Vauxhall & Opel timing belt renewal manual

Barnes BSc

(3577 - 288)

ABCDE
FGHIJ
KLMNO
PQRST

Printed by **J H Haynes & Co Ltd, Sparkford, Nr Yeovil, Somerset BA22 7JJ, England**

Haynes Publishing
Sparkford, Nr Yeovil, Somerset BA22 7JJ, England

Haynes North America, Inc
861 Lawrence Drive, Newbury Park, California 91320, USA

Editions Haynes S.A.
Tour Aurore - La Défense 2, 18 Place des Reflets,
92975 PARIS LA DEFENSE Cedex, France

Haynes Publishing Nordiska AB
...SALA, Sweden

© Haynes Publishing 1999

A book in the **Haynes Service and Repair Manual Series**

ISBN 1 85960 577 X

British Library Cataloguing in Publication Data
A catalogue record for this book is available from the British Library

Contents

Contents

Contents

Contents

Contents

This timing belt renewal manual is aimed at the more experienced mechanic who has some experience of the work involved, and already has most of the specialised tools needed for such work.

Tasks are described and photographed in a clear step-by-step sequence. The illustrations are numbered by the Section number and paragraph number to which they relate - if there is more than one illustration per paragraph, the sequence is denoted alphabetically.

A brief history of timing belts

The timing belt (also known as a camshaft drivebelt) first appeared on mass-produced vehicles in the early 1970s. Traditionally, camshaft drive had been via gears or by sprockets and chains, both of which were adequate for a block-mounted camshaft and pushrod valvegear. The development of overhead camshaft designs, however, implied long chain runs with problems of noise, lubrication, wear and tensioning. By comparison the toothed belt offered the advantages of relatively silent running and much reduced cost and complexity of manufacture and assembly. With a couple of notable exceptions, most manufacturers adopted belt drive with enthusiasm.

At first the timing belt was thought to be everlasting, or at least as long-lived as any other engine component. (To put this optimism in perspective, remember that vehicle manufacturers were still experimenting with novelties such as timing gears made of reinforced cardboard, or timing chain tensioners which caused a catastrophic loss of oil pressure when the chain stretched beyond a certain point. Many drivers accepted the idea that engine rebuilds and overhauls were an inevitable part of the motoring year.) Reality soon intruded, however, and regular inspection became part of the service schedules, followed by regular renewal as mechanics' X-ray vision proved unable to detect incipient belt failure.

Timing belt failure in service would have been no more than an irritant had it not been for other developments in engine design. Higher compression ratios and larger valves meant that in many cases a piston passing TDC would collide with the head of an open valve when the timing belt broke. The resulting damage could range from no more than a bent valve stem and a souvenir scar on the piston crown, to an engine which was effectively a write-off. Most modern engines will suffer serious damage if the timing belt breaks or slips in service. Diesel engines are worst affected because their combustion space is necessarily smaller.

This brings us to the present day. The design and construction of toothed belts has improved considerably, but regular renewal is still required.

Types of belt

Timing belts have a core made of fibreglass strands. The teeth are made of an elastic nylon facing material and are bonded to the core with a flexible rubber compound. The precise characteristics of the various construction materials will vary to meet the vehicle manufacturer's specification.

The belt tooth profile was originally trapezoidal (straight-sided). This was superseded by a semi-circular type which is stronger and longer-wearing. There are numerous variations on these two basic profiles, some of them matched to particular sprocket teeth. For this reason it is essential that belts are only used for their catalogued applications, even if they appear similar to belts used in other applications.

Storage and handling of belts

Like any rubber product, timing belts should be stored in dry temperate conditions and out of direct sunlight. Do not allow them to become contaminated by oil or solvents. Ideally the belts should be stored in their original packaging. Do not bend them tightly, roll them up or hang them on pegs or hooks.

When fitting a new belt, be careful not to bend or kink it sharply. Avoid contamination of the belt by engine fluids and make sure that any fuel, oil or coolant leaks near the belt run are rectified.

Renewal intervals

Manufacturers' specified renewal intervals vary widely and sometimes apparently arbitrarily. In the absence of any specific recommendation to the contrary, an interval of 36 000 to 40 000 miles (60 000 to 65 000 km) is suggested.

Some manufacturers specify a shorter renewal interval for vehicles operating under adverse conditions. 'Adverse conditions' include taxi work, full-time towing, driving on unmade roads and operation in extremes of climate. If in doubt, the only safe course of action is to opt for the shorter interval.

As a general rule, a used timing belt should not be refitted once it has been removed. This is because the tensioning procedure laid down by the manufacturer applies to a new belt; once the old belt has stretched in service it is virtually impossible to regain the correct tension.

Reasons for belt failure

A belt which has been in service for longer than the recommended period can be expected to fail simply as a result of ageing and fatigue. Premature failure can be caused by a number of factors, some of which leave characteristic signs.

The photographs overleaf showing various types of failure have been provided by AE Auto Parts Ltd.

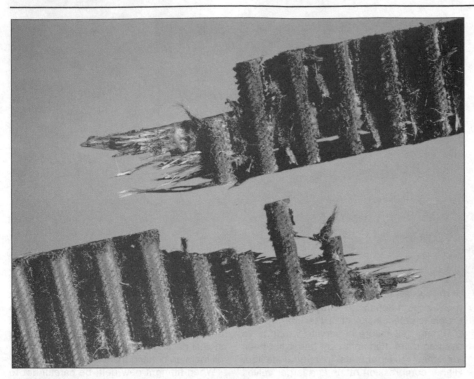

Foreign Body Entrapment

Cause

A foreign body (nut, bolt, washer, etc) has become trapped in the drive and has over-stretched and broken the tensile cords.

Symptom

Belt breakage, in a curved or ragged tear.

Remedy

Attempt to locate and identify foreign body

Ensure belt covers are effective.

Land Wear

Cause

Excessive tension, causing the belt to wear on the pulley lands.

Rough sprocket(s) abrading the belt.

Symptom

Wear, or polishing, on the lands between the teeth, possibly wearing down to the tension cords; with polishing on the tooth crests of trapezoidal belts.

Remedy

Replace sprocket(s) if required.

Edge Wear

Cause

Damaged sprocket flange, or misaligned sprockets.

Symptom

Excessive wear and damage to the belt edges.

Remedy

Replace damaged sprockets and ensure correct belt alignment.

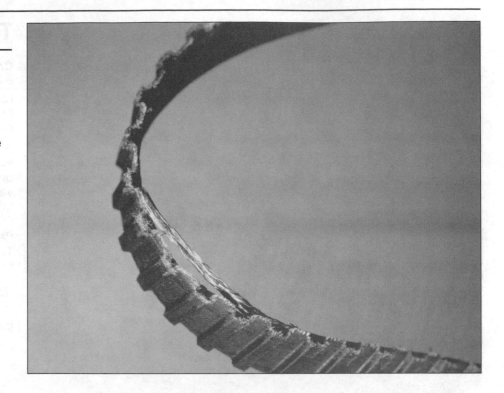

Back Cracks

Cause

The rubber has been over-heated and has degraded, possibly from friction on a siezed idler or water pump. Extreme cold may have the same effect.

Symptom

A series of cracks across the back of the rubber stock.

Remedy

Ensure all spindles driven off the back of the belt, including water pumps, rotate freely.

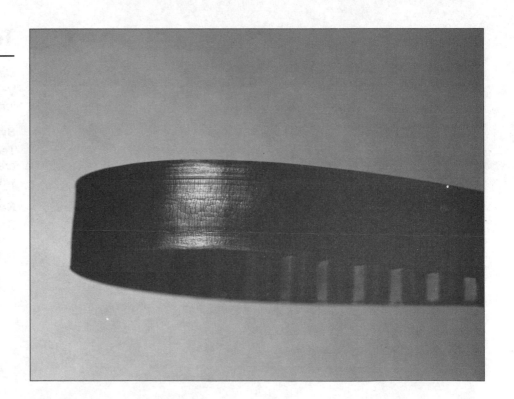

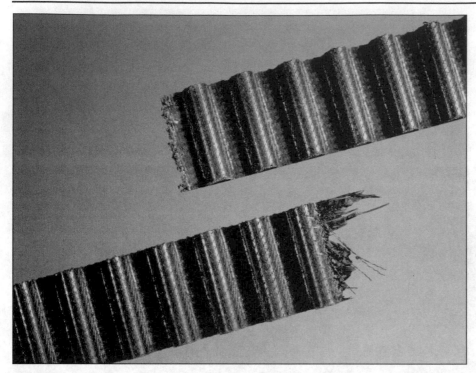

Tensile Failure

Cause

Some of the tensile cord's fibres have broken due to crimping (folding) before or during assembly, creating a weak point.

A belt running over-tensioned may sometimes cause teeth to ride up onto sprocket lands, resulting in vast over-stretching and tensile failure.

Symptom

Tensile breakage, with a straight break between two teeth.

Remedy

Replace belt carefully, without pinching or levering.

Set new belt to correct tension.

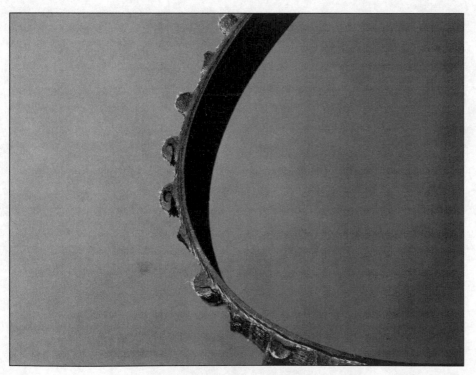

Tooth Peel

Cause

Very low tension allowing the belt to jump teeth.

Symptom

Teeth peeling, emanating from root cracks. Often is present together with tooth shear.

Remedy

Set new belt to correct tension and ensure tensioner mechanism is tight.

Tooth Wear

Cause

Extremely low tension allows the belt to ride out on the sprocket, causing localised wear on edge of the thrust face.

Sometimes excessive tension, pulling the belt up the land, may wear the tooth face, before a tensile failure.

Symptom

Hollows through the facing fabric.

Remedy

Set new belt to correct tension.

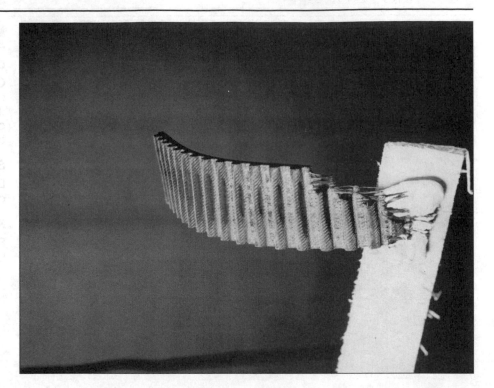

Tooth Shear

Cause

May be due to sudden overload of the drive from the seizure of a driven pump, such as a water pump.

Also may be due to low tension, which allows the belt to ride high on the sprocket, producing excessive bending moments, and deflection of the teeth until cracks form.

Symptom

Six or more teeth missing, often with cracking in roots of a number of teeth.

Remedy

Ensure all driven items rotate freely.

Set new belt to correct tension and ensure tensioner mechanism is tight.

Oil Contamination

Cause

Contamination from a failed oil seal, or an oil or diesel leak, breaks down the adhesion of the rubber. Swelling can also cause mis-meshing leading to other types of failure.

Symptom

Dirty or smelly belt, with a ragged decomposing structure.

Remedy

Ensure oil leak is stopped. Check belt covers and dust shields.

Consequences of timing belt breaking in service

Almost all modern engines will suffer some damage if the timing belt breaks in service. The severity of such damage varies according to the design of the engine, the speed at which it was turning when the belt broke and a certain amount of good or bad luck. Belts often break when the engine is being started or when pulling away - in these cases damage may not be severe.

If engine damage is suspected, the only sure way of checking is by removing the cylinder head and dismantling the valvegear. Some authorities recommend that a compression test be performed before going to the trouble of dismantling, but this will only be possible if a spare timing belt can be fitted. A cylinder leak-down test can be performed instead, rotating the camshaft as necessary to close the appropriate pair of valves, but this will only detect gross damage (holes in pistons, valve heads snapped off).

When faced with an engine on which the belt has broken, the following course of action is suggested:

(a) *Remove the camshaft cover and check for visible damage (broken rocker fingers or valve springs, valves stuck open, etc).*

(b) *Position the pistons at mid-stroke and rotate the camshaft. If the camshaft will not turn, or jams at some point, further investigation is required.*

(c) *If the camshaft turns satisfactorily, position the crankshaft and camshaft in their correct relative positions and fit a timing belt - for preference an old one. Perform a compression test.*

(d) *If the compression test is satisfactory, the engine has probably escaped damage. If the compression on one or more cylinders is low, suspect a bent valve stem or other damage.*

Tensioning gauges and units

On some engines timing belt tension is set automatically by a spring-loaded tensioner. Provided the tensioner is in good condition and the correct procedure is followed, no problems will be encountered and no tensioning gauge wili be needed.

More usually, belt tension is set manually and checked using a particular gauge specified by the vehicle manufacturer. The experienced mechanic may rely on the 'feel' of the belt to judge when tension is correct. As a rule of thumb, it should not be possible to twist the belt further than 90° (a quarter of a turn) with the fingers. A further check can be made when the engine is running: a belt which is too tight will often make a characteristic droning or honking noise. However, even in experienced hands it is only possible to achieve an approximately correct setting without a tensioning gauge and in the worst case it is a recipe for disaster.

A universal belt tensioning gauge would be welcomed by many mechanics, but it appears not to exist. Conversion of (often arbitrary and non-linear) units from one make of gauge to another is not always possible, because not only are the gauges calibrated differently, they also work in different ways. Some gauges are also sensitive to belt thickness.

It will be seen, therefore, that the only way to be certain of correctly tensioning manually-adjusted timing belts is to use the manufacturer's specified gauge. Other methods may work, but unless specifically recommended they must be regarded as second best.

Acknowledgements

Thanks are due to AE Auto Parts Ltd, Bradford, West Yorkshire, for the provision of timing belt fault finding information. Certain illustrations are the copyright of Vauxhall Motors Ltd, and are used with their permission. Thanks are also due to Draper Tools Limited, who provided some of the workshop tools, and to all those people at Sparkford who helped in the production of this manual, especially Mark Coombs, Spencer Drayton, Andy Legg, John Mead, Matthew Minter and Steve Rendle.

We take great pride in the accuracy of information given in this manual, but vehicle manufacturers make alterations and design changes during the production run of a particular vehicle of which they do not inform us. No liability can be accepted by the authors or publishers for loss, damage or injury caused by errors in, or omissions from, the information given.

Working on your car can be dangerous. This page shows just some of the potential risks and hazards, with the aim of creating a safety-conscious attitude.

General hazards

Scalding

• Don't remove the radiator or expansion tank cap while the engine is hot.
• Engine oil, automatic transmission fluid or power steering fluid may also be dangerously hot if the engine has recently been running.

Burning

• Beware of burns from the exhaust system and from any part of the engine. Brake discs and drums can also be extremely hot immediately after use.

Crushing

• When working under or near a raised vehicle, always supplement the jack with axle stands, or use drive-on ramps. *Never venture under a car which is only supported by a jack.*
• Take care if loosening or tightening high-torque nuts when the vehicle is on stands. Initial loosening and final tightening should be done with the wheels on the ground.

Fire

• Fuel is highly flammable; fuel vapour is explosive.
• Don't let fuel spill onto a hot engine.
• Do not smoke or allow naked lights (including pilot lights) anywhere near a vehicle being worked on. Also beware of creating sparks (electrically or by use of tools).
• Fuel vapour is heavier than air, so don't work on the fuel system with the vehicle over an inspection pit.
• Another cause of fire is an electrical overload or short-circuit. Take care when repairing or modifying the vehicle wiring.
• Keep a fire extinguisher handy, of a type suitable for use on fuel and electrical fires.

Electric shock

• Ignition HT voltage can be dangerous, especially to people with heart problems or a pacemaker. Don't work on or near the ignition system with the engine running or the ignition switched on.

• Mains voltage is also dangerous. Make sure that any mains-operated equipment is correctly earthed. Mains power points should be protected by a residual current device (RCD) circuit breaker.

Fume or gas intoxication

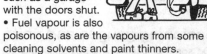

• Exhaust fumes are poisonous; they often contain carbon monoxide, which is rapidly fatal if inhaled. Never run the engine in a confined space such as a garage with the doors shut.
• Fuel vapour is also poisonous, as are the vapours from some cleaning solvents and paint thinners.

Poisonous or irritant substances

• Avoid skin contact with battery acid and with any fuel, fluid or lubricant, especially antifreeze, brake hydraulic fluid and Diesel fuel. Don't syphon them by mouth. If such a substance is swallowed or gets into the eyes, seek medical advice.
• Prolonged contact with used engine oil can cause skin cancer. Wear gloves or use a barrier cream if necessary. Change out of oil-soaked clothes and do not keep oily rags in your pocket.
• Air conditioning refrigerant forms a poisonous gas if exposed to a naked flame (including a cigarette). It can also cause skin burns on contact.

Asbestos

• Asbestos dust can cause cancer if inhaled or swallowed. Asbestos may be found in gaskets and in brake and clutch linings. When dealing with such components it is safest to assume that they contain asbestos.

Special hazards

Hydrofluoric acid

• This extremely corrosive acid is formed when certain types of synthetic rubber, found in some O-rings, oil seals, fuel hoses etc, are exposed to temperatures above 400ºC. The rubber changes into a charred or sticky substance containing the acid. *Once formed, the acid remains dangerous for years. If it gets onto the skin, it may be necessary to amputate the limb concerned.*
• When dealing with a vehicle which has suffered a fire, or with components salvaged from such a vehicle, wear protective gloves and discard them after use.

The battery

• Batteries contain sulphuric acid, which attacks clothing, eyes and skin. Take care when topping-up or carrying the battery.
• The hydrogen gas given off by the battery is highly explosive. Never cause a spark or allow a naked light nearby. Be careful when connecting and disconnecting battery chargers or jump leads.

Air bags

• Air bags can cause injury if they go off accidentally. Take care when removing the steering wheel and/or facia. Special storage instructions may apply.

Diesel injection equipment

• Diesel injection pumps supply fuel at very high pressure. Take care when working on the fuel injectors and fuel pipes.

⚠ *Warning: Never expose the hands, face or any other part of the body to injector spray; the fuel can penetrate the skin with potentially fatal results.*

Remember...

DO

• Do use eye protection when using power tools, and when working under the vehicle.

• Do wear gloves or use barrier cream to protect your hands when necessary.

• Do get someone to check periodically that all is well when working alone on the vehicle.

• Do keep loose clothing and long hair well out of the way of moving mechanical parts.

• Do remove rings, wristwatch etc, before working on the vehicle – especially the electrical system.

• Do ensure that any lifting or jacking equipment has a safe working load rating adequate for the job.

DON'T

• Don't attempt to lift a heavy component which may be beyond your capability – get assistance.

• Don't rush to finish a job, or take unverified short cuts.

• Don't use ill-fitting tools which may slip and cause injury.

• Don't leave tools or parts lying around where someone can trip over them. Mop up oil and fuel spills at once.

• Don't allow children or pets to play in or near a vehicle being worked on.

1

Chapter 1 Bedford Rascal & Suzuki Supercarry 1986 to 1994

Contents

Specifications

Timing belt renewal interval . . . . Every 36 000 miles (60 000 km) or 4 years - whichever comes first

Note: *This is not included in the manufacturer's maintenance schedule, but is strongly recommended as a precaution against the timing belt failing in service. If the timing belt fails while the engine is running, extensive engine damage could be caused.*

Torque wrench settings	Nm	lbf ft
Camshaft cover bolts	5	4
Camshaft sprocket bolt	55	41
Cooling fan bolts	10	7
Crankshaft pulley bolt	55	41
Roadwheel nuts	65	48
Spark plugs	25	18
Timing belt cover:		
Inner cover nuts and bolts	10	7
Outer cover nuts and bolts	4	3
Timing belt tensioner bolts	20	15

1.3 Remove the auxiliary drivebelt

1.4 Checking the auxiliary drivebelt tension

1 Auxiliary drivebelt - removal, refitting and adjustment

Removal

1 Disconnect the battery negative lead, then raise or remove (according to model) the front seats for access to the engine.
2 Loosen the alternator adjustment and pivot bolts, and swivel the alternator in towards the engine as far as possible.
3 Slip the drivebelt off the crankshaft, water pump and alternator pulleys, and remove it over the fan blades **(see illustration)**.

Refitting

4 Locate the drivebelt on the pulleys, and swivel out the alternator to apply moderate tension. Lightly tighten the adjustment and pivot bolts.

Adjustment

5 Depress the drivebelt with moderate thumb pressure (10 kg/22 lb) midway between the water pump and alternator pulleys **(see illustration)**. The drivebelt is correctly adjusted if it deflects by 6 to 9 mm.

6 If adjustment is necessary, loosen the adjustment and pivot bolts slightly, and use a lever at the pulley end of the alternator housing to reposition it until the drivebelt deflection is correct. Tighten the bolts on completion.
7 Remove the socket and extension bar, and reconnect the battery negative lead. Refit the front seats.

2 Top Dead Centre (TDC) for No 1 cylinder - locating

1 To ensure correct reassembly and synchronisation of the engine components, a method of setting the engine in a 'reference' condition during dismantling is required. Setting a particular piston to Top Dead Centre (TDC) achieves this. TDC refers to the highest position a piston reaches within its respective cylinder. In a four-stroke engine, each piston reaches TDC twice per cycle; once on the compression stroke, and once on the exhaust stroke. TDC normally refers to the piston position on the compression stroke. Note that the cylinders are numbered 1 to 4 from the timing belt end **(see illustration)**. The following paragraphs describe the location of TDC on cylinder No 1.

2 Before starting work, disconnect the battery negative cable. Disable the ignition system by removing the distributor centre HT lead and earthing it on the cylinder block using a jumper wire. Prevent any vehicle movement by putting the transmission in neutral, applying the handbrake and chocking the rear wheels.
3 Note the position of the No 1 cylinder HT terminal with respect to the distributor body. If the terminal is not numbered, follow the HT lead from the No 1 cylinder spark plug back to the distributor cap. Using chalk or a pen (**not** a pencil), place a mark on the distributor body directly under the terminal. Unclip and remove the distributor cap.
4 Disconnect the HT leads from the spark plugs, noting their fitted sequence (if the leads are not marked for cylinder number, mark them 1 to 4 from the front of the engine). Remove all four spark plugs.
5 To bring any piston up to TDC, it will be necessary to rotate the crankshaft manually. This can be done by using a ratchet wrench and socket on the crankshaft bolt at the front of the engine.
6 Rotate the crankshaft clockwise until the distributor rotor arm electrode approaches the mark that was made on the distributor body.
7 Locate the timing inspection hole on the transmission bellhousing, and remove the rubber bung **(see illustration)**. This exposes

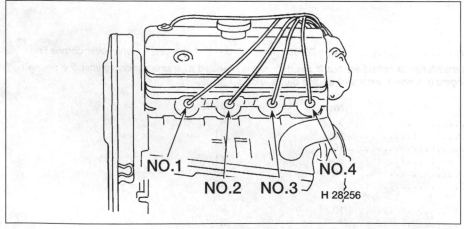

2.1 Cylinder numbering order

2.7 Remove the bung from the timing inspection hole

2.8 Align the T timing mark with the pointer on the bellhousing

3.5a Remove the crankshaft pulley centre bolt . . .

3.5b . . . and pulley

3.6a Remove the timing belt outer cover bolts . . .

3.6b . . . and cover

the edge of the flywheel, on which there are a number of timing marks.

8 Continue rotating the crankshaft clockwise until the T timing mark is aligned exactly with the pointer marked on the bellhousing **(see illustration)**. **Note:** *Observe from directly above the inspection hole, to ensure correct alignment.*

9 Check that the distributor rotor arm is now aligned with the mark on the distributor body. If it is offset by 180°, then the cylinder is on the exhaust stroke; rotate the crankshaft through one complete revolution, and repeat paragraph 8 above.

10 Cylinder No 1 is now at TDC. This process can also be used to find TDC for cylinder No 4 if required, by repeating the above process but marking the position of the No 4 cylinder HT terminal on the distributor body.

3 Timing belt and cover - removal and refitting

Removal

1 Disconnect the battery negative cable, and position it away from the terminal.

2 Slacken the alternator mounting and adjustment bolts, and pivot the alternator towards the engine. Remove the auxiliary drivebelt **(see illustration)**.

3 Refer to Section 5 and remove the cooling fan and spacer. Lift off the auxiliary drivebelt pulley.

4 Referring to Section 2, set the engine to TDC on cylinder No 4 (not No 1 - this is because the timing marks used to align the camshaft sprocket for TDC on No 4 are much easier to see than those for No 1).

5 Remove the crankshaft pulley by extracting the centre bolt **(see illustrations)**. To do this, the crankshaft must be prevented from rotating - this can be achieved by selecting fourth gear and firmly applying the handbrake. If this method fails to lock the crankshaft in position, remove the timing mark inspection plug on the bellhousing, and get an assistant to insert a stout, wide-bladed screwdriver between two of the starter ring gear teeth -

this should lock the flywheel (and hence the crankshaft) in position.

6 The timing belt outer cover can now be taken off by removing the bolts securing it to the inner cover **(see illustrations)**. Recover the rubber gasket - if it is serviceable, retain it for refitting later.

7 At this point, identify the timing alignment marks stamped onto both the camshaft and crankshaft sprockets. These should both be lined up with the timing arrows stamped on the inner timing belt cover. Note that there are

two arrows provided on the cover for aligning the camshaft sprocket; one at 12 o'clock and one at 6 o'clock. The 12 o'clock arrow is used for setting cylinder No 4 at TDC - the 6 o'clock one is for setting cylinder No 1 at TDC. As the engine has already been set to TDC on No 4, use the 12 o'clock arrow for alignment.

8 Slacken the two bolts securing the timing belt tensioner to the engine block, and prise the tensioner spring off the water pump retaining bolt **(see illustration)**. This will relieve the tension on the belt.

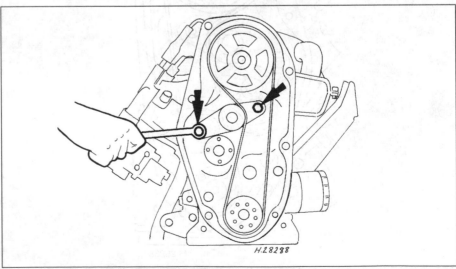

3.8 Tensioner bolts (arrowed)

3.9 Remove the timing belt

3.11a Camshaft sprocket correctly aligned with marks on timing belt cover

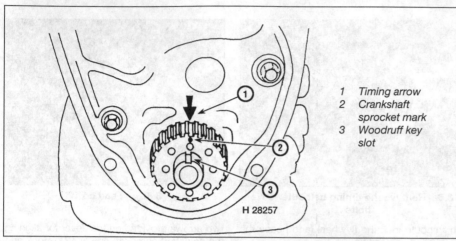

1 Timing arrow
2 Crankshaft sprocket mark
3 Woodruff key slot

3.11b Crankshaft sprocket correctly aligned with marks on timing belt cover

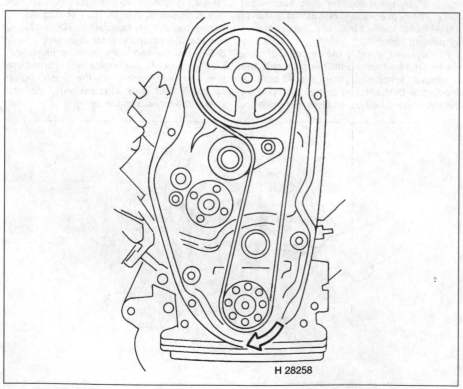

3.12 Correct routing of timing belt around sprockets and tensioner

9 Unless they are already printed on, mark the timing belt with arrows indicating its direction of rotation. The belt can now be slid off the timing sprockets (see illustration). Do not allow either the camshaft or crankshaft to rotate until the belt is refitted.
10 If signs of oil contamination are found, trace the source of the oil leak and rectify it, then wash down the engine timing belt area and all related components to remove all traces of oil.

Refitting

11 Check that both the camshaft and crankshaft are still correctly aligned with the relevant marks on the timing belt inner cover (see illustrations).
12 Fit the timing belt over the camshaft and crankshaft sprockets, ensuring that the arrows on the belt correspond with the rotation of the crankshaft (clockwise) (see illustration). Make sure that any slack in the belt is on the tensioner side - the flat side of the belt should pass around the tensioner roller. Ensure that the teeth on the belt engage positively with those on the sprockets.
13 Push the tensioner pulley against the belt to eliminate the slack, and clip the tensioner spring over the water pump retaining bolt.
14 *Temporarily* refit the crankshaft bolt, and put the transmission into neutral. Rotate the crankshaft clockwise through two complete turns, to even out the tension in the belt.
Caution: Turn the crankshaft directly - do not apply effort to the camshaft sprocket. Check that the timing marks on both sprockets are again aligned with those on the inner cover. Tighten first the inner, then the outer tensioner bolt to the specified torque.
15 Rotate the crankshaft through two more clockwise revolutions. The timing belt tension can now be checked using a spring balance and ruler. Hook the spring balance over the timing belt on the side that is not routed around the tensioner roller, at a point mid-way between the two sprockets (see illustration). Pull the balance at right-angles to the belt until 3 kg (6.6 lb) registers on the scale. Use the ruler to measure how much the belt is deflected from its normal position.

3.15 Checking the tension of the timing belt

3.17 Tighten the tensioner retaining bolts to the specified torque

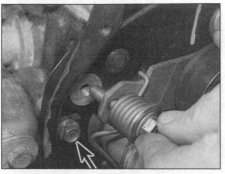

4.2a Unclip the spring from water pump retaining bolt (arrowed) and remove the timing belt tensioner outer . . .

4.2b . . . and inner retaining bolts

16 If the deflection is not between 5.5 and 6.5 mm, the belt tension will have to be adjusted. Loosen the tensioner retaining bolts, slacken or tighten the belt as required, and repeat the steps in paragraph 15. This process may have to be repeated more than once to achieve the correct belt tension.

17 When the belt deflection is within specification, tighten the tensioner retaining bolts to the correct torque **(see illustration)**. Refit the outer timing belt cover and rubber gasket. If necessary, use a light coating of silicon sealant to hold the gasket in place during refitting.

18 Slide the crankshaft pulley into place, engaging the key and keyway correctly. Refit the bolt and the tighten it to the specified torque, locking the crankshaft using one of the methods described in the removal process.

19 Refit the cooling fan, spacer and water pump drive pulley, and tighten the bolts.

20 Route the auxiliary drivebelt around the crankshaft, water pump and alternator pulleys. Tension the belt using the alternator, as described in Seciton 1.

21 Reconnect the battery negative cable.

4 Timing belt sprockets and tensioner - removal and refitting

Removal

1 Working as described in Section 3, paragraphs 1 to 7 inclusive, remove the auxiliary drivebelt and pulleys, the cooling fan, and the timing belt outer cover.

2 Unclip the belt tensioner spring from water pump retaining bolt, and remove the timing belt tensioner outer and inner retaining bolts **(see illustrations)**. Extract the entire tensioner assembly. Remove the timing belt.

3 Using a suitable implement to hold the sprocket stationary, remove the camshaft sprocket bolt **(see illustration 4.6)**. Whatever method is used, hold the sprocket directly - do not be tempted to use the timing belt to hold the sprocket. Slide the sprocket off the camshaft, and recover the Woodruff key **(see illustrations)**.

4 Prise the crankshaft sprocket off the shaft using suitable lever (not a screwdriver). Recover the Woodruff key and the belt guide washer **(see illustrations)**.

Refitting

5 Follow the above steps in reverse order. Ensure that the Woodruff keys are inserted

4.3a Remove the camshaft sprocket bolt

4.3b Slide the sprocket off the camshaft . . .

4.3c . . . and recover the Woodruff key

4.4a Remove the crankshaft sprocket

4.4b Recover the Woodruff key . . .

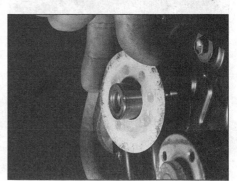

4.4c . . . and the belt guide washer

4.6 Tightening the camshaft sprocket bolt - note the forked holding tool bolted through the sprocket

5.3 Prise the brake servo vacuum hose off the rigid pipe mounted on the radiator bracket

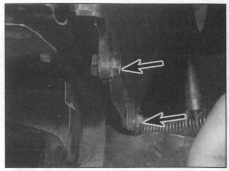

5.4a Remove the bolts securing the cowling (left-hand side bolts arrowed) . . .

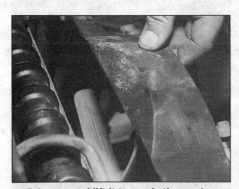

5.4b . . . then unclip it from the upper and lower edge of the radiator . . .

correctly when refitting the timing belt sprockets; the curved edge should be inserted into the shaft, with the flat edge facing outwards. Ensure that all fixings are tightened to the correct torque.

6 When tightening the camshaft sprocket bolt, hold it stationary using the same method employed during removal **(see illustration)**.

7 Ensure that the sprockets are correctly aligned as described in Section 3, paragraphs 7 and 11, then refit the timing belt and all other disturbed components.

5 Cooling fan - removal and refitting

Removal

1 Disconnect the battery negative cable, and position it away from the terminal.

2 Slacken the alternator mounting and adjustment bolts, and pivot the alternator

towards the engine. Remove the auxiliary drivebelt as described in Section 1.

3 Slacken the worm-drive clip, and prise the brake servo vacuum hose off the rigid pipe mounted on the radiator bracket **(see illustration)**.

4 Remove the radiator cowling, to give greater access to the cooling fan bolts, as follows. Remove the bolts securing the cowling, then unclip it from the lower and upper edges of the radiator, and lift it towards the engine. Remove the four retaining bolts and washers, then lift off the cooling fan - recover the alloy spacer if it is loose **(see illustrations)**.

Refitting

5 To refit the fan, simply reverse the removal steps, referring to Section 1 for details of refitting and tensioning the auxiliary drivebelt.

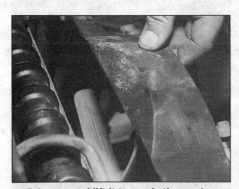

5.4c . . . and lift it towards the engine

5.4d Lift off the cooling fan . . .

5.4e . . . recover the alloy spacer if it is loose

Chapter 2A
Vauxhall Astra &
Opel Kadett petrol 1979 to 1984

Contents

Specifications

Timing belt renewal interval . . . . Every 36 000 miles (60 000 km) or 4 years - whichever comes first
Note: *Although the mileage interval for timing belt renewal is 50 000 miles (80 000 km), it is strongly recommended that the interval is reduced on vehicles which are subjected to intensive use, ie, mainly short journeys or a lot of stop-start driving. The actual belt renewal interval is therefore very much up to the individual owner. That being said, it is highly recommended to err on the side of safety, and renew the belt at this earlier interval, bearing in mind the drastic consequences resulting from belt failure.*

Torque wrench settings	Nm	lbf ft
Camshaft sprocket bolt	45	33
Coolant pump bolts	8	6
Coolant temperature sender	10	7
Crankshaft pulley bolt:		
1.3 litre engines	55	40
1.6 and 1.8 litre engines	60	44
Roadwheel bolts	90	66

1 Auxiliary drivebelt - removal, refitting and tensioning

1 Loosen the alternator mounting bolts and nuts just sufficiently to allow the unit to be pivoted in towards the engine. This will release all tension from the belt which can now be slipped off the respective pulleys. Fit a new belt after checking that it is of the correct type and take up the slack in the belt by swinging the alternator away from the engine and lightly tightening the bolts just to hold it in that position.

2 Although special tools are available for measuring the belt tension a good approximation can be achieved if the belt is tensioned so that there is 0.5 in (13 mm) of movement at the mid-point position on the longest run of belt between pulleys **(see illustration)**. With the alternator bolts just holding the unit firm, lever the alternator away from the engine using a wooden lever at the mounting bracket end until the correct tension in the belt is reached and then tighten the alternator bolts. On no account apply any loads at the free end of the alternator as serious damage can be caused internally.

2 Cooling system - draining and refilling

Draining

Note: *Take care to protect the hands from escaping steam when removing the expansion tank filler cap if the system is hot.*

1 Before draining the system park the car on level ground, remove the filler cap on the expansion tank and move the heater control to full heat.

2 Position a clean container such as a basin under the radiator bottom hose and loosen a hose clip. If the hose joint has not been disturbed for some time it will be necessary to manipulate the hose to break the joint and allow the coolant to flow into the container.

1.2 Checking the auxiliary drivebelt tension

Refilling

3 Before attempting to fill the cooling system make sure that all the hoses and hose clips are in good condition and that the clips are tight.

4 Check that the heater control is in the full heat position and then remove the filler cap from the expansion tank. To release air from the system as it is being filled, remove the temperature sender from the induction manifold (1.3 litre engines) or slacken the bleed screw on the thermostat housing (1.6 and 1.8 litre engines). Fill the system slowly (by pouring coolant into the expansion tank) to prevent air locks forming and either refit the temperature switch or tighten the bleed screw, as appropriaten when coolant, free of air, emerges. Fill to 0.4 in (10 mm) above the level marked KALT (ie COLD) on the expansion tank. Repeated squeezing of the large coolant hoses will induce surging of the mixture in the system which will help to dislodge any air bubbles. Refit the expansion tank filler cap tightly and mop up any spilt fluid **(see illustration)**.

5 Run the engine at a fast tickover until the cooling fan motor engages and, particularly if the system has been disturbed in any way, examine carefully for leaks. Stop the engine and allow it to cool before topping up the level in the expansion tank as necessary. Remember that the system must be cold before an accurate level is indicated in the expansion tank.

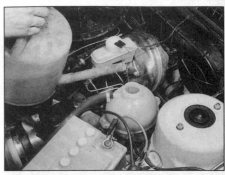

2.4 Filling the expansion tank

3 Coolant pump - removal and refitting

Removal

1 Drain the coolant as described in Section 2.

2 Slacken the alternator mounting nuts and bolts, swing the alternator in towards the engine and remove the drivebelt.

3 Undo the securing bolts and remove the timing belt cover. Turn the crankshaft to align the timing mark on the camshaft sprocket with the mark at the top of the housing behind the sprocket, and at the same time align the notch in the rim of the crankshaft pulley with the timing pointer **(see illustrations 4.10a and 4.10b)**.

4 Disconnect the main hose to the coolant pump, then remove the timing belt rear cover. Remove the three bolts which hold the pump in the engine block. The pump shaft is eccentric in the pump body so that, by rotating the pump body, the tension in the toothed timing belt can be released. Turn the body of the pump inwards to slacken the timing belt and slip the belt off the pump pulley. Make sure that the crankshaft and the camshaft are not turned while the belt is removed as, apart from losing the valve timing, the valves or pistons could be damaged. Withdraw the coolant pump from the engine block **(see illustrations)**.

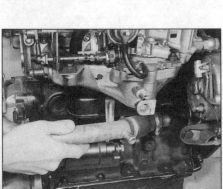

3.4a Coolant hose and pipe connection to rear of pump

3.4b Removing coolant pump (engine partly dismantled)

3.4c Coolant pump drive sprocket

Refitting

5 Before fitting the coolant pump, clean its mounting in the engine block and fit a new O-ring seal to the pump body **(see illustration)**. Install the pump in the block and fit the three retaining bolts and washers, but only hand tighten them at this stage.

6 Fit the toothed timing belt to the pump pulley and refer to Section 4 for the procedure on tensioning the belt. Tighten the three bolts securing the pump to the specified torque **(see illustration)**.

7 Refit the timing belt cover and then fit the drivebelt to the crankshaft and alternator pulleys. Refer to Section 8 for the procedure for tensioning the belt and tighten the alternator mounting bolts.

8 Reconnect the coolant hose at the back of the pump and then refill the system as described in Section 2. Finally run the engine up to its normal operating temperature and check for leaks.

4 Timing belt - removal, refitting and tensioning

Removal

Note: *The following procedure will necessitate re-positioning of the coolant pump which, in*

3.5 Coolant pump O-ring seal

turn, is likely to cause leakage from around the sealing flange. Minor leakage can normally be rectified by using a suitable product in the cooling system, although it is preferable to remove the coolant pump completely and fit a new sealing ring (for further information see Section 3).

1 Unscrew and remove the belt cover.

2 Apply a spanner to the crankshaft pulley bolt and turn the crankshaft until No 1 piston is on the firing stroke. The BTDC notch on the pulley should be in approximate alignment with the ignition timing pointer, but to ensure that it is No 1 piston that is on the firing stroke and not No 4, either remove the No 1 spark plug and feel the compression being

3.6 Coolant pump mounting bolts

generated as the crankshaft is turned, or remove the distributor cap and check that the rotor is in alignment with No 1 spark plug contact in the cap **(see illustration 4.10a)**.

3 Release the alternator adjustment link and mounting bolts, push the alternator in towards the engine and slip the drivebelt from the pulleys.

4 Unscrew the crankshaft pulley bolt without disturbing the set position of the crankshaft. To prevent the crankshaft rotating as the bolt is unscrewed, either engage a gear and apply the brakes, or remove the flywheel housing lower cover and jam the flywheel ring.

5 Drain the cooling system. (This operation is not essential if the coolant pump is not going to be removed - see note at beginning of Section).

6 Release the coolant pump mounting bolts just enough to be able to swivel the pump and to release the tension of the timing belt. The pump has a hexagon to enable a large spanner to be fitted but, since access is very restricted, it may be preferable to temporarily remove the alternator.

7 Take the belt off the sprockets without moving the set position of the camshaft or crankshaft.

8 If signs of oil contamination are found, trace the source of the oil leak and rectify it, then wash down the engine timing belt area and all related components to remove all traces of oil.

Refitting

9 Engage the new belt over the sprockets and apply some tension by moving the coolant pump **(see illustrations)**.

10 Refit the crankshaft pulley and then check that the pulley notch is still in alignment with the timing pointer and that the camshaft sprocket mark is aligned with the groove in the plate behind it. If not, release the belt tension and readjust the position of the sprockets as necessary **(see illustrations)**.

11 The belt tension should now be adjusted

4.9a Engaging timing belt with sprockets

4.9b Moving the coolant pump to tension the timing belt

4.10a Crankshaft pulley timing marks aligned

4.10b Camshaft timing marks (No 1 piston firing)

using the official tool (KM 510). Adjust the tension as necessary by moving the water pump **(see illustration)**. If the belt is overtight, it will be heard to hum when the engine is running. Gauge readings are:

	New belt	Used belt
1.3 litre	6.0	5.0
1.6 litre	4.5	2.5
1.8 litre	4.5	2.5

When the adjustment is correct, tighten the coolant pump bolts, turn the crankshaft through one full turn, and check the tension again. Repeat this procedure until the correct tension is obtained.

12 Refit the belt cover **(see illustration)** and the auxiliary drivebelt.

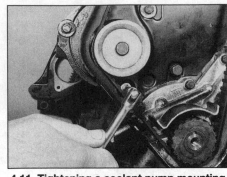

4.11 Tightening a coolant pump mounting screw

4.12 Fitting timing belt cover

Chapter 2B
Vauxhall Astra & Opel Kadett diesel 1979 to 1984

Contents

Specifications

Timing belt renewal interval . . . .   Every 36 000 miles (60 000 km) or 4 years - whichever comes first

Auxiliary drivebelts
Tension (using gauge KM-128-A):
   Alternator:
      New . . . .   450 N
      Used . . . .   250 to 400 N
   Power steering pump:
      New . . . .   450 N
      Used . . . .   250 to 300 N

Timing belt tension
Using tension gauge KM-510-A:
   New belt, warm 9.0
   New belt, cold 6.5
   Run-in belt, warm 8.0
   Run-in belt, cold 4.0

Injection pump
Timing setting . . . . 1.0 ± 0.05 mm

Torque wrench settings

	Nm	lbf ft
Alternator:		
Adjuster strap nuts and bolts	25	18
Pivot bolt	25	18
Camshaft sprocket bolt:*		
Stage 1	75	55
Stage 2	Angle-tighten a further 60°	
Coolant pump to cylinder block	25	18
Crankshaft pulley-to-sprocket bolt	20	15
Crankshaft sprocket centre bolt	155	114
Engine mountings:		
Except right-hand bracket to cylinder block	40	30
Right-hand mounting bracket to cylinder block	50	37
Fuel injection pump and brackets:		
Main bracket to block	25	18
Pump sprockets bolts	25	18
Subsidiary brackets:		
M6 bolts	14	10
M8 bolts	25	18
Power steering pump:		
Drivebelt tensioner to pump	40	30
Vacuum pump to camshaft housing	28	21
Wheel bolts	90	66

* Bolts tightened by the angular method must be renewed every time.

2B

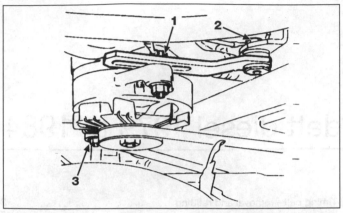

1.2 Alternator drivebelt adjustment points

1 Alternator to adjuster strap bolt
2 Adjuster strap pivot bolt
3 Alternator pivot boltr

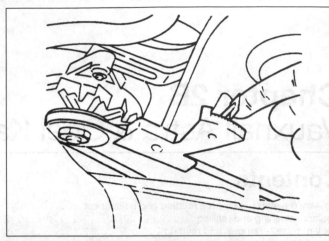

1.8 Using special tool KM-128-A to tension the alternator drivebelt

1 Auxiliary drivebelts - removal, refitting and adjustment

Alternator

Removal and refitting

1 Gain full access to the drivebelt by raising the car, supporting it on axle stands and removing the right-hand front roadwheel. Remove the air cleaner housing assembly.

2 To remove the drivebelt, first slacken the alternator pivot and adjuster strap nuts and bolts **(see illustration)**.

3 Where fitted, remove the power steering pump drivebelt.

4 Move the alternator towards the engine and slip the drivebelt off its pulleys.

5 Fit the new drivebelt in position over the pulleys and adjust it as follows:

Adjustment

6 Tighten the alternator fastening slightly, so that the alternator can just be moved by hand.

7 Move the alternator away from the engine until the belt tension is correct.

8 Vauxhall recommend the use of a special tool (KM-128-A) for tensioning the belt to the specified amount **(see illustration)**. In the absence of this tool, aim for a tension such that the belt can be deflected about 12 mm by firm finger pressure in the middle of its run. The belt tension must, however, be checked with the special tool as soon as possible. If using a lever to move the alternator, only use a wooden or plastic one and only lever at the pulley end.

9 Tighten the alternator fastenings to the specified torque setting once the belt tension is correct.

10 Where applicable, refit and tension the steering pump drivebelt.

11 Refit the air cleaner housing assembly.

Power steering pump

Removal and refitting

12 Gain full access to the drivebelt by jacking up the front right-hand side of the vehicle and supporting it on axle stands.

13 To remove the drivebelt, first loosen the pump mounting and tensioner bolts shown **(see illustration)**. Release the tensioner screw locknuts and rotate them to allow the drivebelt to slacken **(see illustration)**. Slip the drivebelt off its pulleys.

14 Fit the new drivebelt in position over the pulleys and adjust it as follows:

Adjustment

15 Rotate the tensioner screw locknuts until the belt tension is correct.

16 Vauxhall recommend the use of a special tool (KM-128-A) for tensioning the belt to the specified amount. In the absence of this tool, aim for a tension such that the belt can be deflected approximately 12 mm by firm finger pressure in the middle of its run. The belt tension must, however, be checked with the special tool as soon as possible.

17 Once belt tension is correct, tighten the tensioner screw locknuts and lower the vehicle.

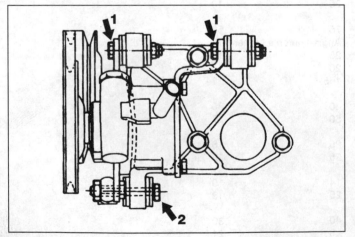

1.13a Power steering pump drivebelt adjustment points

1 Pump mounting bolts   2 Tensioner bolt

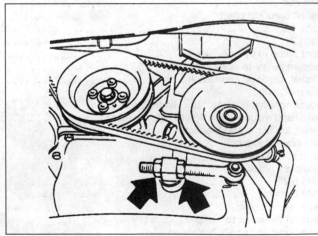

1.13b Rotate the tensioner screw locknuts (arrowed) to adjust drivebelt tension

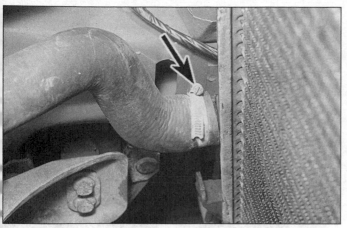

2.3 Release the radiator bottom hose clamp (arrowed) to drain the cooling system

2.8 The thermostat elbow coolant bleed screw (arrowed)

2 Coolant -
draining and refilling

⚠ **Warning: Take care to avoid scalding when removing the cooling system expansion tank cap. Place a thick cloth over the cap before turning it anti-clockwise.**
Caution: Never operate the vehicle with plain water in the cooling system, except in an emergency. Apart from the risk of freezing in winter weather, serious corrosion and rust and scale formation may occur.
Warning: Antifreeze is poisonous and must be handled with due care.

Draining

1 The system should only be drained when it is cool. If it must be drained hot, take great care to avoid scalding.
2 Remove the expansion tank cap. If the system is hot, place a thick cloth over the cap before turning it anti-clockwise.

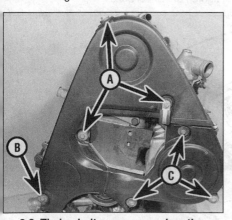

3.2 Timing belt cover screw location

A *Large cover - short screws*
B *Large cover - long screw*
C *Pump sprocket cover screws*

3 Place a container underneath the radiator bottom hose. Disconnect the hose from the radiator and allow the system to drain (**see illustration**).
4 There is no cylinder block drain plug, making it impossible to drain the system completely.

Filling

5 Make sure that all hoses and clips are in good condition. Refit any disturbed hoses and see that their clips are tight.
6 Fill the system via the expansion tank cap. If new coolant is being put in, start by pouring in the required quantity of neat antifreeze and follow it up with the water.
7 Massage the large coolant hoses to help displace air pockets during filling.
8 Most vehicles will be fitted with a self-venting cooling system this can be recognised by the two small vent hoses which enter the top of the expansion tank. If the system is not self-venting, open the bleed screw on the thermostat elbow during filling and close it when coolant runs out at the bleed screw (**see illustration**).
9 When the system appears full, refit the expansion tank cap. Run the engine up to operating temperature, keeping a look-out for coolant leaks, then stop it and allow it to cool. Recheck the coolant level and top-up if necessary.

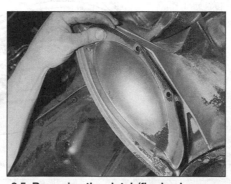

3.5 Removing the clutch/flywheel access cover

10 Recheck the tightness of all hose clips when the engine has cooled, and again after a few hundred miles.

3 Timing belt -
removal and refitting

Caution: A timing belt which is damaged, oil-soaked or fuel soaked must be renewed or it will fail, resulting in serious engine damage.

Removal

1 Remove the alternator drivebelt (Section 1).
2 Remove the timing belt covers. The large cover is secured by four screws - note the fuel pipe clip under one of them. The injection pump sprocket cover is secured by three screws (**see illustration**).
3 Remove the crankshaft pulley - it is secured to the sprocket by four Allen screws.
4 Disconnect the battery earth lead.
5 Remove the clutch/flywheel access cover from the bottom of the gearbox bellhousing (**see illustration**).
6 Turn the crankshaft in the normal direction of rotation, using a spanner on the sprocket bolt, until the timing mark on the injection pump sprocket aligns with the reference mark on the pump bracket. In this position No 1 piston is at TDC on the firing stroke (**see illustration**).

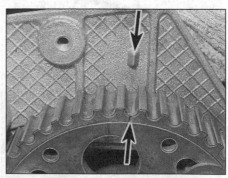

3.6 Injection pump sprocket timing mark aligned with mark on pump bracket

2B

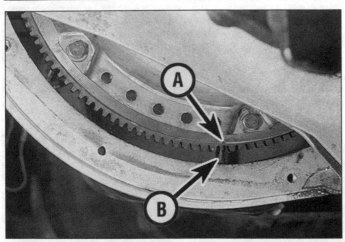

3.7 TDC mark on flywheel (A) and pointer on clutch housing (B)

3.10 Undoing a coolant pump bolt - other two arrowed (engine removed)

7 Check that the TDC mark on the flywheel and the pointer on the clutch housing are aligned **(see illustration)**.

8 If tool KM-537 or equivalent is available, remove the vacuum pump and lock the camshaft in position by fitting the tool. If the tool is not available or cannot be fitted, make alignment marks between the camshaft sprocket and its backplate for use when refitting.

9 Drain the coolant.

10 Slacken the three bolts which secure the coolant pump to the block **(see illustration)**. Using a large open-ended spanner on the flats of the pump, pivot it to release the tension on the belt.

11 Separate the right-hand front engine mounting by undoing the two bolts which are accessible from the top.

12 Mark the running direction of the belt if it is to be re-used. Also take care not to kink the belt, nor get oil, grease etc. on it.

13 Slip the belt off the sprockets and jockey wheel. Remove the belt by feeding it through the engine mounting.

14 If signs of oil contamination are found,

trace the source of the oil leak and rectify it, then wash down the engine timing belt area and all related components to remove all traces of oil.

Refitting

15 Commence refitting by threading the belt through the engine mounting. Refit and tighten the engine mounting bolts.

16 Place the belt over the sprockets and the jockey wheel **(see illustration)**. Make sure that No 1 piston is still at TDC, the injection pump sprocket mark is aligned and the camshaft position is still correct.

17 Move the coolant pump so as to put some tension on the timing belt. Nip up the pump securing bolts, but do not tighten them fully yet.

18 Remove the camshaft locking tool, if used, and refit and secure the crankshaft pulley.

19 Belt tension can only be adjusted accurately using tension gauge KM-510-A or equivalent **(see illustration)**. A belt which is

too tight will usually hum when running and a belt which is too slack will wear rapidly and may jump teeth.

20 Settle the belt by rotating the crankshaf through half a turn in the normal direction o rotation. Fit the tension gauge to the slack side of the belt (the alternator side) and read the tension. Desired values are given in the *Specifications*.

21 If adjustment is necessary, slacken the coolant pump bolts and pivot the pump to increase or decrease the tension. Nip up the coolant pump bolts.

22 Turn the crankshaft through one full turn then recheck the tension. Keep adjusting the belt tension until a stable value is obtained.

23 Tighten the coolant pump bolts to the specified torque. Refill the cooling system (Section 2).

24 Check the injection pump timing (Section 6).

25 Refit the belt covers, clutch/flywheel cover and other disturbed components.

26 Refit the roadwheel, lower the vehicle and tighten the wheel bolts.

3.16 Timing belt correctly fitted

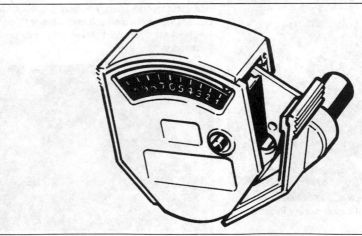

3.19 Timing belt tension gauge

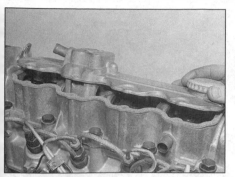

4.6 Removing the camshaft cover

4.8a Fitting the camshaft alignment tool KM-537

4.8b Home-made tool for locking the camshaft in a set position

4 Valve timing - checking and adjustment

1 Valve timing on these engines is more complicated than on the petrol equivalents because there are no timing marks as such on the camshaft or sprocket, neither is the sprocket keyed or pegged to the camshaft.

2 Note that the camshaft sprocket bolt should be renewed whenever it has been slackened.

3 If the valve timing has been lost completely, be careful when turning the crankshaft or camshaft in case piston/valve contact occurs.

4 Two methods of checking the valve timing are described. For either method, begin by checking the timing belt tension.

5 Bring the engine to TDC, No 1 firing, by turning the crankshaft in the normal direction of rotation, using a spanner on the sprocket bolt, until the timing mark on the injection pump sprocket aligns with the reference mark on the pump bracket (see illustration 3.6). Check that the TDC mark on the flywheel and the pointer on the clutch housing are aligned (see illustration 3.7).

6 Remove the air cleaner. Disconnect the breather hose and remove the camshaft cover (see illustration). If necessary, also remove the vacuum pump.

Using tool KM-537 or equivalent

7 The maker's tool KM-537 consists of a plate which bolts onto the camshaft carrier in place of the vacuum pump. When the peg on the plate will enter the hole in the tail of the camshaft, the camshaft is correctly positioned for TDC, No 1 piston firing.

Making the tool

8 It is possible to make a substitute for tool KM-537 (see illustration), but the valve timing must be known to be correct first - thereafter the tool can be used to check the timing. As can be seen, the home-made tool is simply a metal bar with three holes drilled in it (see illustration). The accuracy of the tool depends on the precision with which the holes are drilled, and the snug fit of the screws or bolts in their holes. The crankshaft must be at

TDC, No 1 firing, before marking up and constructing the tool.

9 Drill one of the end holes in the metal bar. Insert a short stud or dowel into the camshaft peg hole, marking the end with chalk or paint. The stud should be just long enough to touch the metal bar in its fitted position.

10 Secure the bar, using one of the vacuum pump screws, so that it is just free to move. Swing the bar past the stud or dowel so that an arc is marked on the bar. Remove the bar and drill a hole in the centre of the arc to accept a bolt or screw which will fit snugly into the camshaft peg hole. Fit this bolt or screw and clamp it with a couple of nuts.

11 Mark around the other vacuum pump screw hole with paint or chalk. Offer the tool to the camshaft and carrier so that the peg hole bolt and first fixing screw are snug and the position of the second fixing screw hole is marked. Remove the tool and drill the second fixing screw hole.

12 Offer up the tool again and make sure that it fits without strain or slack; repeat the construction exercise if necessary.

Using the tool

13 With the crankshaft and injection pump timing marks correctly positioned, offer the tool to the camshaft carrier in place of the vacuum pump. If the tool can be located and secured so that the peg enters the hole in the camshaft, valve timing is correct. In fact, a tolerance of 1.0 mm in either direction at the flywheel TDC mark is allowed.

14 If the tool will not enter, remove it. Hold the

camshaft using a spanner on the flats provided and slacken the camshaft sprocket bolt. Break the taper between the sprocket and camshaft if necessary by tapping the sprocket with a wooden or plastic mallet. Turn the camshaft until the alignment tool enters snugly. Remove the old camshaft sprocket bolt and insert a new bolt. Nip the bolt up until the sprocket taper bites, then remove the alignment tool. Hold the camshaft again and tighten the sprocket bolt to the specified torque.

15 Back off the crankshaft a quarter turn, then regain TDC and check that the alignment tool still fits snugly.

Using a dial test indicator

16 Tool KM-537 cannot be used on later models (mid-1984 on) because the holes into which it screws have been deleted. The home-made tool which screws into the vacuum pump holes is not affected. Instead of tool KM-537, the makers specify the use of a dial test indicator (DTI or clock gauge) and suitable support. The support must allow the DTI to move across the camshaft carrier without changing height relative to the carrier top surface. The DTI foot (the part which will rest on the cam lobe) should have a flat bottom and be 7 to 10 mm in diameter.

17 To check the valve timing, position the timing marks as specified in paragraph 5, then place the DTI and support over the second cam from the sprocket end (No 1 cylinder inlet cam).

18 Zero the DTI on the base circle of the cam (see illustration).

19 Carefully move the DTI, and its support if

4.18 Dial test indicator zeroed on base circle of second cam . . .

4.19 . . . another reading is taken towards the top of the cam

2B

5.4a Fitting a new O-ring to the coolant pump

5.4b Fitting the coolant pump (engine removed)

applicable, exactly 10 mm towards the top of the cam. In this position the DTI should show a lift of 0.55 ± 0.05 mm. If so, the valve timing is correct (see illustration).

20 If adjustment is necessary, proceed as described in paragraph 14, but working towards a correct DTI reading instead of a correct fit of the tool.

All methods

21 Check the injection pump timing, then refit the belt covers, flywheel/clutch cover, cam cover and other disturbed components.

5 Coolant pump -
removal and refitting

Removal

1 Drain the cooling system, saving the coolant if it is fit for re-use.

2 Remove the timing belt, the timing belt idler pulley and backplate.

3 Remove the three bolts which retain the coolant pump. Lift out the pump - some coolant will be released. It may be necessary

to remove the alternator to provide sufficient clearance to remove the pump completely.

Refitting

4 Use a new O-ring when refitting the pump. In order to prevent corrosion and the resultant impossibility of moving the coolant pump to tension the timing belt, apply silicone grease to the pump O-ring and cylinder block mating surface. Insert but do not tighten the retaining bolts (see illustrations).

5 Refit the timing belt backplate and the idler pulley.

6 Refit and tension the timing belt.

7 Refit the other disturbed components, then refill the cooling system.

6 Fuel injection pump timing -
checking and adjustment

Checking

1 Timing of the injection pump should only be necessary in the following circumstances:

a) *When fitting a new or overhauled pump*

b) *If the timing is suspected of being wrong*

c) *If the timing belt has been re-tensioned or renewed*

A dial test indicator with a long probe and a suitable support will be needed.

2 The procedure as shown here was carried out during engine rebuilding. With the engine in the vehicle, it will be necessary to remove the timing belt covers, the air cleaner snorkel and the clutch/flywheel cover.

3 Check the valve timing (Section 4).

4 Bring the engine to TDC, No 1 firing. The timing mark on the pump sprocket must be aligned with the pip on the pump bracket (see illustration).

5 Turn the engine against the normal direction of rotation so that the flywheel TDC mark is approximately 5.0 cm away from the TDC pointer.

6 Remove the central plug from the rear of the injection pump (see illustration).

7 Mount the dial test indicator with its probe entering the central plug hole. Zero the indicator (see illustration).

8 Be prepared for fuel spillage during subsequent operations. The manufacturers specify the use of a probe which screws into and presumably seals, the plug hole.

9 Bring the engine back to TDC, No 1 firing. When the timing marks are aligned, the dial

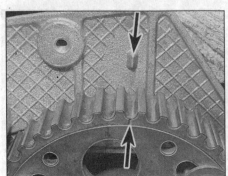

6.4 Injection pump sprocket timing mark aligned with mark on pump bracket

6.6 Removing the plug from the rear of the injection pump

6.7 Dial test indicator mounted with its probe in the plug hole

6.10a Slacken the injection pump sprocket clamping bolts . . .

test indicator should show a lift corresponding to the desired timing setting - see *Specifications*.

Adjustment

10 If adjustment is necessary, slacken the three bolts which clamp together the two halves of the pump sprocket **(see illustration)**. Turn the inner part of the sprocket anti-clockwise (against the normal direction of rotation) as far as the slots will allow. The fit between the two parts of the

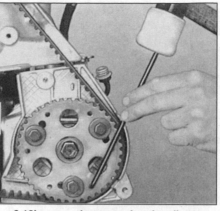

6.10b . . . and use a rod and mallet to move the inner part of the sprocket

sprocket is tight and a rod or soft metal drift may be needed to encourage the inner part to move **(see illustration)**.

11 With the sprocket positioned as just described and the engine still at TDC, No 1 firing, the dial test indicator should again read zero. Reset it if necessary.

12 Turn the inner part of the sprocket clockwise

until the dial test indicator shows the desired lift, then tighten the sprocket clamp bolts.

13 Repeat the checking procedure from paragraph 5.

14 When the injection timing is correct, remove the test gear and refit the plug to the rear of the pump.

15 Refit the timing belt covers and other disturbed components.

---

7 Vacuum pump - removal and refitting

Removal

1 Disconnect the servo vacuum pipe from the pump. Do this by counterholding the large union nut and unscrewing the small one **(see illustration)**.

2 Remove the two pump securing screws and withdraw the pump from the camshaft housing **(see illustrations)**. Be prepared for some oil spillage.

3 Recover the small central oil pipe and the driving dog.

4 Discard the two O-rings fitted to the central oil pipe and also the pump body to camshaft housing seal **(see illustration)**.

Refitting

5 Fit new sealing rings to the pump assembly.

6 Refit the central oil pipe and the driving dog to the pump **(see illustration)**.

7 Offer the pump to the camshaft housing, making sure that the teeth of the driving dog engage with the slot in the camshaft end. Fit the pump securing screws and tighten them to the specified torque.

8 Reconnect and secure the vacuum pipe connection(s).

2B

7.1 Disconnecting the servo vacuum pipe from the vacuum pump

7.2a Remove the two pump securing screws . . .

7.2b . . . and withdraw the vacuum pump from the camshaft housing

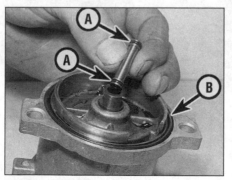

7.4 Renew the O-rings fitted to the central oil pipe (A) and the pump body to camshaft housing seal (B)

7.6 Refitting the central oil pipe with driving dog to the vacuum pump

Notes

Chapter 3A
Vauxhall Astra/Belmont &
Opel Kadett petrol 1984 to 1991

Contents

Specifications

Timing belt renewal interval .... Every 36 000 miles (60 000 km) or 4 years - whichever comes first

Timing belt tension (using gauge KM-510-A)	1.3 and 1.4 litre	1.6, 1.8 and 2.0 litre
New belt, cold	6.0	3.0
New belt, warm	8.0	8.0
Used belt, cold	5.0	3.0
Used belt, warm	7.5	8.0

Torque wrench settings	Nm	lbf ft
Alternator mounting bracket bolts	40	30
Alternator pivot and adjustment bolts	34	25
Camshaft sprocket bolts:		
SOHC engine	45	33
DOHC engine:*		
Stage 1	50	37
Stage 2	Angle-tighten a further 40° to 50°	
Crankshaft pulley bolt:		
1.3, 1.4 and 1.6 (16SV and C16NZ) litre engine:		
Bolt with 23 mm thread length	55	41
Bolt with 30 mm thread length:*		
Stage 1	55	41
Stage 2	Angle tighten a further 45 to 60°	
1.6, 1.8 and 2.0 litre SOHC engine	20	15
Crankshaft pulley-to-sprocket screws with splined heads	20	15
Crankshaft sprocket bolt:*		
SOHC engine:		
Stage 1	130	96
Stage 2	Angle tighten a further 40 to 50°	
DOHC engine:		
Stage 1	250	185
Stage 2	Angle-tighten a further 40 to 50°	
Roadwheel bolts	90	66
Spark plugs	20	15
Timing belt tensioner and idler rollers-to-block bolts:*		
Stage 1	25	18
Stage 2	Angle-tighten a further 45° to 60°	
Water pump bolts:		
1.2, 1.3 and 1.4 litre models	8	6
1.6, 1.8 and 2.0 litre models	25	18

Note: *All bolts which are angle tightened must be renewed whenever they are disturbed*

1 Auxiliary drivebelt - removal, refitting and adjustment

Alternator

1 To remove the belt, simply loosen the mounting nuts and bolts, and the bolt securing the adjuster bracket, and slacken the belt sufficiently to slip it from the pulleys. On models with power steering it will first be necessary to remove the power steering pump drivebelt as described below.

2 Refit the the pulleys.

3 Although special tools are available for measuring the belt tension, a good approximation can be achieved if the belt is tensioned so that there is approximately 13 mm of free movement under firm thumb pressure at the mid-point of the longest run between pulleys. If in doubt, err on the slack side, as an excessively-tight belt may cause damage to the alternator or other components.

4 If adjustment is required, loosen the alternator upper mounting nut and bolt - use two spanners, one to counterhold the bolt. Lever the alternator away from the engine using a wooden lever at the mounting bracket until the correct tension is achieved, then tighten the bolt securing the adjuster bracket, and the alternator mounting nuts and bolts. On no account lever at the free end of the alternator, as serious internal damage could be caused to the alternator.

Power steering pump

5 To remove the belt, simply loosen the locknut and fully slacken the adjuster nut sufficiently to slip the drivebelt from the pulleys.

6 Refit the belt over the pulleys

7 Although special tools are available for measuring the belt tension, a good approximation can be achieved if the belt is tensioned so that there is approximately 8 mm of free movement under firm thumb pressure at the mid-point of the longest run between pulleys. If in doubt, err on the slack side, as an excessively-tight belt may cause damage to the alternator or other components.

8 If adjustment is required, slacken the adjuster bolt locknut (situated on the base of the pump) and rotate the adjuster nut as necessary to tension the belt. Once the belt tension is correct, securely tighten the locknut.

Alternator/power steering pump - later 1.6 litre models

9 From March 1987 onwards, a single drivebelt is used for the alternator and power steering pump on 1.6 litre engines. The drivebelt is of the ribbed type and runs at a higher tension than the previous (V) belt.

10 To remove the belt, simply loosen the alternator pivot and strap bolts and slip the drivebelt from the pulleys.

11 Refit the belt over the pulleys.

12 To set the tension accurately, make up or obtain an adapter as shown (see illustration).

13 Slacken the alternator pivot and adjusting strap bolts and fit the adapter. Using a torque wrench apply a load of 55 Nm (41 lbf ft) for a new belt, or 50 Nm (37 lbf ft) for an old belt. Keep the tension applied and securely tighten the alternator bolts.

2 Coolant - draining and refilling

Draining

⚠️ **Warning: Wait until the engine is cold before starting this procedure. Do not allow antifreeze to come in contact with your skin or painted surfaces of the vehicle. Rinse off spills immediately with plenty of water. Never leave antifreeze lying around in an open container or in a puddle in the driveway or on the garage floor. Children and pets are attracted by its sweet smell. Antifreeze is fatal if ingested.**

1 To drain the cooling system, remove the expansion tank filler cap. Turn the cap anti-clockwise until it reaches the first stop. Wait until any pressure remaining in the system is released then push the cap down, turn it anti-clockwise to the second stop and lift off.

2 Position a suitable container beneath the radiator bottom hose union.

3 Slacken the hose clip and ease the hose from the radiator stub. If the hose joint has not been disturbed for some time, it will be necessary to gently manipulate the hose to break the joint. Do not use excessive force, or the radiator stub could be damaged. Allow the coolant to drain into the container.

4 Reconnect the hose and securely tighten its retaining clip on completion of draining.

Refilling

5 Before attempting to fill the cooling system make sure that all hoses and clips are in good condition, and that the clips are tight.

6 Remove the expansion tank filler cap.

7 On 1.3, 1.4 and later 1.6 litre engines models, disconnect the wire and unscrew the coolant temperature sender from the inlet manifold. On early 1.6, and all 1.8 and 2.0 litre models, unscrew the bleed screw which is situated in the thermostat housing cover (where no bleed screw is fitted, unscrew the temperature sender unit) (see illustration).

8 Fill the system by slowly pouring the coolant into the expansion tank to prevent airlocks from forming.

9 When coolant free of air bubbles emerges from the orifice, reconnect the heater hose (1.2 litre models) or refit the coolant temperature sender/bleed screw (as applicable) and tighten it securely (all other models).

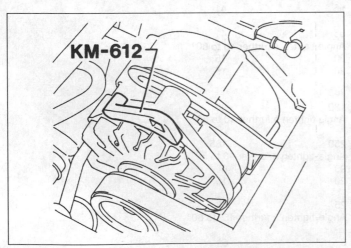

1.12 Adapter KM-612 used for setting auxiliary drivebelt tension on later 1.6 litre models

2.7 On 1.3 litre models, unscrew temperature gauge sender unit from the manifold to bleed the cooling system

3.3 Removing the water pump - 1.8 litre model shown

3.4 Fitting a new sealing ring to the pump

10 Top-up the coolant level to the KALT (or COLD) mark on the expansion tank, then refit the expansion tank cap.

11 Start the engine and run it until it reaches normal operating temperature, then stop the engine and allow it to cool.

12 Check for leaks, particularly around disturbed components. Check the coolant level in the expansion tank, and top-up if necessary. Note that the system must be cold before an accurate level is indicated in the expansion tank.

3 Water pump (SOHC engine) - removal and refitting

Removal

1 Drain the cooling system as described in Section 1 then disconnect the battery earth lead.

2 Remove the timing belt and the timing belt backplate as described in Section 4.

3 Remove the three securing bolts and withdraw the water pump **(see illustration)**. Note that it may be necessary to remove the alternator completely (see Section 8) to provide enough room to remove the pump from the engine bay.

Refitting

4 Refitting is the reverse of removal, noting the following points.

a) *Fit a new sealing ring to the pump* **(see illustration)**.

b) *Ensure that the pump and its recess are clean and dry and coat the sealing ring and cylinder block mating surface with silicone grease or petroleum jelly. This will prevent contact corrosion between the pump and the block, and make things easier if the pump has to be moved for adjustment of the timing belt.*

c) *Fit the timing belt and tension it as described in Section 4 and tighten the pump bolts to the specified torque.*

d) *On completion refill the cooling system and adjust the alternator drivebelt as described in Sections 2 and 1.*

4 Timing belt (SOHC engine) - removal and refitting

Note: *The following procedure will necessitate re-positioning of the water pump which, in turn, is likely to cause leakage from around the sealing flange. Minor leakage can normally be rectified by using a proprietary radiator sealing product in the cooling system, although it is preferable to remove the water pump completely and fit a new sealing ring (for further information see Section 3).*

Removal

1 Undo the belt cover retaining bolts (early models) or release the retaining clips (later models) and remove the cover.

2 Use a socket or spanner on the crankshaft pulley to turn the crankshaft until No 1 piston is at its firing point, indicated by the notch on the crankshaft pulley being in line with the pointer on the oil pump housing, and the mark on the camshaft sprocket being in line with the rib on the camshaft housing **(see illustrations)**.

3A

4.2a Crankshaft pulley notch and oil pump pointer in alignment (arrowed)

4.2b Camshaft sprocket mark and housing rib (both arrowed) should be aligned

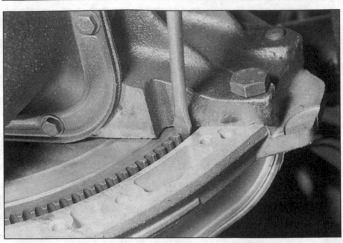

4.4 Jamming the flywheel ring gear

4.8 Slackening a water pump bolt

3 Slacken the alternator mounting and adjustment bolts, move the alternator towards the engine and remove its drivebelt. Where necessary, unscrew the union nuts and disconnect the oil cooler pipes from the filter housing to improve access to the crankshaft pulley.

4 On 1.3, 1.4 and 1.6 (16SV and C16NZ) litre engines, release the crankshaft pulley central bolt without disturbing the set position of the crankshaft. To prevent the crankshaft turning it may be sufficient to engage a gear (manual gearbox only) and apply the brakes; a better way is to remove the flywheel bottom cover plate and jam the flywheel ring gear with a large screwdriver or a tyre lever **(see illustration)**. Remove the bolt and the pulley.

5 On 1.6 (16SH), 1.8 and 2.0 litre engines, remove the four Allen screws which secure the pulley to the sprocket. Remove the pulley.

6 On all models, drain the cooling system as described in Section 2.

7 On later (June 1990 onwards) 1.4 litre and 1.6 (16SV and C16NZ) litre engines which are

fitted with a spring-loaded automatic tensioner, lock the tensioner in its slackest position. To do this move the tensioner indicator arm clockwise until the holes in the baseplate and arm align and lock the tensioner in position with a suitable rod **(see illustration 4.15)**.

8 On all models, slacken the three bolts which secure the water pump. The bolts are accessible through holes in the belt backplate **(see illustration)**.

9 Swivel the pump to release the tension on the timing belt. There are flats behind the pump sprocket for this purpose **(see illustration)**. Note the belt's running direction if it is to be used again, then slip it off the sprockets.

10 A new belt, or one which is to be re-used, must not be kinked or be contaminated with oil, grease etc

Refitting

Later (June 1990 onwards) 1.4 litre and 1.6 (16SV and C16NZ) litre engines

11 Fit the new belt without disturbing the set position of the crankshaft and camshaft sprockets. Apply some tension by moving the water pump and check that the timing marks are correctly aligned **(see illustration)**.

12 Refit the crankshaft pulley bolt and withdraw the locking rod from the spring loaded automatic tensioner.

13 Rotate the water pump and set the belt tension so that the automatic tensioner indicator arm and backplate holes are aligned (the tensioner arm will have moved fully clockwise). Tighten the water pump bolts securely.

14 Rotate the crankshaft smoothly throug

4.9 Swivelling the water pump using a spanner on the flats

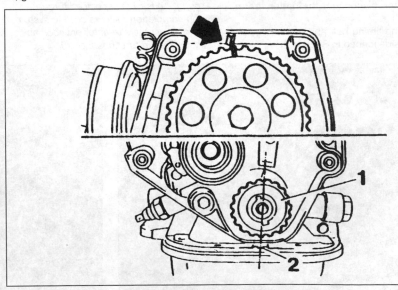

4.11 On 1.4 and 1.6 (16SV and C16NZ) litre engines, align the camshaft sprocket mark with the backplate rib. The crankshaft sprocket (1) is aligned with the backplate/oil pump housing groove (2)

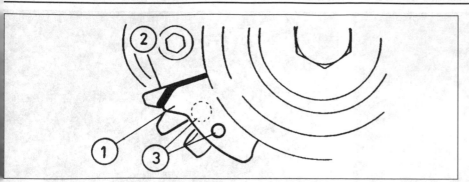

4.15 Timing belt tensioner indicator arm (1), baseplate (2) and locking holes (3) - later 1.4 litre and 1.6 (16SV and C16NZ) litre engines

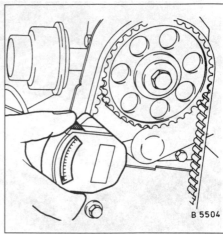

4.21 Checking the timing belt tension with gauge KM-510-A

two complete turns clockwise until the timing marks are realigned **(see illustration 4.11)**.

15 Slacken the water pump bolts and rotate the pump anti-clockwise slightly until the automatic tensioner arm is positioned in the centre of backplate notch **(see illustration)**. When the tensioner is correctly positioned, tighten the water pump bolts to the specified torque setting.

16 Rotate the crankshaft through two more complete turns clockwise (so that the timing marks are aligned again) and check that the tensioner arm and backplate notch are still correctly aligned. If not, repeat the operation in paragraph 15.

17 Once the tensioner position is correct, remove the crankshaft pulley bolt.

18 Refit all disturbed components by reversing the removal sequence. Adjust the auxiliary drivebelt and refill the cooling system as described in Sections 1 and 2.

All other models

19 Fit the new belt without disturbing the set position of the crankshaft and camshaft sprockets. Apply some tension by moving the water pump.

20 Refit the crankshaft pulley and check that

the pulley and camshaft sprocket marks are still correctly aligned (paragraph 2). If not, release the belt tension and align the sprockets correctly. Tighten the crankshaft pulley bolt to the specified torque, using locking compound on the bolt threads.

21 To adjust the tension of the belt, the tension gauge (KM-510-A) should be used **(see illustration)**.

22 Turn the crankshaft through at least half a turn in the normal direction of rotation. Set the tension gauge, apply it to the slack side of the belt (above the alternator) and release it. Read the gauge and compare the figure with that given in the Specifications.

23 If adjustment is necessary, move the water pump to increase or decrease belt tension, rotate the crankshaft through one full turn and take another gauge reading. Repeat as necessary until the desired tension is achieved.

24 When adjustment is correct, tighten the water pump bolts to the specified torque. Refit and secure the belt cover.

25 Refit and tension the alternator drivebelt and refill the cooling system, as described in Sections 1 and 2. Refit the flywheel bottom cover if it was removed.

5 Timing belt (DOHC engine) - removal and refitting

Note: *The timing belt must be renewed every time it is removed, even if it is apparently in good condition.*

Removal

1 Raise and support the front of the vehicle. Remove the engine undertray and the wheelarch splash shields as a unit.

2 Disconnect the battery negative lead.

3 Unclip the throttle cable from the air cleaner-to-air mass meter trunking. Slacken the clips and remove the trunking.

4 Remove the air cleaner as described in Section 7.

5 Remove the steering pump drivebelt (when applicable) and the alternator drivebelt.

6 Remove the three bolts and rubber bushes which secure the timing belt cover. Remove the cover and its seal **(see illustrations)**.

3A

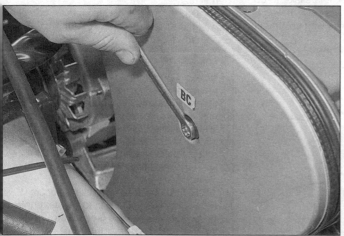

5.6a Removing a belt cover bolt . . .

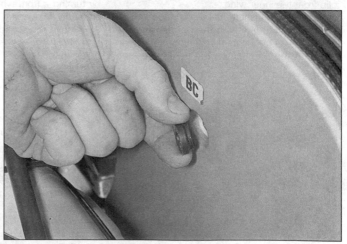

5.6b . . . and the rubber bush

5.6c The belt cover seal

5.8a Pulley notch and pointer must be aligned . . .

5.8b . . . and sprocket marks aligned with backplate notches (arrowed)

5.10 Slackening the camshaft belt tensioner screw

7 Working through the wheelarch, slacken the six screws with splined heads which secure the crankshaft pulley to the sprocket. For better access, unbolt the oil cooler hose clip from the inner wing.

8 Turn the crankshaft until the timing mark on the pulley is in line with the pointer and the timing marks on the camshaft sprockets are in line with the notches on the backplate (see

illustrations). (To turn the crankshaft by means of the central bolt, a Torx socket, size E20, will be needed. If this is not available, engage 4th or 5th gear and turn the crankshaft by turning a front wheel. It is easier to do this smoothly if the spark plugs are removed.)

9 Remove the six screws with splined heads and lift off the crankshaft pulley. The screw holes are offset so it will only fit one way.

10 Slacken the camshaft belt tensioner screw using a 6 mm Allen key (see illustration). Move the tensioner to slacken the belt and slip the belt off the sprockets and rollers.

11 Do not turn the crankshaft or camshafts while the belt is removed, or piston/valve contact may occur.

Refitting

12 Commence refitting by checking that the pulley and sprocket timing marks are still correctly aligned. Temporarily refit the pulley and secure it with two screws to do this. When satisfied, remove the pulley.

13 Fit the new belt over the sprockets and rollers, being careful not to kink it. Observe any arrows or other indication of running direction.

14 Refit the crankshaft pulley. Secure it with the six screws with splined heads, tightened to the specified torque (see illustration).

15 The belt tension must now be set. The makers specify the use of a special tool (KM-666) (see illustration).

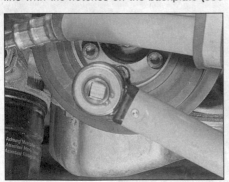

5.14 Tightening one of the crankshaft pulley screws

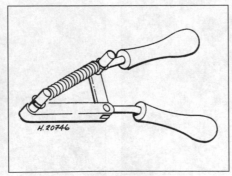

H.20746

5.15 Special tool KM-666 for tensioning the timing belt

16 Fit the special tool to the tensioner. Make sure the tensioner is free to move.

17 Make a mark on the exhaust camshaft sprocket, seven teeth anti-clockwise from the timing mark. Turn the crankshaft clockwise until the new mark is aligned with the notch on the belt backplate. In this position tighten the tensioner screw to the specified torque, then remove the special tool.

18 Turn the crankshaft through two full turns clockwise and check that the pulley and sprocket timing marks come back into correct alignment. If they do not, remove the belt and start again.

19 The remainder of refitting is the reverse of the removal procedure.

6 Timing belt tensioner and idler rollers (DOHC engine) - removal and refitting

Removal

1 Remove the timing belt as described in Section 5.

2 Remove the Allen screw which secures the belt tensioner. Lift off the tensioner and its mounting plate and recover the spacer sleeve.

3 Similarly unbolt and remove the idler roller and recover its sleeve.

4 Renew the rollers if they show roughness when spun, or if they have been noisy in operation.

Refitting

5 Refitting is the reverse of the removal procedure, noting the following points:

a) *Make sure the spacer sleeves are the right way round. The smaller diameter of the tensioner sleeve goes towards the block. The smaller diameter of the idler sleeve goes away from the block.*

b) *Tighten the screws to the specified torque.*

c) *Fit a new timing belt.*

7 Air cleaner housing (DOHC engine) - removal and refitting

Removal

1 Remove the trunking which connects the air cleaner to the air mass meter **(see illustration)**.

2 Remove the three bolts which secure the air cleaner. Remove the air cleaner **(see illustrations)**.

Refitting

3 Refit by reversing the removal operations.

8 Alternator - removal and refitting

Removal

1 Disconnect the battery earth (negative) lead.

2 Make a note of the electrical connections at the rear of the alternator, then disconnect the multi-plug, spade terminals or other connectors as appropriate.

3 Remove the alternator strap bolts, noting the short earth lead which links the alternator to the engine. Slacken the pivot bolt, swing the alternator towards the engine and remove the drivebelt.

4 Remove the pivot bolt and lift off the alternator. On one car examined, the pivot bolt had been inserted from the wrong side so that it could not be withdrawn far enough to release the alternator: in this case it is necessary to unbolt the alternator mounting from the block.

5 Take care not to knock or drop the alternator.

Refitting

6 Refit in the reverse order to removal; tension the drivebelt as described in Section 1.

7.1 Disconnecting the trunking from the air cleaner

7.2a Two of the air cleaner securing bolts (arrowed)

7.2b The third air cleaner bolt

7.2c Removing the air cleaner

3A

Notes

Chapter 3B
Vauxhall Astra/Belmont & Opel Kadett diesel 1984 to 1991

Contents

3B

Specifications

Timing belt renewal interval .... Every 36 000 miles (60 000 km) or 4 years - whichever comes first

Auxiliary drivebelts
Tension (using gauge KM-128-A):
  Alternator:
    New .... 450 N
    Used .... 250 to 400 N
  Power steering pump:
    New .... 450 N
    Used .... 250 to 300 N

Timing belt tension
16D and 16DA engines (using tension gauge KM-510-A):
  New belt, warm 9.0
  New belt, cold 6.5
  Run-in belt, warm 8.0
  Run-in belt, cold 4.0
17D engine (using tension gauge KM-510-A):
  New belt, warm 7.5
  New belt, cold 9.5
  Run-in belt, warm 5.0
  Run-in belt, cold 9.0
17DR and 17DTL engines .... Automatic tensioner

Injection pump timing setting
16D engine .... 1.0 ± 0.05 mm
16DA engine .... 0.9 ± 0.05 mm
17D, 17DR and 17DTL engines:
  Bosch .... $0.80 + 0.05$ mm
  Lucas/CAV .... $x - 0.15$ mm (where x = manufacturer's calibration marked on pump)

Torque wrench settings

	Nm	lbf ft

16D and 16DA engines

Alternator:
Adjuster strap nuts and bolts	25	18
Pivot bolt	25	18

Camshaft sprocket bolt:*
Stage 1	75	55
Stage 2	Angle-tighten a further 60°	
Coolant pump to cylinder block	25	18
Crankshaft pulley-to-sprocket bolt	20	15

Crankshaft sprocket centre bolt:
16D engine	155	114

16DA engine:*
Stage 1	130	96
Stage 2	Angle-tighten a further 45°	

Engine mountings:
Except right-hand bracket to cylinder block	40	30
Right-hand mounting bracket to cylinder block	50	37

Fuel injection pump and brackets:
Main bracket to block	25	18
Pump sprockets bolts	25	18

Subsidiary brackets:
M6 bolts	14	10
M8 bolts	25	18

Power steering pump:
Drivebelt tensioner to pump	40	30
Vacuum pump to camshaft housing	28	21
Wheel bolts	90	66

17D, 17DR and 17DTL engines

Alternator:
Adjuster strap nuts and bolts	25	18
Pivot bolt	25	18

Camshaft sprocket bolt:*
Stage 1	75	55
Stage 2	Angle tighten a further 60°	
Stage 3	Angle tighten a further 5°	
Coolant pump bolts	25	18
Crankcase pulley to sprocket	20	15

Engine mountings:

Left-hand:
Mounting bracket to transmission	60	44
Flexible mounting to bracket	60	44
Flexible mounting to sidemember	65	48

Right-hand:
Mounting bracket to cylinder block	60	44
Flexible mounting to bracket	35	26
Flexible mounting to sidemember	65	48

Rear:
Mounting bracket to transmission	60	44
Flexible mounting to bracket	45	33
Flexible mounting to sidemember	40	30

Fuel injection pump:
Fuel lines to pump	25	18
Hub to pump	25	18
Pump to bracket(s)	25	18
Pump to support - M6 bolts	12	9
Sprocket to hub	25	18
Vent bolt to pump	25	18

Power steering pump:
Drivebelt tensioner to pump	40	30

Timing belt:
Guide roller to cylinder block	40	30
Tension roller to cylinder block	25	18
Vacuum pump to camshaft housing	28	21
Wheel bolts	90	66

Bolts must be renewed every time

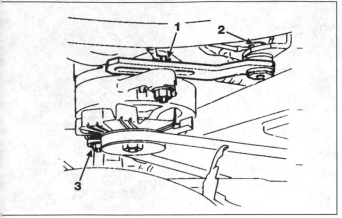

1.2 Alternator drivebelt adjustment points

1 *Alternator to adjuster strap bolt*   3 *Alternator*
2 *Adjuster strap pivot bolt*   *pivot bolt*

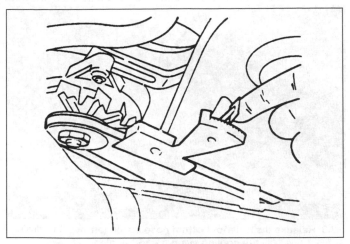

1.8 Using special tool KM-128-A to tension the alternator drivebelt

1 Auxiliary drivebelts - removal, refitting and adjustment

Alternator
Removal and refitting

1 Gain full access to the drivebelt by raising the car, supporting it on axle stands and removing the right-hand front roadwheel. Remove the air cleaner housing assembly.
2 To remove the drivebelt, first slacken the alternator pivot and adjuster strap nuts and bolts **(see illustration)**.
3 Where fitted, remove the power steering pump drivebelt.
4 Move the alternator towards the engine and slip the drivebelt off its pulleys.
5 Fit the new drivebelt in position over the pulleys and adjust it as follows:

Adjustment

6 Tighten the alternator fastening slightly, so

that the alternator can just be moved by hand.
7 Move the alternator away from the engine until the belt tension is correct.
8 Vauxhall recommend the use of a special tool (KM-128-A) for tensioning the belt to the specified amount **(see illustration)**. In the absence of this tool, aim for a tension such that the belt can be deflected about 12 mm by firm finger pressure in the middle of its run. The belt tension must, however, be checked with the special tool as soon as possible. If using a lever to move the alternator, only use a wooden or plastic one and only lever at the pulley end.
9 Tighten the alternator fastenings to the specified torque setting once the belt tension is correct.
10 Where applicable, refit and tension the steering pump drivebelt.
11 Refit the air cleaner housing assembly.

Power steering pump
Removal and refitting

12 Gain full access to the drivebelt by jacking

up the front right-hand side of the vehicle and supporting it on axle stands.
13 To remove the drivebelt, first loosen the pump mounting and tensioner bolts shown **(see illustration)**. Release the tensioner screw locknuts and rotate them to allow the drivebelt to slacken **(see illustration)**. Slip the drivebelt off its pulleys.
14 Fit the new drivebelt in position over the pulleys and adjust it as follows:

Adjustment

15 Rotate the tensioner screw locknuts until the belt tension is correct.
16 Vauxhall recommend the use of a special tool (KM-128-A) for tensioning the belt to the specified amount. In the absence of this tool, aim for a tension such that the belt can be deflected approximately 12 mm by firm finger pressure in the middle of its run. The belt tension must, however, be checked with the special tool as soon as possible.
17 Once belt tension is correct, tighten the tensioner screw locknuts and lower the vehicle.

3B

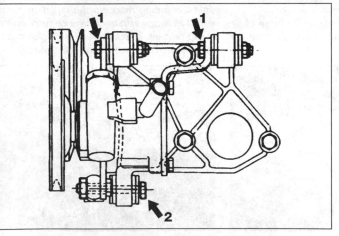

1.13a Power steering pump drivebelt adjustment points

1 *Pump mounting bolts*   2 *Tensioner bolt*

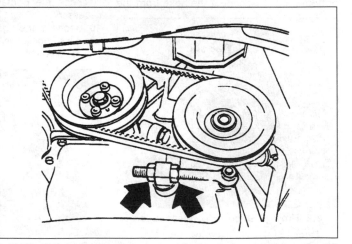

1.13b Rotate the tensioner screw locknuts (arrowed) to adjust drivebelt tension

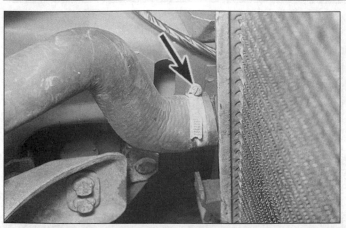

2.3 Release the radiator bottom hose clamp (arrowed) to drain the cooling system - 16D engine

2.8 The thermostat elbow coolant bleed screw (arrowed) - 16D engine

2 Coolant - draining and refilling

⚠️ **Warning: Take care to avoid scalding when removing the cooling system expansion tank cap. Place a thick cloth over the cap before turning it anti-clockwise.**
Caution: Never operate the vehicle with plain water in the cooling system, except in an emergency. Apart from the risk of freezing in winter weather, serious corrosion and rust and scale formation may occur.
Warning: Antifreeze is poisonous and must be handled with due care.

Draining

1 The system should only be drained when it is cool. If it must be drained hot, take great care to avoid scalding.
2 Remove the expansion tank cap. If the system is hot, place a thick cloth over the cap before turning it anti-clockwise.
3 Place a container underneath the radiator bottom hose. Disconnect the hose from the radiator and allow the system to drain (see illustration).
4 There is no cylinder block drain plug, making it impossible to drain the system completely.

Filling

5 Make sure that all hoses and clips are in good condition. Refit any disturbed hoses and see that their clips are tight.
6 Fill the system via the expansion tank cap. If new coolant is being put in, start by pouring in the required quantity of neat antifreeze and follow it up with the water.
7 Massage the large coolant hoses to help displace air pockets during filling.
8 Most vehicles will be fitted with a self-venting cooling system this can be recognised by the two small vent hoses which enter the top of the expansion tank. If the system is not self-venting, open the bleed screw on the thermostat elbow during filling and close it when coolant runs out at the bleed screw (see illustration).
9 When the system appears full, refit the expansion tank cap. Run the engine up to operating temperature, keeping a look-out for coolant leaks, then stop it and allow it to cool. Recheck the coolant level and top-up if necessary.
10 Recheck the tightness of all hose clips when the engine has cooled, and again after a few hundred miles.

3 Timing belt - removal and refitting

Caution: A timing belt which is damaged, oil-soaked or fuel soaked must be renewed or it will fail, resulting in serious engine damage.

16D and 16DA engines

Removal

1 Remove the alternator drivebelt (Section 1).
2 Remove the timing belt covers. The large cover is secured by four screws - note the fuel pipe clip under one of them. The injection pump sprocket cover is secured by three screws (see illustration).
3 Remove the crankshaft pulley - it is secured to the sprocket by four Allen screws.
4 Disconnect the battery earth lead.
5 Remove the clutch/flywheel access cover from the bottom of the gearbox bellhousing (see illustration).
6 Turn the crankshaft in the normal direction of rotation, using a spanner on the sprocket bolt, until the timing mark on the injection pump sprocket aligns with the reference mark on the pump bracket. In this position No 1 piston is at TDC on the firing stroke (see illustration).

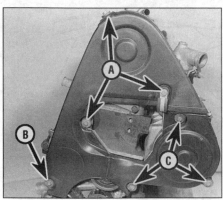

3.2 Timing belt cover screw location
A   Large cover - short screws
B   Large cover - long screw
C   Pump sprocket cover screws

3.5 Removing the clutch/flywheel access cover

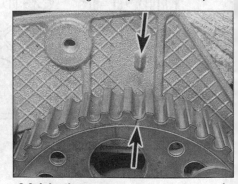

3.6 Injection pump sprocket timing mark aligned with mark on pump bracket

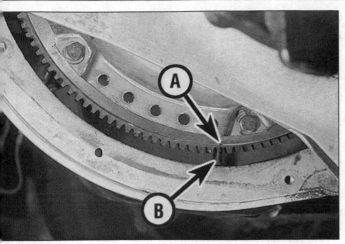

3.7 TDC mark on flywheel (A) and pointer on clutch housing (B)

3.10 Undoing a coolant pump bolt - other two arrowed (engine removed)

7 Check that the TDC mark on the flywheel and the pointer on the clutch housing are aligned **(see illustration)**.

8 If tool KM-537 or equivalent is available, remove the vacuum pump and lock the camshaft in position by fitting the tool. If the tool is not available or cannot be fitted, make alignment marks between the camshaft sprocket and its backplate for use when refitting.

9 Drain the coolant.

10 Slacken the three bolts which secure the coolant pump to the block **(see illustration)**. Using a large open-ended spanner on the flats of the pump, pivot it to release the tension on the belt.

11 Separate the right-hand front engine mounting by undoing the two bolts which are accessible from the top.

12 Mark the running direction of the belt if it is to be re-used. Also take care not to kink the belt, nor get oil, grease etc. on it.

13 Slip the belt off the sprockets and jockey wheel. Remove the belt by feeding it through the engine mounting.

14 If signs of oil contamination are found, trace the source of the oil leak and rectify it, then wash down the engine timing belt area and all related components to remove all traces of oil.

Refitting

15 Commence refitting by threading the belt through the engine mounting. Refit and tighten the engine mounting bolts.

16 Place the belt over the sprockets and the jockey wheel **(see illustration)**. Make sure that No 1 piston is still at TDC, the injection pump sprocket mark is aligned and the camshaft position is still correct.

17 Move the coolant pump so as to put some tension on the timing belt. Nip up the pump securing bolts, but do not tighten them fully yet.

18 Remove the camshaft locking tool, if used, and refit and secure the crankshaft pulley.

19 Belt tension can only be adjusted accurately using tension gauge KM-510-A or equivalent **(see illustration)**. A belt which is too tight will usually hum when running and a belt which is too slack will wear rapidly and may jump teeth.

20 Settle the belt by rotating the crankshaft through half a turn in the normal direction of rotation. Fit the tension gauge to the slack side of the belt (the alternator side) and read the tension. Desired values are given in the *Specifications*.

21 If adjustment is necessary, slacken the coolant pump bolts and pivot the pump to increase or decrease the tension. Nip up the coolant pump bolts.

22 Turn the crankshaft through one full turn, then recheck the tension. Keep adjusting the belt tension until a stable value is obtained.

23 Tighten the coolant pump bolts to the specified torque. Refill the cooling system (Section 2).

24 Check the injection pump timing (Section 6).

25 Refit the belt covers, clutch/flywheel cover and other disturbed components.

26 Refit the roadwheel, lower the vehicle and tighten the wheel bolts.

17D engine

Removal

27 Remove the alternator drivebelt (Section 1).

3B

3.16 Timing belt correctly fitted

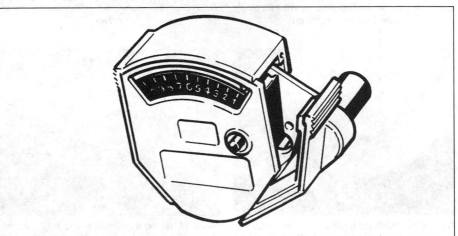

3.19 Timing belt tension gauge

3.28a Removing the timing belt upper cover

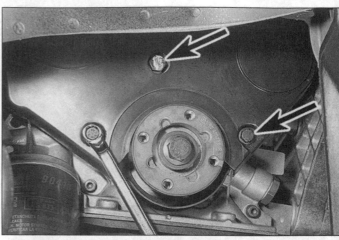

3.28b Removing the timing belt lower cover retaining bolts

28 Remove the air filter housing. Remove the timing belt covers. Two versions of the moulded plastic timing belt covers have been used since the introduction of this engine, the later version being identified by the squared-off top surface of the outer belt cover. On the earlier version, a screwdriver blade can be used to release the outer cover retaining clips and the cover sections can then be removed as required to gain access to the timing belt. On the later version, the method of retention is by bolts instead of clips. This arrangement is, in fact, the same as used on the 17DR engine (see illustrations).

29 Remove the crankshaft pulley - it is secured to the sprocket by four Allen screws (see illustration).

30 Disconnect the battery earth lead.

31 Remove the clutch/flywheel access cover from the bottom of the gearbox bellhousing (see illustration).

32 Turn the crankshaft in the normal direction of rotation, using a spanner on the sprocket bolt, until the timing mark on the injection

pump sprocket aligns with the reference mark on the pump bracket. In this position No 1 piston is at TDC on the firing stroke.

33 Check that the TDC mark on the flywheel and the pointer on the clutch housing are aligned (see illustration).

34 If tool KM-537 or equivalent is available, remove the vacuum pump and lock the camshaft in position by fitting the tool. If the tool is not available or cannot be fitted, make alignment marks between the camshaft sprocket and its backplate for use when refitting.

35 Drain the coolant.

36 Slacken the three bolts which secure the coolant pump to the block (see illustration). Using a large open-ended spanner on the flats of the pump, pivot it to release the tension on the belt.

37 Separate the right-hand front engine mounting by undoing the two bolts which are accessible from the top (see illustration).

38 Mark the running direction of the belt if it is to be re-used. Also take care not to kink the belt, nor get oil, grease etc. on it.

39 Slip the belt off the sprockets and jockey wheel. Remove the belt by feeding it through the engine mounting.

3.29 The crankshaft pulley viewed through the front wheel arch

3.31 Removing the clutch/flywheel access cover

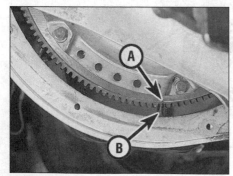

3.33 TDC mark on flywheel (A) and pointer on clutch housing (B)

3.36 Undoing a coolant pump bolt - other two arrowed (engine removed)

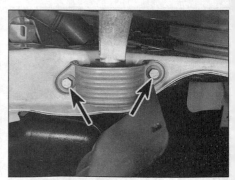

3.37 Right-hand front engine mounting-to-side chassis member securing bolts (arrowed)

3.42 Timing belt correctly fitted

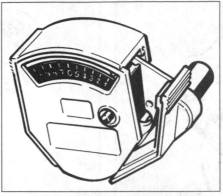

3.45 Timing belt tension gauge

3.54 Release the drivebelt tensioner securing bolt, then turn the tensioner arm with an Allen key until the belt is slack

40 If signs of oil contamination are found, trace the source of the oil leak and rectify it, then wash down the engine timing belt area and all related components to remove all traces of oil.

Refitting

41 Commence refitting by threading the belt through the engine mounting. Refit and tighten the engine mounting bolts.

42 Place the belt over the sprockets and the jockey wheel (see illustration). Make sure that No 1 piston is still at TDC, the injection pump sprocket mark is aligned and the camshaft position is still correct.

43 Move the coolant pump so as to put some tension on the timing belt. Nip up the pump securing bolts, but do not tighten them fully yet.

44 Remove the camshaft locking tool, if used, and refit and secure the crankshaft pulley.

45 Belt tension can only be adjusted accurately using tension gauge KM-510-A or equivalent (see illustration). A belt which is too tight will usually hum when running and a belt which is too slack will wear rapidly and may jump teeth.

46 Settle the belt by rotating the crankshaft through half a turn in the normal direction of rotation. Fit the tension gauge to the slack side of the belt (the alternator side) and read the tension. Desired values are given in the *Specifications*.

47 If adjustment is necessary, slacken the coolant pump bolts and pivot the pump to increase or decrease the tension. Nip up the coolant pump bolts.

48 Turn the crankshaft through one full turn, then recheck the tension. Keep adjusting the belt tension until a stable value is obtained.

49 Tighten the coolant pump bolts to the specified torque. Refill the cooling system (Section 2).

50 Check the injection pump timing (Section 6).

51 Refit the belt covers, clutch/flywheel cover and other disturbed components.

52 Refit the roadwheel, lower the vehicle and tighten the wheel bolts.

17DR and 17DTL engines

Removal, refitting and tensioning

53 The procedure for these engines with an automatic timing belt tensioner is essentially the same as described for the 17D engine, except that it is not necessary to drain the coolant, remove the engine mounting, nor to slacken the coolant pump mounting bolts and move the pump to adjust the belt tension. Instead, belt adjustment is catered for by means of the automatic tensioner, as follows.

54 To release the belt tension prior to removal, unscrew the timing belt tensioner securing bolt slightly then, with a suitable Allen key inserted in the slot on the tensioner arm, turn the tensioner arm until the timing belt is slack (see illustration). Tighten the securing bolt slightly to hold the tensioner in this position. The timing belt can now be removed.

55 Prior to fitting the timing belt, first ensure that the coolant pump is correctly positioned by checking that the lug on the pump flange is aligned with the corresponding lug on the cylinder block. If this is not the case, slacken the pump mounting bolts slightly and move the pump accordingly. Tighten the bolts to the specified torque on completion.

56 Initially refit the timing belt as described above, ensuring that No 1 piston is still at TDC, that the injection pump sprocket mark is still aligned and the camshaft position is still correct (see illustration). On 17DTL engines,

3B

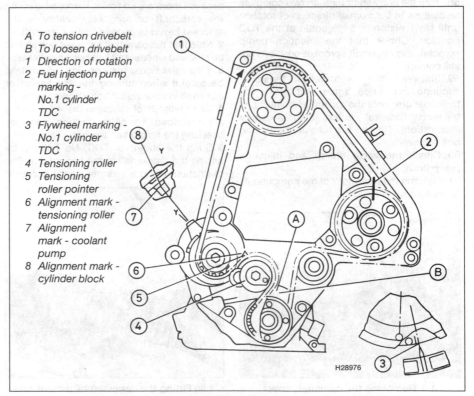

A To tension drivebelt
B To loosen drivebelt
1 Direction of rotation
2 Fuel injection pump marking - No.1 cylinder TDC
3 Flywheel marking - No.1 cylinder TDC
4 Tensioning roller
5 Tensioning roller pointer
6 Alignment mark - tensioning roller
7 Alignment mark - coolant pump
8 Alignment mark - cylinder block

3.56a Timing belt routing

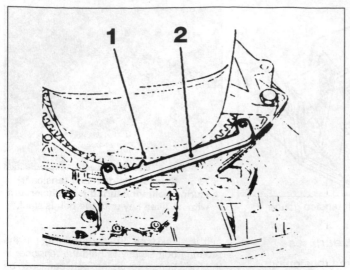

3.56b On 17DTL engines, flywheel position for TDC must be determined by the use of a setting tool (Adjuster KM-851)

1 Flywheel marking - No.1 cylinder TDC   2 Setting tool

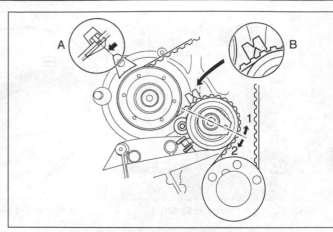

3.59 Timing belt automatic tensioner details - 17DR and 17DTL engines

A   Alignment lugs on coolant pump and cylinder block
B   Tensioner pointer aligned with notch in tensioner bracket
1   Move the tensioner arm anti-clockwise to release the belt tension
2   Move the tensioner arm clockwise to tension the belt

flywheel position for TDC must be determined by the use of a setting tool (Adjuster KM-851) fitted next to the flywheel as shown **(see illustration)**.

57 Tension the timing belt by first slackening the automatic tensioner securing bolt and moving the tensioner arm anti-clockwise until the tensioner pointer is at its stop. Tighten the tensioner securing bolt to hold the tensioner in this position.

58 Turn the crankshaft through two complete revolutions in the normal direction of rotation until No 1 piston is once again at the TDC position. Check that the injection pump sprocket and camshaft sprocket positions are still correct.

59 Slacken the automatic tensioner securing bolt once again and move the tensioner arm until the tensioner pointer and tensioner bracket notch coincide **(see illustration)**. Tighten the tensioner securing bolt securely.

60 Check the valve timing and injection pump timing.

61 Refitting the remainder of the components is the reversal of removal.

4   Valve timing - checking and adjustment

16D and 16DA engines up to May 1989

1 Valve timing on these engines is more complicated than on the petrol equivalents because there are no timing marks as such on the camshaft or sprocket, neither is the sprocket keyed or pegged to the camshaft.

2 Note that the camshaft sprocket bolt should be renewed whenever it has been slackened.

3 If the valve timing has been lost completely, be careful when turning the crankshaft or camshaft in case piston/valve contact occurs.

4 Two methods of checking the valve timing are described. For either method, begin by checking the timing belt tension.

5 Bring the engine to TDC, No 1 firing, by turning the crankshaft in the normal direction of rotation, using a spanner on the sprocket

bolt, until the timing mark on the injection pump sprocket aligns with the reference mark on the pump bracket **(see illustration 3.6)**. Check that the TDC mark on the flywheel and the pointer on the clutch housing are aligned **(see illustration 3.7)**.

6 Remove the air cleaner. Disconnect the breather hose and remove the camshaft cover **(see illustration)**. If necessary, also remove the vacuum pump.

Using tool KM-537 or equivalent

7 The maker's tool KM-537 consists of a plate which bolts onto the camshaft carrier in place of the vacuum pump. When the peg on the plate will enter the hole in the tail of the camshaft, the camshaft is correctly positioned for TDC, No 1 piston firing.

Making the tool

8 It is possible to make a substitute for tool KM-537 **(see illustration)**, but the valve timing must be known to be correct first - thereafter the tool can be used to check the timing. As can be seen, the home-made tool is simply a metal bar with three holes drilled in it **(see illustration)**. The accuracy of the tool

4.6 Removing the camshaft cover

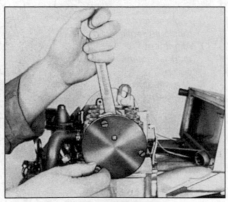

4.8a Fitting the camshaft alignment tool KM-537

4.8b Home-made tool for locking the camshaft in a set position

depends on the precision with which the holes are drilled, and the snug fit of the screws or bolts in their holes. The crankshaft must be at TDC, No 1 firing, before marking up and constructing the tool.

9 Drill one of the end holes in the metal bar. Insert a short stud or dowel into the camshaft peg hole, marking the end with chalk or paint. The stud should be just long enough to touch the metal bar in its fitted position.

10 Secure the bar, using one of the vacuum pump screws, so that it is just free to move. Swing the bar past the stud or dowel so that an arc is marked on the bar. Remove the bar and drill a hole in the centre of the arc to accept a bolt or screw which will fit snugly into the camshaft peg hole. Fit this bolt or screw and clamp it with a couple of nuts.

11 Mark around the other vacuum pump screw hole with paint or chalk. Offer the tool to the camshaft and carrier so that the peg hole bolt and first fixing screw are snug and the position of the second fixing screw hole is marked. Remove the tool and drill the second fixing screw hole.

12 Offer up the tool again and make sure that it fits without strain or slack; repeat the construction exercise if necessary.

Using the tool

13 With the crankshaft and injection pump timing marks correctly positioned, offer the tool to the camshaft carrier in place of the vacuum pump. If the tool can be located and secured so that the peg enters the hole in the camshaft, valve timing is correct. In fact, a tolerance of 1.0 mm in either direction at the flywheel TDC mark is allowed.

14 If the tool will not enter, remove it. Hold the camshaft using a spanner on the flats provided and slacken the camshaft sprocket bolt. Break the taper between the sprocket and camshaft if necessary by tapping the sprocket with a wooden or plastic mallet. Turn the camshaft until the alignment tool enters snugly. Remove the old camshaft sprocket bolt and insert a new bolt. Nip the bolt up until the sprocket taper bites, then remove the alignment tool. Hold the camshaft again and tighten the sprocket bolt to the specified torque.

15 Back off the crankshaft a quarter turn, then regain TDC and check that the alignment tool still fits snugly.

Using a dial test indicator

16 Tool KM-537 cannot be used on later models (mid-1984 on) because the holes into which it screws have been deleted. The home-made tool which screws into the vacuum pump holes is not affected. Instead of tool KM-537, the makers specify the use of a dial test indicator (DTI or clock gauge) and suitable support. The support must allow the DTI to move across the camshaft carrier without changing height relative to the carrier top surface. The DTI foot (the part which will rest on the cam lobe) should have a flat bottom and be 7 to 10 mm in diameter.

4.18 Dial test indicator zeroed on base circle of second cam . . .

17 To check the valve timing, position the timing marks as specified in paragraph 5, then place the DTI and support over the second cam from the sprocket end (No 1 cylinder inlet cam).

18 Zero the DTI on the base circle of the cam (see illustration).

19 Carefully move the DTI, and its support if applicable, exactly 10 mm towards the top of the cam. In this position the DTI should show a lift of 0.55 ± 0.05 mm. If so, the valve timing is correct (see illustration).

20 If adjustment is necessary, proceed as described in paragraph 14, but working towards a correct DTI reading instead of a correct fit of the tool.

All methods

21 Check the injection pump timing, then refit the belt covers, flywheel/clutch cover, cam cover and other disturbed components.

16DA engines from May 1989

22 The valve timing on this engine is adjusted using the dial test indicator method described above but modified as follows. Before starting work, it is necessary to make sure that the drivebelt tension is set correctly.

23 You will need a dial test indicator (DTI) with a 10 mm diameter measuring foot. Special tool KM-661-1 should ideally be available. This is a support bar which rests on

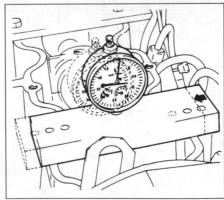

4.23 Dial test indicator (DTI) in position above camshaft

Note dotted lines indicating the two base positions during the test procedure

4.19 . . . another reading is taken towards the top of the cam

the top face of the camshaft carrier and positions the DTI above the camshaft (see illustration). A home-made support can be used if tool KM-661-1 is not available.

24 An additional tool (KM-661-2) is prescribed by the manufacturer. This comprises a slotted steel plate with a stop screw which is secured by bolts to the camshaft carrier, immediately above the flats on the camshaft. The second part of the tool is effectively an open-jawed spanner which fits over the flats on the camshaft and passes up through the slotted plate. The stop screw bears on the spanner handle, allowing precise positioning of the camshaft (see illustrations). In the absence of the manufacturer's tool, it should not prove difficult to make up an equivalent device at home.

Checking

25 To check the valve timing, turn the crankshaft in the normal direction of rotation and stop when the crankshaft is approximately 90° BTDC, with No 1 cylinder

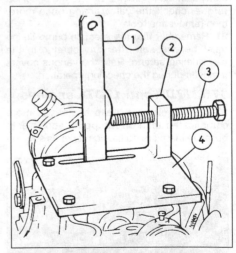

4.24 Service tool KM-661-2 in use

1 Open-jawed spanner
2 Stop screw bracket welded to baseplate
3 Stop screw
4 Baseplate located by camshaft cover bolts

3B

on the compression stroke. Fit the DTI to the support bar and position the foot of the gauge over the base circle of the second cam from the sprocket end (No 1 cylinder inlet cam). Set the DTI to zero.

26 Carefully move the DTI and the support bar (without disturbing the position of the DTI in the support bar) exactly 10 mm to the left, as viewed from the camshaft sprocket end of the engine (ie. towards the peak of the cam lobe). Turn the crankshaft to the TDC position for No 1 cylinder (see Section 3). In this position, the DTI should show a lift of 0.55 ± 0.03 mm. If so, the valve timing is correct.

Adjustment

27 If adjustment is necessary, slacken the camshaft sprocket bolt, noting that since this must be renewed each time it is disturbed. It is as well to fit a new bolt loosely at this stage. Release the taper between the sprocket and the camshaft, if necessary by tapping the sprocket with a wooden or plastic mallet.

28 Using the flats on the camshaft, turn it until the DTI reads approximately 0.80 mm of lift. Check that the crankshaft is still set to TDC.

29 Assemble and fit the holding tool, KM-661-2 or equivalent. Using the stop screw, gradually set the cam lift to 0.60 to 0.64 mm. Tighten the camshaft sprocket bolt tight enough for the camshaft taper to lock the sprocket, then remove the holding tool.

30 Carefully lift away the DTI and its support bar, taking care not to disturb the DTI position in the bar. Turn the crankshaft through two complete revolutions, then position the DTI once more and check that a lift figure of 0.55 ± 0.03 mm is shown at TDC. If the correct figure is not shown, repeat the adjustment sequence. If the figure is correct, tighten the (new) camshaft sprocket bolt to the specified torque, check the valve timing once more, then remove the tools.

31 Remember that the injection pump timing must be checked after any change in the valve timing setting. Refit the various covers removed during the checking operation.

17D, 17DR and 17DTL engines

32 Valve timing on these engines is more complicated than on the petrol equivalents because there are no timing marks as such on the camshaft or sprocket, neither is the sprocket keyed or pegged to the camshaft.

33 Note that the camshaft sprocket bolt should be renewed whenever it has been slackened.

34 If the valve timing has been lost completely, be careful when turning the crankshaft or camshaft in case piston/valve contact occurs.

35 The valve timing on this engine is checked using a dial test indicator. Before starting work, it is necessary to make sure that the drivebelt tension is set correctly.

36 Bring the engine to TDC, No 1 firing, by turning the crankshaft in the normal direction of rotation, using a spanner on the sprocket bolt, until the timing mark on the injection pump sprocket aligns with the reference mark on the belt cover (see illustration 6.19). Check that the TDC mark on the flywheel and the pointer on the clutch housing are aligned (see illustration 3.7).

37 Remove the air cleaner. Disconnect the breather hose and remove the camshaft cover (see illustration). If necessary, also remove the vacuum pump.

38 You will need a dial test indicator (DTI) with a 10 mm diameter measuring foot. Special tool KM-661-1 should ideally be available. This is a support bar which rests on the top face of the camshaft carrier and positions the DTI above the camshaft (see illustration). A home-made support can be used if tool KM-661-1 is not available.

39 An additional tool (KM-661-2) is prescribed by the manufacturer. This comprises a slotted steel plate with a stop screw which is secured by bolts to the camshaft carrier, immediately above the flats on the camshaft. The second part of the tool is effectively an open-jawed spanner which fits over the flats on the camshaft and passes up through the slotted plate. The stop screw bears on the spanner handle, allowing precise positioning of the camshaft (see illustration). In the absence of the manufacturer's tool, it should not prove difficult to make up an equivalent device at home.

Checking

40 To check the valve timing, turn the crankshaft in the normal direction of rotation and stop when the crankshaft is approximately 90° BTDC, with No 1 cylinder on the compression stroke. Fit the DTI to the support bar and position the foot of the gauge over the base circle of the second cam from the sprocket end (No 1 cylinder inlet cam). Set the DTI to zero.

41 Carefully move the DTI and the support bar (without disturbing the position of the DTI in the support bar) exactly 10 mm to the left, as viewed from the camshaft sprocket end of the engine (ie. towards the peak of the cam lobe). Turn the crankshaft to the TDC position for No 1 cylinder (see Section 3). In this position, the DTI should show a lift of 0.55 ± 0.03 mm. If so, the valve timing is correct.

Adjustment

42 If adjustment is necessary, slacken the camshaft sprocket bolt, noting that since this must be renewed each time it is disturbed. It is as well to fit a new bolt loosely at this stage. Release the taper between the sprocket and the camshaft, if necessary by tapping the sprocket with a wooden or plastic mallet.

43 Using the flats on the camshaft, turn it until the DTI reads approximately 0.80 mm of lift. Check that the crankshaft is still set to TDC.

44 Assemble and fit the holding tool, KM-661-2 or equivalent. Using the stop screw, gradually set the cam lift to 0.60 to 0.64 mm. Tighten the camshaft sprocket bolt tight enough for the camshaft taper to lock the sprocket, then remove the holding tool.

45 Carefully lift away the DTI and its support bar, taking care not to disturb the DTI position in the bar. Turn the crankshaft through two

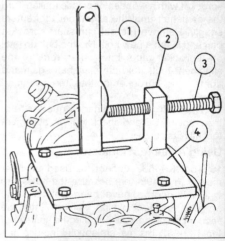

4.39 Service tool KM-661-2 in use

1   Open-jawed spanner
2   Stop screw bracket welded to baseplate
3   Stop screw
4   Baseplate located by camshaft cover bolts

4.37 Removing the camshaft cover

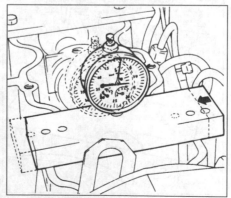

4.38 Dial test indicator (DTI) in position above camshaft

Note dotted lines indicating the two base positions during the test procedure

5.4a Fitting a new O-ring to the coolant pump

5.4b Fitting the coolant pump (engine removed)

complete revolutions, then position the DTI once more and check that a lift figure of 0.55 ± 0.03 mm is shown at TDC. If the correct figure is not shown, repeat the adjustment sequence. If the figure is correct, tighten the (new) camshaft sprocket bolt to the specified torque, check the valve timing once more, then remove the tools.

46 Remember that the injection pump timing must be checked after any change in the valve timing setting. Refit the various covers removed during the checking operation.

5 Coolant pump -
removal and refitting

Removal

1 Drain the cooling system, saving the coolant if it is fit for re-use.
2 Remove the timing belt, the timing belt idler pulley and backplate.
3 Remove the three bolts which retain the coolant pump. Lift out the pump - some coolant will be released. It may be necessary to remove the alternator to provide sufficient clearance to remove the pump completely.

Refitting

4 Use a new O-ring when refitting the pump. In order to prevent corrosion and the resultant impossibility of moving the coolant pump to tension the timing belt, apply silicone grease to the pump O-ring and cylinder block mating surface. Insert but do not tighten the retaining bolts (see illustrations).
5 Refit the timing belt backplate and the idler pulley.
6 Refit and tension the timing belt.
7 Refit the other disturbed components, then refill the cooling system.

6 Fuel injection pump timing -
checking and adjustment

16D and 16DA engines

Checking

1 Timing of the injection pump should only be necessary in the following circumstances:

a) When fitting a new or overhauled pump
b) If the timing is suspected of being wrong
c) If the timing belt has been re-tensioned or renewed

A dial test indicator with a long probe and a suitable support will be needed.
2 The procedure as shown here was carried out during engine rebuilding. With the engine in the vehicle, it will be necessary to remove the timing belt covers, the air cleaner snorkel and the clutch/flywheel cover.
3 Check the valve timing (Section 4).
4 Bring the engine to TDC, No 1 firing. The timing mark on the pump sprocket must be aligned with the pip on the pump bracket (see illustration).
5 Turn the engine against the normal direction of rotation so that the flywheel TDC mark is approximately 5.0 cm away from the TDC pointer.
6 Remove the central plug from the rear of the injection pump (see illustration).
7 Mount the dial test indicator with its probe entering the central plug hole. Zero the indicator (see illustration).
8 Be prepared for fuel spillage during subsequent operations. The manufacturers specify the use of a probe which screws into, and presumably seals, the plug hole.
9 Bring the engine back to TDC, No 1 firing. When the timing marks are aligned, the dial test indicator should show a lift corresponding

3B

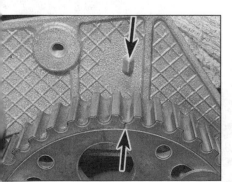

6.4 Injection pump sprocket timing mark aligned with mark on pump bracket

6.6 Removing the plug from the rear of the injection pump

6.7 Dial test indicator mounted with its probe in the plug hole

6.10a Slacken the injection pump sprocket clamping bolts . . .

to the desired timing setting - see *Specifications*.

Adjustment

10 If adjustment is necessary, slacken the three bolts which clamp together the two halves of the pump sprocket **(see illustration)**. Turn the inner part of the sprocket anti-clockwise (against the normal direction of rotation) as far as the slots will allow. The fit between the two parts of the sprocket is tight and a rod or soft metal drift may be needed to encourage the inner part to move **(see illustration)**.

11 With the sprocket positioned as just described and the engine still at TDC, No 1

6.20 Flywheel timing marks are visible through clutch housing inspection cover - 17D and 17DR engines

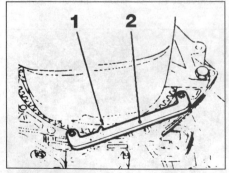

6.21 Determining flywheel position for TDC by the use of a setting tool (Adjuster KM-851) - 17DTL engines

1 Flywheel TDC mark   2 Setting tool

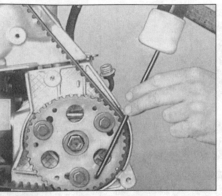

6.10b . . . and use a rod and mallet to move the inner part of the sprocket

firing, the dial test indicator should again read zero. Reset it if necessary.

12 Turn the inner part of the sprocket clockwise until the dial test indicator shows the desired lift, then tighten the sprocket clamp bolts.

13 Repeat the checking procedure from paragraph 5.

14 When the injection timing is correct, remove the test gear and refit the plug to the rear of the pump.

15 Refit the timing belt covers and other disturbed components.

17D, 17DR and 17DTL engines - Bosch pump

Checking

16 Timing of the injection pump should only be necessary in the following circumstances:

a) *When fitting a new or overhauled pump*
b) *If the timing is suspected of being wrong*
c) *If the timing belt has been re-tensioned or renewed*

A dial test indicator with a long probe and a suitable support will be needed.

17 The procedure as shown here was carried out during engine rebuilding. With the engine in the vehicle, it will be necessary to remove the timing belt covers, the air cleaner snorkel and the clutch/flywheel cover.

18 Check the valve timing (Section 4).

19 Bring the engine to TDC, No 1 firing. The

6.23 Removing the plug from the rear of the injection pump

6.19 Fuel injection pump sprocket timing mark aligned with moulded mark on drivebelt inner cover

timing mark on the pump sprocket must be aligned with the moulded mark on the timing belt inner cover **(see illustration)**.

20 On 17D and 17DR engines, remove the clutch housing cover plate. With No 1 piston set to TDC on the firing stroke, the TDC mark on the flywheel and the pointer on the clutch housing will be aligned **(see illustration)**.

21 On 17DTL engines, remove the flywheel cover plate. Flywheel position for TDC must be determined by the use of a setting tool (Adjuster KM-851) fitted next to the flywheel as shown **(see illustration)**. With No 1 piston set to TDC on the firing stroke, the TDC mark on the flywheel and the pointer on the setting tool will be aligned.

22 Turn the engine against the normal direction of rotation so that the flywheel TDC mark is approximately 5.0 cm away from the TDC pointer.

23 Remove the central plug from the rear of the injection pump **(see illustration)**.

24 Mount the dial test indicator with its probe entering the central plug hole. Zero the indicator **(see illustration)**.

25 Be prepared for fuel spillage during subsequent operations. The manufacturers specify the use of a probe which screws into, and presumably seals, the plug hole.

26 Bring the engine back to TDC, No 1 firing. When the timing marks are aligned, the dial test indicator should show a lift corresponding to the desired timing setting - see *Specifications*.

6.24 Dial test indicator mounted with its probe in the plug hole

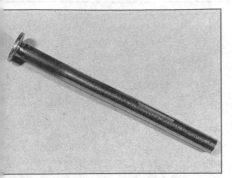

6.34a Home-made probe used for checking Lucas/CAV pump timing

Adjustment

27 If adjustment is necessary, slacken the three bolts which clamp together the two halves of the pump sprocket. Turn the inner part of the sprocket anti-clockwise (against the normal direction of rotation) as far as the slots will allow. The fit between the two parts of the sprocket is tight and a rod or soft metal drift may be needed to encourage the inner part to move.

28 With the sprocket positioned as just described and the engine still at TDC, No 1 firing, the dial test indicator should again read zero. Reset it if necessary.

29 Turn the inner part of the sprocket clockwise until the dial test indicator shows the desired lift, then tighten the sprocket clamp bolts.

30 Repeat the checking procedure from paragraph 22.

31 When the injection timing is correct, remove the test gear and refit the plug to the rear of the pump.

32 Refit the timing belt covers and other disturbed components.

17D, 17DR and 17DTL engines - Lucas/CAV pump

33 There are some slight changes from the

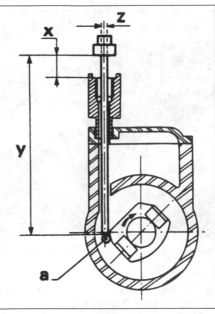

6.34b Special DTI probe shown in position during pump timing check - Lucas/CAV injection pump

a   Timing piece
x   Timing value (as shown on plate)
y 95.5 ± 0.01 mm
z   7.00 mm shank diameter

timing procedure above when dealing with the Lucas/CAV injection pump as detailed below.

34 Note that the closing plug is located on the upper surface of the pump rather than at the end of the pump casing as on the Bosch pump. In the absence of the measuring tool KM-690-A and the dial test indicator KM-571-B, you will need a standard dial test indicator (DTI), together with some method of mounting it above the timing hole at the appropriate height. Also required is a headed probe made to the dimensions shown, this being placed in the timing hole before the DTI is mounted in position **(see illustrations)**.

6.35 Lucas/CAV pump showing DTI set up for timing check. Individual value for each pump is stamped on plate (arrowed)

35 Check the amount of lift indicated on the DTI when the crankshaft timing marks are brought into alignment. There is no standard specified lift figure for Lucas/CAV pumps. Each pump is calibrated during manufacture and the lift figure marked on a plate which is fitted to the pump lever **(see illustration)**. If the lift figure shown on the DTI does not correspond with that given on the plate, adjust the pump sprocket as described in above. Once adjustment is complete, remove the DTI with probe and refit the closing plug.

7 Vacuum pump - removal and refitting

Removal

1 Disconnect the servo vacuum pipe from the pump. Do this by counterholding the large union nut and unscrewing the small one **(see illustration)**.

2 On 17DR and 17DTL engines, disconnect the EGR system vacuum supply hose from the pump **(see illustration)**.

3B

7.1 Disconnecting the servo vacuum pipe from the vacuum pump

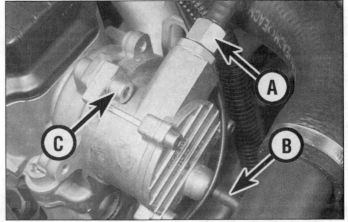

7.2 Vacuum pump connections - 17DR and 17DTL engines

A   Servo vacuum pipe
B   EGR system vacuum supply hose
C   Pump securing screws (2 off)

7.3a Remove the two pump securing screws . . .

7.3b . . . and withdraw the vacuum pump from the camshaft housing

3 Remove the two pump securing screws and withdraw the pump from the camshaft housing (see illustrations). Be prepared for some oil spillage.

4 Recover the small central oil pipe and the driving dog.

5 Discard the two O-rings fitted to the central oil pipe and also the pump body to camshaft housing seal (see illustration).

Refitting

6 Fit new sealing rings to the pump assembly.

7 Refit the central oil pipe and the driving dog to the pump (see illustration).

8 Offer the pump to the camshaft housing, making sure that the teeth of the driving dog engage with the slot in the camshaft end. Fit the pump securing screws and tighten them to the specified torque.

9 Reconnect and secure the vacuum pipe connection(s).

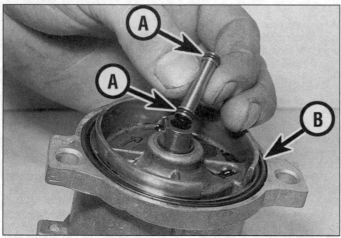

7.5 Renew the O-rings fitted to the central oil pipe (A) and the pump body to camshaft housing seal (B)

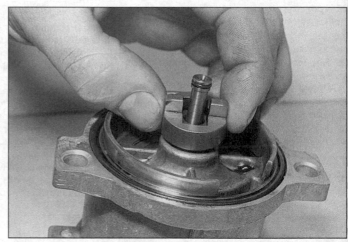

7.7 Refitting the central oil pipe with driving dog to the vacuum pump

Chapter 4A
Vauxhall/Opel Astra petrol 1991 to 1998

Contents

Specifications

Timing belt renewal interval . . . .   Every 36 000 miles (60 000 km) or 4 years - whichever comes first

Timing belt tension (using gauge KM-510-A)

1.8 and 2.0 litre SOHC engines up to 1993
New belt, cold 4.5
New belt, warm 7.5
Used belt, cold 2.5
Used belt, warm 7.0

Torque wrench settings

	Nm	lbf ft
SOHC engine		
Alternator adjuster bracket:		
1.4 and 1.6 litre models	25	18
1.8 and 2.0 litre models:		
Pre 1993 models	25	18
1993-on models	18	13
Alternator to mounting bracket:		
M8 bolts	30	22
M10 bolts	40	30
Camshaft cover bolts	8	6
Camshaft sprocket bolt	45	33
Coolant pump bolts:		
M6 (1.4 and 1.6 litre engines)	8	6
M8 (1.8 and 2.0 litre engines)	25	18
Crankshaft pulley/crankshaft sprocket bolt (1.4 and 1.6 litre engines):		
Models with V-belt	55	41
Models with ribbed belt:*		
M10 bolt:		
Stage 1	55	41
Stage 2	Angle-tighten a further 45°	
Stage 3	Angle-tighten a further 15°	
M12 bolt:		
Stage 1	95	70
Stage 2	Angle-tighten a further 45°	
Stage 3	Angle-tighten a further 15°	
Crankshaft sprocket bolt (1.8 and 2.0 litre engines):*		
Stage 1	130	96
Stage 2	Angle-tighten a further 45°	
Crankshaft pulley-to-sprocket bolts (1.8 and 2.0 litre engines)	55	41
Engine/transmission mounting bolts:		
Front left-hand mounting:		
Mounting-to-body bolts	65	48
Mounting-to-bracket bolts	60	44
Front right-hand mounting:		
Mounting-to-body bolts*	65	48
Mounting-to-bracket bolts	35	26
Rear mounting:		
Mounting-to-bracket bolts	45	33
Mounting-to-subframe bolts	40	30
Power steering pump mounting bolts:		
With V-belts	30	22
With ribbed V-belts	20	15
Power steering pump pulley bolts (1.4 and 1.6 litre, V-belt models)	25	18
Roadwheel bolts	110	81
Spark plugs	25	18
Timing belt tensioner bolt	20	15
1.4 and 1.6 litre DOHC engines		
Alternator adjuster bracket	25	18
Alternator to mounting bracket:		
M8 bolts	30	22
M10 bolts	40	30
Camshaft cover bolts	8	6
Camshaft sensor	15	11
Camshaft sprocket bolt:*		
Stage 1	50	37
Stage 2	Angle-tighten a further 60°	
Stage 3	Angle-tighten a further 15°	
Crankshaft pulley bolt:*		
Stage 1	95	70
Stage 2	Angle-tighten a further 30°	
Stage 3	Angle-tighten a further 15°	
Engine/transmission mounting bolts:		
Front left-hand mounting:		
Mounting-to-body bolts	65	48
Mounting-to-bracket bolts	60	44

Torque wrench settings

	Nm	lbf ft
1.4 and 1.6 litre DOHC engines (continued)		
Engine/transmission mounting bolts:		
Front right-hand mounting:		
Mounting-to-body bolts*	65	48
Mounting-to-bracket bolts	35	26
Rear mounting:		
Mounting-to-bracket bolts	45	33
Mounting-to-subframe bolts	40	30
Power steering pump mounting bolts:		
Fastenings A and C **(see illustration 1.11)**	25	18
Fastening B **(see illustration 1.11):**		
With V-belt	40	30
With ribbed V-belt	18	13
Roadwheel bolts	110	81
Spark plugs	25	18
Timing belt cover bolts:		
Upper and lower covers	4	3
Rear cover	6	4
Timing belt idler pulley bolt	25	18
Timing belt tensioner bolt	20	15
1.8 and 2.0 litre DOHC engines		
Alternator adjuster bracket:		
Pre 1993 models	25	18
1993-on models	18	13
Alternator to mounting bracket:		
M8 bolts	30	22
M10 bolts	40	30
Camshaft cover bolts	8	6
Camshaft sprocket bolt:*		
Stage 1	50	37
Stage 2	Angle-tighten a further 60°	
Stage 3	Angle-tighten a further 15°	
Crankshaft pulley bolts	20	15
Crankshaft sprocket bolt:*		
Stage 1	130	96
Stage 2	Angle-tighten a further 40 to 50°	
Engine/transmission mounting bolts:		
Front left-hand mounting:		
Mounting-to-body bolts	65	48
Mounting-to-bracket bolts	60	44
Front right-hand mounting:		
Mounting-to-body bolts*	65	48
Mounting-to-bracket bolts	35	26
Rear mounting:		
Mounting-to-bracket bolts	45	33
Mounting-to-subframe bolts	40	30
Power steering pump mounting bolts:		
Fastenings A and C **(see illustration 1.11)**	25	18
Fastening B **(see illustration 1.11):**		
With V-belt	40	30
With ribbed V-belt	18	13
Roadwheel bolts	110	81
Spark plugs	25	18
Timing belt idler pulley bolt:		
Engines up to 1993:*		
Stage 1	25	18
Stage 2	Angle-tighten a further 45°	
Stage 3	Angle-tighten a further 15°	
Engines from 1993	25	18
Timing belt idler pulley bracket bolt (models from 1993)	25	18
Timing belt tensioner bolt:		
Engines up to 1993:*		
Stage 1	25	18
Stage 2	Angle-tighten a further 45°	
Stage 3	Angle-tighten a further 15°	
Engines from 1993	25	18

* **Note:** *Use new bolts.*

4A

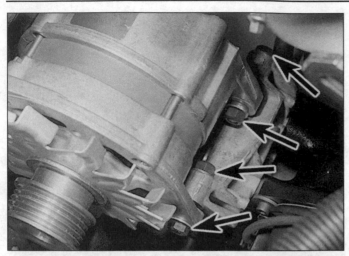

1.4 Lower alternator mounting nuts and bolts (arrowed). Viewed with top alternator mounting disconnected - Bosch type

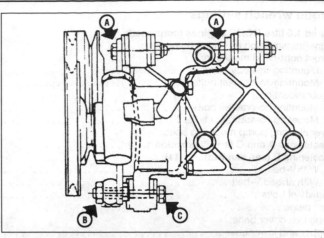

1.11 Mounting and adjuster bolts (arrowed) must be loosened to adjust power steering pump drivebelt tension

For A, B and C see Torque wrench settings

1 Auxiliary drivebelts - removal, refitting and adjustment

Manually-adjusted belts

Alternator

1 Disconnect the air intake trunking from the air cleaner, and from the airbox or the throttle body, as applicable, and remove it for improved access.
2 On 1.4 and 1.6 litre models with power steering, the drivebelt also drives the power steering pump.
3 To remove the belt on 1.8 and 2.0 litre models, first remove the power steering pump drivebelt, as described below.
4 Loosen the alternator mounting nuts and bolts sufficiently to allow the alternator to be pivoted in towards the engine **(see illustration)**.
5 Slide the belt from the pulleys.
6 Fit the belt around the pulleys, ensuring that the belt is of the correct type if it is being renewed, and take up the slack in the belt by swinging the alternator away from the engine

and lightly tightening the mounting nuts and bolts.
7 On 1.8 and 2.0 litre models, refit and tension the power steering pump drivebelt, as described below.
8 Although special tools are available for checking the belt tension, a good approximation can be achieved if the belt is tensioned so that there is approximately 13.0 mm of free movement under firm thumb pressure at the mid-point of the longest run between pulleys.
9 With the mounting bolts just holding the unit firm, lever the alternator away from the engine using a wooden lever at the mounting bracket end until the correct tension is achieved, then tighten the mounting nuts and bolts. **On no account** lever at the free end of the alternator, as serious internal damage could be caused.
10 Refit the air trunking.

Power steering pump

11 Slacken the adjuster and mounting bolts shown in **(see illustration)**.

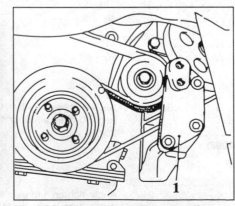

1.20 Remove the engine mounting bracket (1) - DOHC models

12 Slacken the adjuster nuts, and adjust the length of the threaded rod in order to tension or remove the belt, as necessary **(see illustration)**.
13 Fit the belt around the pulleys, then tension the belt.
14 Although special tools are available for measuring the belt tension, a good approximation can be achieved if the belt is tensioned so that there is approximately 10.0 mm of free movement under firm thumb pressure at the mid-point of the belt run between pulleys. If in doubt, err on the slack side, as an excessively tight belt may cause damage to the pump.
15 Tighten the adjuster nuts, and tighten the adjuster and mounting bolts to the specified torque on completion.

Automatically-adjusted belts

Note: *Replacement requires the engine to be supported and the mounting removed. Sealing Compound (Vauxhall P/N 90167347, or equivalent) will be required when refitting the bolts.*
16 On models with an intake air temperature sensor, first disconnect the negative lead from the battery and then remove its wiring plug.
17 Remove the air intake pipe. On some models it may be necessary to remove the complete air cleaner assembly and engine cover. If fitted, remove the panel from behind the right-hand front wheel.
18 Support the engine using hoist or a trolley jack. If using a trolley jack, place a piece of wood between the jack and the engine to prevent damaging the sump.
19 Release the tension roller, turning in a clock-wise direction and remove the belt from the roller.
20 Remove the right-hand engine mounting from the chassis member. On DOHC models remove the engine mounting bracket from the support **(see illustration)**.

1.12 Adjusting the length of the power steering pump threaded rod - 1.8 and 2.0 litre SOHC models

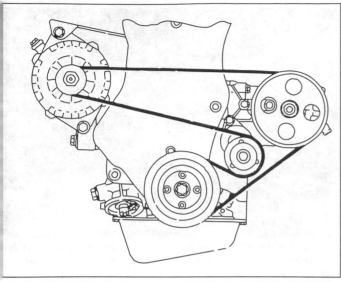

1.22a Ribbed V-belt shown correctly fitted - C 18 XE, C 18 XEL and C 20 XE models

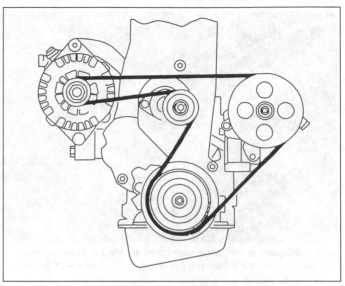

1.22b Ribbed V-belt shown correctly fitted - 1.4 and 1.6 litre SOHC models with power steering

21 Slowly and carefully lower the engine and remove the belt, noting how is fitted.

22 Refitting is a reversal of the removal procedure. However, locate the belt as the original was fitted **(see illustrations)**.

23 Recut the threads of the engine mounting bolts and replace using Sealing Compound (Vauxhall P/N 90167347, or equivalent).

24 Tighten the engine mountings to their correct torque.

2 Air cleaner housing assembly - removal and refitting

Carburettor models
Removal

1 Disconnect the air hose from the airbox on the carburettor.

2 Release the clips securing the cover to the air cleaner casing, then lift the cover sufficiently to remove the element **(see illustrations)**.

3 Slacken the air cleaner housing assembly securing nuts (one front and one rear), and pull the assembly from the body panel.

Refitting

4 Refitting is a reversal of removal. Fit the new element, noting that the rubber locating flange should be uppermost, then refit the air cleaner cover and secure with the clips.

Fuel injection models
Removal

5 Disconnect the battery negative lead.
6 Disconnect the wiring from the air flow meter, if applicable.
7 Remove the air intake hose from the air cleaner housing.

8 Unclip the retaining clamps from the top cover.
9 Unscrew the two housing securing nuts and release the air flow guide hose.
10 The lower part of the housing can now be removed, complete with its rubber support.

Refitting

11 Refitting is a reversal of removal.

3 Top dead centre (TDC) for No 1 piston (SOHC) - locating

1 Top Dead Centre (TDC) is the highest point that each piston reaches in its travel up and down its cylinder bore, as the crankshaft rotates. While each piston reaches TDC both at the top of the compression stroke and again at the top of the exhaust stroke, for the purpose of timing the engine, TDC refers to

4A

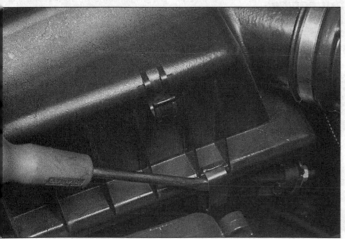

2.2a Release the clips securing the cover to the air cleaner casing . . .

2.2b . . . then lift the cover sufficiently to remove the element

3.6a TDC pointer on timing belt cover aligned with timing notch in crankshaft sensor wheel (arrowed) - 1.6 litre fuel injection engine

3.6b TDC pointer on timing belt cover aligned with timing notch in crankshaft pulley (arrowed) - 2.0 litre fuel injection engine

3.6c Timing mark on camshaft sprocket aligned with notch in timing belt rear cover (arrowed) - 1.6 litre fuel injection engine

the position of No 1 piston at the top of its compression stroke.

2 Number 1 piston (and cylinder) is at the timing belt end of the engine, and its TDC position is located as follows. Note that the crankshaft rotates clockwise when viewed from the timing belt end of the engine.

3 Disconnect the battery negative lead. If necessary, remove all the spark plugs to enable the crankshaft to be turned more easily.

4 To gain access to the camshaft sprocket timing mark, remove the timing belt upper cover as described in Section 9.

5 Using a socket and extension bar on the crankshaft pulley bolt, turn the crankshaft to bring No 1 piston to TDC as follows.

All engines except 1.4 litre carburettor engine

6 The pointer on the timing belt cover must be aligned with the notch in the crankshaft pulley, or the timing mark on the crankshaft sensor wheel, as applicable, and the timing mark on the camshaft sprocket must be aligned with the notch in the top of the timing belt rear cover (see illustrations).

7 Note that there is also a timing mark on the crankshaft sprocket (visible with the crankshaft pulley/sensor wheel removed). When No 1 piston is positioned at TDC, the mark on the crankshaft sprocket should be aligned with the corresponding mark at the bottom of the oil pump flange – ie, the mark on the sprocket should be pointing vertically downwards.

1.4 litre carburettor engines

8 The pointer on the rear timing belt cover must be aligned with the 10° BTDC notch in the crankshaft pulley, and the timing mark on

the camshaft sprocket must be aligned with the notch in the top of the rear timing belt cover (see illustration). Note that when the timing marks are aligned as described although No 1 piston is positioned at 10° BTDC, this is acceptable for all the tasks in this manual requiring No 1 piston to be positioned at TDC.

9 Note that there is also a timing mark on the crankshaft sprocket (visible with the crankshaft pulley/sensor wheel removed). When No 1 piston is positioned at TDC, the mark on the crankshaft sprocket should be aligned with the corresponding mark at the bottom of the oil pump flange – ie, the mark on the sprocket should be pointing vertically downwards (see illustration).

4 Top dead centre (TDC) for No 1 piston (DOHC) - locating

1 Top Dead Centre (TDC) is the highest point that each piston reaches in its travel up and down its cylinder bore, as the crankshaft rotates. While each piston reaches TDC both at the top of the compression stroke and again at the top of the exhaust stroke, for the purpose of timing the engine, TDC refers to the position of No 1 piston at the top of its compression stroke.

2 Number 1 piston (and cylinder) is at the timing belt end of the engine, and its TDC position is located as follows. Note that the crankshaft rotates clockwise when viewed from the timing belt end of the engine.

3 Disconnect the battery negative lead. If necessary, remove all the spark plugs to enable the crankshaft to be turned more easily.

1.4 and 1.6 litre engines

4 To gain access to the camshaft sprocket timing marks, remove the timing belt upper cover as described in Section 10.

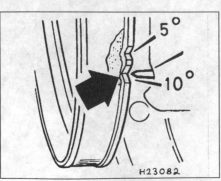

3.8 Crankshaft pulley 10° BTDC notch aligned with pointer on rear timing belt cover - 1.4 litre carburettor engine

3.9 Timing mark on crankshaft sprocket aligned with mark at bottom of timing belt rear cover - 1.6 litre engine

4.5 On 1.6 litre engines align the camshaft sprocket timing marks (A) with the cylinder head upper surface (B) as shown to position No 1 cylinder at TDC on its compression stroke

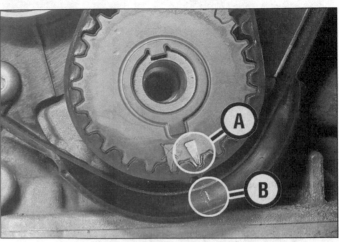

4.6 Crankshaft sprocket (A) and belt cover (B) timing marks - 1.6 litre engine

5 Using a socket and extension bar on the crankshaft pulley bolt, rotate the crankshaft until the timing marks on the camshaft

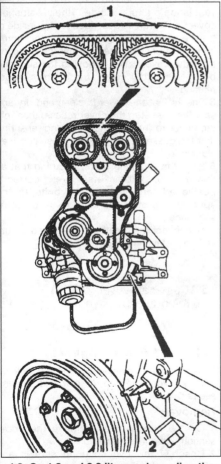

4.8 On 1.8 and 2.0 litre engines align the camshaft sprocket timing marks with the marks (1) on the cylinder head cover, and the crankshaft pulley notch with the pointer (2) to position No 1 cylinder at TDC on its compression stroke

sprockets are facing towards each and are both correctly aligned with the cylinder head upper surface. With the camshaft sprocket marks correctly positioned, the notch on the crankshaft pulley rim should align with the mark on the timing belt lower cover (see illustration). The engine is now positioned with No 1 piston at TDC on its compression stroke.

6 Note that there is also a timing mark on the crankshaft sprocket (visible with the crankshaft pulley/sensor wheel removed). When No 1 piston is positioned at TDC, the mark on the crankshaft sprocket should be aligned with the corresponding mark at the bottom of the oil pump flange (see illustration).

1.8 and 2.0 litre models

7 To gain access to the camshaft sprocket timing marks, remove the timing belt outer cover as described in Section 10.

8 Using a socket and extension bar on the crankshaft sprocket bolt, rotate the crankshaft until the timing marks on the camshaft sprockets are both pointing vertically upwards, and are correctly aligned with the timing marks on the camshaft cover. With the camshaft sprocket marks correctly

positioned, the notch on the crankshaft pulley rim should be aligned with the pointer on the rear timing belt cover (see illustration). The engine is now positioned with No 1 piston at TDC on its compression stroke.

9 Note that there is also a timing mark on the crankshaft sprocket (visible with the crankshaft pulley/sensor wheel removed). When No 1 piston is positioned at TDC, the mark on the crankshaft sprocket should be aligned with the corresponding mark at the bottom of the oil pump flange – ie, the mark on the sprocket should be pointing vertically downwards.

4A

5 Camshaft cover (SOHC) - removal and refitting

Removal

Note: A new gasket will almost certainly be required on refitting.

1 Release the retaining clip(s) and disconnect the breather hose(s) from the camshaft cover (see illustrations).

2 Slacken and remove the retaining bolts, noting the correct fitted location of any clips

5.1a Disconnect the breather hoses . . .

5.1b . . . from the camshaft cover - 1.6 litre engine

5.2 Note the positions of any brackets and clips (arrowed) secured by the camshaft cover bolts - 1.6 litre engine

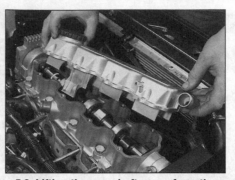

5.3 Lifting the camshaft cover from the cylinder head

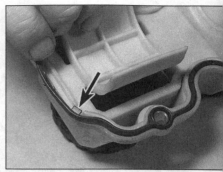

5.5 Tag (arrowed) on gasket engages with notch in camshaft cover - 1.6 litre engine

or brackets retained by the bolts **(see illustration)**.

3 Lift the camshaft cover from the camshaft housing **(see illustration)**. If the cover is

stuck, do not lever between the cover and camshaft housing mating surfaces - if necessary, gently tap the cover sideways to free it. Recover the gasket; if it shows signs

of damage or deterioration it must be renewed.

Refitting

4 Prior to refitting, examine the inside of the cover for a build-up of oil sludge or any other contamination, and if necessary clean the cover with paraffin, or a water-soluble solvent. Examine the condition of the crankcase ventilation filter inside the camshaft cover, and clean as described for the inside of the cover if clogging is evident (on some engines, if desired, the filter can be removed from the cover, after removing the securing bolts). Dry the cover thoroughly before refitting.

5 Ensure that the cover is clean and dry and seat the gasket in the cover recess, then refit the cover to the camshaft housing, ensuring that the gasket remains correctly seated **(see illustration)**.

6 Refit the retaining bolts, ensuring that all relevant clips/brackets are correctly positioned, and tighten the bolts to the specified torque, working in a diagonal sequence.

7 Reconnect the breather hose(s) and secure with the retaining clip(s).

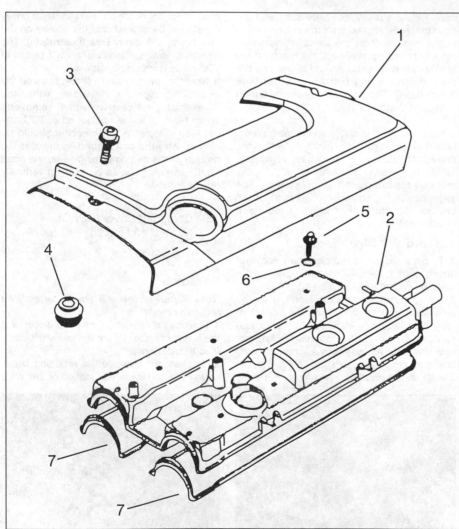

6.2 Engine/spark plug cover and camshaft cover - 1.4 and 1.6 litre engines

1 Engine/spark plug cover	3 Engine/spark plug cover securing bolts	5 Camshaft cover bolts
2 Camshaft cover	4 Bushes	6 Washers
		7 Gaskets

6 Camshaft cover (DOHC) - removal and refitting

1.4 and 1.6 litre engines

Note: *Suitable sealing compound will be required when refitting the camshaft cover - see text.*

Removal

1 On 1.6 litre engines, remove the upper section of the inlet manifold.

2 Unscrew the two securing screws and withdraw the spark plug cover **(see illustration)**. If necessary, mark the spark plug HT leads for position (to avoid confusion when refitting), then disconnect them from the plugs and unclip them from the camshaft cover.

3 Release the retaining clips and disconnect

6.3 On 1.6 litre engines slacken the retaining clips and disconnect the breather hoses (arrowed) from the left-hand end of the camshaft cover

6.4 Unscrew the retaining bolts . . .

6.5 . . . and lift the camshaft cover away from the engine - 1.6 litre engine

the breather hoses from the camshaft cover (see illustration).

4 Evenly and progressively slacken and remove the camshaft cover retaining bolts (see illustration).

5 Lift the camshaft cover away from the cylinder head and recover the cover seals, and the sealing rings which are fitted to each of the retaining bolt locations (see illustration). Examine the seals and sealing rings for signs of wear or damage and renew if necessary.

Refitting

6 Ensure that the cover and cylinder head surfaces are clean and dry, then fit the camshaft cover seals securely to the cover grooves. Fit the sealing rings to the recesses around each retaining bolt location, holding them in position with a smear of grease (see illustrations).

7 Apply sealing compound to the edges of the inlet and exhaust camshaft bearing cap locations at the timing belt end of the engine, and to the semi-circular cut-outs at the transmission end of the cylinder head.

8 Carefully manoeuvre the camshaft cover into position, taking great care to ensure all the sealing rings remain correctly seated. Refit the cover retaining bolts and tighten the retaining bolts to the specified torque, working in a spiral pattern from the centre outwards.

9 Reconnect the breather hoses, securing them in position with the retaining clips.

10 Reconnect the HT leads to the spark plugs, ensuring that they are correctly connected as noted before removal. Clip the HT leads into position in the camshaft cover, then refit the spark plug cover and tighten the securing screws.

11 On 1.6 litre engines, refit the inlet manifold upper section.

1.8 and 2.0 litre engines

Removal

12 On C 20 XE engines, remove the outer timing belt cover as described in Section 10.

13 Slacken the retaining clips and disconnect

6.6a Ensure the seals are correctly seated in the cover recesses . . .

the breather hoses from the rear of the cover (see illustration).

14 Unscrew the two securing screws and withdraw the spark plug cover. If necessary, mark the spark plug HT leads for position (to avoid confusion when refitting), then disconnect them from the plugs and unclip them from the camshaft cover.

15 Where applicable, disconnect the camshaft sensor wiring connector and unclip the wiring from the camshaft cover.

16 Evenly and progressively slacken and remove the camshaft cover retaining bolts (see illustration).

6.13 On 1.8 and 2.0 litre engines release the retaining clips and disconnect the breather hoses (arrowed) from the rear of the cover

6.6b . . . and fit the sealing rings to the recess around each retaining bolt hole - 1.6 litre engine

17 Lift the camshaft cover away from the cylinder head and recover the cover seal(s) and the sealing rings which are fitted to each of the retaining bolt holes. Examine the seal(s) and sealing rings for signs of wear or damage and renew if necessary.

Refitting

18 Ensure that the cover and cylinder head surfaces are clean and dry, then fit the camshaft cover seal(s) securely to the cover grooves. Fit the sealing rings to the recesses around each retaining bolt location, holding them in position with a smear of grease.

4A

6.16 Removing a camshaft cover retaining bolt - 2.0 litre engine

19 Carefully manoeuvre the camshaft cover into position, taking great care to ensure that all the sealing rings remain correctly seated. Refit the cover retaining bolts and tighten the retaining bolts to the specified torque, working in a spiral pattern from the centre outwards.
20 Where applicable, reconnect the camshaft sensor wiring connector and clip the wiring into position on the camshaft cover.
21 Reconnect the breather hoses, securing them in position with the retaining clips.
22 Reconnect the HT leads to the spark plugs, ensuring that they are correctly connected as noted before removal. Clip the HT leads into position in the camshaft cover, then refit the spark plug cover and tighten the securing screws.
23 On C 20 XE engines, refit the outer timing belt cover.

7 Crankshaft pulley (SOHC) - removal and refitting

1.4 and 1.6 litre engines

Note: *A new pulley retaining bolt will be required on refitting.*

Removal

1 Apply the handbrake, then jack up the front of the vehicle and support it on axle stands. Remove the right-hand roadwheel.
2 Remove the auxiliary drivebelt(s) as described in Section 1. Prior to removal, mark the direction of rotation on the belt(s) to ensure that the belt is refitted the same way round.
3 Slacken the crankshaft pulley retaining bolt. To prevent crankshaft rotation on manual transmission models, have an assistant select top gear and apply the brakes firmly. On automatic transmission models prevent rotation by removing one of the torque

converter retaining bolts and bolting the driveplate to the transmission housing using a metal bar, spacers and suitable bolts.
4 Unscrew the retaining bolt and washer and remove the crankshaft pulley from the end of the crankshaft, taking care not to damage the crankshaft sensor, where applicable **(see illustration)**.

Refitting

5 Refit the crankshaft pulley, aligning the pulley cut-out with the raised notch on the timing belt sprocket, then fit the washer and new retaining bolt **(see illustration)**.
6 Prevent the crankshaft from turning by the method used on removal, and tighten the pulley retaining bolt to the specified torque, in the specified stages, where applicable. On engines which require the bolt to be angle-tightened, it is recommended that an angle-measuring gauge is used during the final stages of the tightening, to ensure accuracy **(see illustration)**. If a gauge is not available, use white paint to make alignment marks between the bolt head and pulley prior to tightening; the marks can then be used to check that the bolt has been rotated through the correct angle.
7 Refit the auxiliary drivebelt as described in Section 1 using the mark made prior to removal to ensure that the belt is fitted the correct way around.
8 Refit the roadwheel then lower the vehicle to the ground and tighten the wheel bolts to the specified torque.

1.8 and 2.0 litre engines

Removal

9 Proceed as described above in paragraphs 1 and 2.
10 Slacken the four bolts securing the pulley to the crankshaft sprocket, using a suitable Allen key or hexagon bit, then remove the pulley. To prevent the crankshaft from turning, use a suitable female Torx socket on the crankshaft pulley bolt, or alternatively,

7.4 Removing the crankshaft pulley bolt and washer - 1.6 litre engine

use one of the methods described in paragraph 3.
11 Unscrew the retaining bolts and remove the crankshaft pulley from the end of the crankshaft, taking care not to damage the crankshaft sensor, where applicable.

Refitting

12 Refit the crankshaft pulley, aligning the pulley cut-out with the raised notch on the timing belt sprocket, then fit the retaining bolts.
13 Prevent the crankshaft from turning by the method used on removal, and tighten the pulley retaining bolts to the specified torque.
14 Proceed as described in paragraphs 7 and 8.

8 Crankshaft pulley (DOHC) - removal and refitting

1.4 and 1.6 litre engines

Note: *A new pulley retaining bolt will be required on refitting.*

Removal

1 Apply the handbrake, then jack up the front

7.5 Refit the crankshaft pulley, aligning the cut-out with the raised notch on the crankshaft sprocket (arrowed) - 1.6 litre engine

7.6 Tighten the pulley retaining bolt to the specified torque in the specified stages - 1.6 litre engine

9.3a Unscrew the retaining screws (arrowed) . . .

9.3b . . . and withdraw the timing belt upper cover - 1.6 litre engine

of the car and support it on axle stands. Remove the right-hand roadwheel.

2 Remove the auxiliary drivebelt as described in Section 1. Prior to removal, mark the direction of rotation of the belt to ensure that the belt is refitted the same way round.

3 Slacken the crankshaft pulley retaining bolt. To prevent crankshaft rotation on manual transmission models, have an assistant select top gear and apply the brakes firmly. On automatic transmission models prevent rotation by removing one of the torque converter retaining bolts and bolting the driveplate to the transmission housing using a metal bar, spacers and suitable bolts.

4 Unscrew the retaining bolt and washer and remove the crankshaft pulley from the end of the crankshaft, taking care not to damage the crankshaft sensor, where applicable.

Refitting

5 Refit the crankshaft pulley, aligning the pulley cut-out with the raised notch on the timing belt sprocket, then fit the washer and new retaining bolt.

6 Lock the crankshaft using the method used in removal, and tighten the pulley retaining bolt to the specified stage 1 torque setting, then angle-tighten the bolt through the specified stage 2 angle, using a socket and extension bar, and finally through the specified stage 3 angle. It is recommended that an angle-measuring gauge is used during the final stages of the tightening, to ensure accuracy. If a gauge is not available, use white paint to make alignment marks between the bolt head and pulley prior to tightening; the marks can then be used to check that the bolt has been rotated through the correct angle.

7 Refit the auxiliary drivebelt as described in Section 1 using the mark made prior to removal to ensure the belt is fitted the correct way round.

8 Refit the roadwheel then lower the car to the ground and tighten the wheel bolts to the specified torque.

1.8 and 2.0 litre engines

Removal

9 Carry out the operations described in paragraphs 1 and 2.

10 Using a socket and extension bar on the crankshaft sprocket bolt, turn the crankshaft until the timing notch on the pulley rim is correctly aligned with the pointer on the rear timing belt cover (see Section 4).

11 Slacken and remove the small retaining bolts securing the pulley to the crankshaft sprocket, then remove the pulley from the engine. If necessary, prevent crankshaft rotation by holding the sprocket retaining bolt with a suitable socket.

Refitting

12 Check that the crankshaft sprocket mark is still aligned with the mark on the oil pump flange (see Section 4), then manoeuvre the crankshaft pulley into position. Align the notch on the pulley rim with the pointer on the rear timing belt cover, then seat the pulley on the sprocket and tighten its retaining bolts to the specified torque. If necessary, counterhold the crankshaft using a suitable socket on the sprocket bolt.

13 Proceed as described in paragraphs 7 and 8.

9 Timing belt covers (SOHC) - removal and refitting

1.4 and 1.6 litre engines

Upper cover - removal

1 For improved access, remove the air cleaner housing as described in Section 2.

2 Remove the auxiliary drivebelt(s) as described in Section 1. Prior to removal, mark the direction of rotation on the belt to ensure that the belt is fitted the same way around on refitting. Note that on carburettor and single-

point fuel injection engines, it may be necessary to remove the power steering pump (see Section 20) if the timing belt is to be removed.

3 Unscrew the retaining screws, then unclip the timing belt upper cover and remove it from the engine (see illustrations).

Upper cover - refitting

4 Refitting is the reverse of removal, but refit and tension the auxiliary drivebelt(s) as described in Section 1, observing the direction marking made before removal.

Lower cover - removal

5 Remove the crankshaft pulley, as described in Section 7.

6 Where applicable, unclip the crankshaft sensor wiring from the timing belt lower cover.

7 Unscrew the retaining screws and remove the lower cover from the engine (see illustration). Note that on some models it may be necessary to remove the upper cover as described previously in this Section before the lower cover can be removed.

Lower cover - refitting

8 Refitting is the reverse of removal, but refit the crankshaft pulley as described in Section 7.

4A

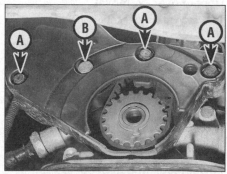

9.7 Timing belt lower cover retaining bolts (A) - 1.6 litre engine

B Timing belt tensioner bolt

9.12a Slacken and remove the retaining bolts and remove the timing belt rear cover - 1.6 litre engine

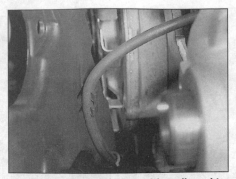

9.12b Crankshaft sensor wiring clipped to rear of timing belt rear cover - 1.6 litre engine

10.2 Removing the timing belt upper cover - 1.6 litre engine

Rear cover - removal

9 Remove the outer covers as described previously in this Section, noting that on some models it may be necessary to remove the power steering pump (see Section 20) to enable the timing belt to be removed.

10 Remove the timing belt as described in Section 11.

11 Remove the camshaft and crankshaft sprockets, and the timing belt tensioner, as described in Section 13.

12 Unscrew and remove the bolts securing the rear cover to the camshaft housing and the cylinder block, then withdraw the rear cover **(see illustrations)**. Where applicable, unclip the crankshaft sensor wiring from the rear of the cover.

Rear cover - refitting

13 Refitting is the reverse of removal, bearing in mind the following points.
a) *Refit the camshaft and crankshaft sprockets, and the timing belt tensioner, as described in Section 13.*
b) *Refit and tension the timing belt as described in Section 11.*
c) *Refit the outer timing belt covers as described previously in this Section.*
d) *Where applicable, refit the power steering pump and bleed the fluid circuit as described in Sections 20 and 19.*

1.8 and 2.0 litre engines

Upper cover - removal

14 Proceed as described in paragraphs 1 and 2.

15 Where applicable, disconnect the wiring from the temperature gauge sender.

16 Release the securing clips, and remove the upper timing belt cover.

Upper cover - refitting

17 Refitting is the reverse of removal, but refit and tension the auxiliary drivebelt(s) as described in Section 1, observing the direction marking made before removal.

Lower (coolant pump) cover - removal

18 Remove the upper timing belt cover as described previously in this Section, then unclip the lower cover from the coolant pump.

Lower (coolant pump) cover - refitting

19 Refitting is the reverse of removal, but refit and tension the auxiliary drivebelt(s) as described in Section 1, observing the direction marking made before removal.

Rear cover - removal

20 Remove the outer timing belt covers as described previously in this Section.

21 Remove the timing belt as described in Section 11.

22 Remove the timing belt sprockets as described in Section 13. Where applicable, disconnect the wiring plug from the crankshaft sensor, and unclip the wiring from the rear belt cover.

23 Unscrew the securing bolts and remove the rear cover, manipulating it from the smaller rear cover on the coolant pump.

24 If desired, the smaller rear belt cover can be removed from the coolant pump, after unscrewing the securing bolt, by rotating it to disengage it from the retaining flange on the pump.

Rear cover - refitting

25 Refitting is a reversal of removal, bearing in mind the following points.
a) *Refit the camshaft and crankshaft sprockets, and the timing belt tensioner, as described in Section 13.*
b) *Refit and tension the timing belt as described in Section 11.*
c) *Refit the outer timing belt covers as described previously in this Section.*

10.6a Timing belt lower cover upper retaining bolt (arrowed) . . .

10 Timing belt covers (DOHC) - removal and refitting

1.4 and 1.6 litre engines

Upper cover

1 Remove the air cleaner housing a described in Section 2.

2 Unscrew the retaining screws, then unclip the upper cover from the rear cover and remove it from the engine compartment **(see illustration)**.

3 Refitting is the reverse of removal tightening the retaining bolts securely.

Lower cover

4 Remove the upper cover as described in paragraphs 1 and 2.

5 Remove the crankshaft pulley as described in Section 5.

6 Unscrew the retaining bolts, then unclip the cover from the rear cover and manoeuvre it out of position **(see illustrations)**.

7 Refitting is the reverse of removal tightening the cover bolts securely. Refit the crankshaft pulley as described in Section 8.

Rear cover

8 Remove the timing belt as described in Section 12.

9 Remove the camshaft sprockets crankshaft sprocket, and timing belt tensioner, and the idler pulley from the inlet

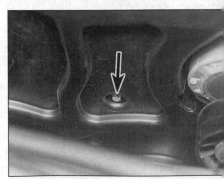

10.6b . . . and lower retaining bolt (arrowed) - 1.6 litre engine

10.10 Timing belt rear cover retaining bolt locations - 1.6 litre engine (shown with timing belt and sprockets still fitted)

10.14a On 1.8 and 2.0 litre engines unscrew the timing belt cover retaining bolts . . .

manifold side of the engine, as described in Section 14.

0 Unscrew the retaining bolts and remove the rear timing belt cover from the engine **(see illustration)**.

1 Refitting is the reverse of removal, tightening the cover bolts securely. Refit the sprockets and the tensioner and idler pulleys as described in Section 14, and refit the timing belt as described in Section 12.

1.8 and 2.0 litre engines

Outer cover

2 Remove the air cleaner housing as described in Section 2.

3 Remove the auxiliary drivebelt(s) as described in Section 1. Prior to removal, mark the direction of rotation on the belt(s) to ensure that the belt is refitted the same way round.

4 Slacken and remove the retaining bolts, along with their washers and rubber spacers,

and remove the cover from the engine, along with its seal **(see illustrations)**.

15 Refitting is the reverse of removal, ensure that the cover seal is correctly fitted **(see illustration)**. Refit the auxiliary drivebelt(s) as described in Section 1, using the mark(s) made prior to removal to ensure that the belt(s) is/are fitted the correct way round.

Rear cover

16 Remove the timing belt as described in Section 12.

17 Remove the camshaft sprockets, crankshaft sprocket, timing belt tensioner idler pulley(s) and, on models from 1993, the idler pulley bracket, as described in Section 14.

18 Where applicable, unbolt the camshaft sensor from the cylinder head.

19 Unscrew the retaining bolts and remove the rear cover from the engine.

20 Refitting is the reverse of removal, tightening all bolts securely. Refit the sprockets, tensioner pulley, idler pulley(s) and

idler pulley bracket (where applicable), as described in Section 14. Refit the timing belt as described in Section 12.

11 Timing belt (SOHC) - removal and refitting

Note: The timing belt must be removed and refitted with the engine cold.

1.4 and 1.6 litre engines

Removal

1 Remove the timing belt upper cover as described in Section 9.

2 Position No 1 cylinder at TDC on its compression stroke as described in Section 3.

3 Remove the crankshaft pulley as described in Section 7.

4 Unbolt the timing belt lower cover and remove it from the engine (see Section 9).

5 Insert a suitable tool (such as a pin punch)

4A

10.14b . . . and recover the rubber spacers

10.15 On refitting ensure the seal is correctly fitted to the outer cover

11.5a Insert a tool (such as a punch) into the hole (arrowed) in the tensioner arm . . .

11.5b . . . then lever the arm clockwise and lock the tensioner in position by locating the tool in the backplate hole

11.7a Slacken the coolant pump bolts . . .

into the hole in the timing belt tensioner arm, then lever the arm clockwise to its stop, and lock it in position by inserting the tool into the corresponding hole in the tensioner backplate (see illustrations). Leave the tool in position to lock the tensioner in position until the belt is refitted.

6 Check the camshaft and crankshaft sprocket timing marks are correctly aligned with the marks on the belt rear cover and oil pump flange.

7 Slacken the coolant pump retaining bolts then, using an open-ended spanner, carefully rotate the pump anti-clockwise to relieve the tension in the timing belt. Adapters to fit the pump are available from most tool shops (Vauxhall/Opel tool KM-421-A or equivalent) and allow the pump to be easily turned using a ratchet or extension bar (see illustrations).

8 Slide the timing belt from its sprockets and remove it from the engine (see illustration). If the belt is to be re-used, use white paint or similar to mark the direction of rotation on the belt. Do not rotate the crankshaft until the timing belt has been refitted.

9 If signs of oil contamination are found, trace the source of the oil leak and rectify it, then wash down the engine timing belt area and all related components to remove all traces of oil.

Refitting

10 On reassembly, thoroughly clean the timing belt sprockets then check that the camshaft sprocket timing mark is still correctly aligned with the cover cut-out and the crankshaft sprocket mark is still aligned with the mark on the oil pump flange.

11 Fit the timing belt over the crankshaft and camshaft sprockets, ensuring that the belt front run is taut (ie, all slack is on the tensioner pulley side of the belt), then fit the belt over the coolant pump sprocket and tensioner pulley. Do not twist the belt sharply while refitting it. Ensure that the belt teeth are correctly seated centrally in the sprockets, and that the timing marks remain in alignment. If a used belt is being refitted, ensure that the running direction mark made on removal points in the normal direction of rotation.

12 Carefully remove the punch from the timing belt tensioner to release the tensioner spring.

13 Check that the sprocket timing marks are still correctly aligned. If adjustment is necessary, lock the tensioner in position again, then disengage the belt from the sprockets and make any necessary adjustments.

14 If the marks are still correctly positioned, tension the timing belt by rotating the coolant pump whilst observing the movement of the tensioner arm. Turn the pump clockwise, so that the tensioner arm is fully over against its stop, without exerting any excess strain on the belt, then tighten the coolant pump retaining bolts.

15 Temporarily refit the crankshaft pulle bolt, then rotate the crankshaft smoothl through two complete turns (720°) in th normal direction of rotation to settle the timin belt in position.

16 Check that both the camshaft an crankshaft sprocket timing marks are sti aligned (see Section 3), then slacken th coolant pump bolts. Adjust the pump so tha the tensioner arm pointer is aligned with th centre of the V-shaped cut-out on th tensioner backplate, then tighten the coolar pump bolts to the specified torque (se illustration). Rotate the crankshaft smoothl through another two complete turns in th normal direction of rotation, to bring th sprocket timing marks back into alignmen Check that the tensioner arm pointer is sti aligned with the centre of the cut-out in th backplate.

17 If the tensioner arm pointer is not correct aligned with the centre of the cut-out, repea the procedure in paragraph 16.

18 Once the tensioner arm and cut-ou remain correctly aligned, ensure that th coolant pump bolts are tightened to th specified torque, then refit the timing be covers and crankshaft pulley as described i Sections 7 and 9.

11.7b . . . and relieve the timing belt tension by rotating the pump with a suitable adapter

11.8 Slip the timing belt off from the sprockets and remove it from the engine

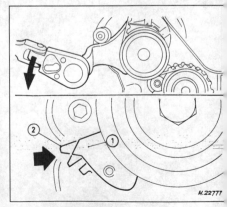

11.16 Rotate the coolant pump until the tensioner arm pointer (1) is correctly aligned with the cut-out (2) on the backplate

1.8 and 2.0 litre engines up to 1993

Note: *The tension of a new belt must be adjusted with the engine cold. The tension of a used belt must be checked with the engine at normal operating temperature. The manufacturers specify the use of a special gauge, Vauxhall/Opel tool KM-510-A, for checking the timing belt tension*

Removal

19 Proceed as described previously for 1.4 and 1.6 litre engines, in paragraphs 1 to 9, but ignore paragraph 5.

20 On reassembly, thoroughly clean the timing belt sprockets then check that the camshaft sprocket timing mark is still correctly aligned with the cover cut-out and the crankshaft sprocket mark is still aligned with the mark on the oil pump flange.

21 Fit the timing belt over the crankshaft and camshaft sprockets, ensuring that the belt front run is taut (ie, all slack is on the coolant pump side of the belt), then fit the belt over the coolant pump sprocket. Do not twist the belt sharply while refitting it. Ensure that the belt teeth are correctly seated centrally in the sprockets, and that the timing marks remain in alignment. If a used belt is being refitted, ensure that the running direction mark made on removal points in the normal direction of rotation.

22 Read the instructions supplied with the gauge (Vauxhall/Opel tool KM-510-A) before proceeding.

23 Place the locked gauge at the centre of the belt run between the coolant pump and the camshaft gear. The gauge should locate on the timing belt as shown **(see illustration)**.

24 Slowly release the operating lever on the

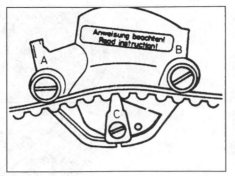

11.23 Tension gauge KM-510-A correctly positioned on timing belt. Belt must pass through points A, B and C - 1.8 and 2.0 litre engines up to 1993

11.24 Note the reading on the scale of the tension gauge - 1.8 and 2.0 litre engines up to 1993

gauge, then lightly tap the gauge two or three times and note the reading on the scale **(see illustration)**.

25 If the reading is not as specified, loosen the three coolant pump securing bolts, using an Allen key or hexagon bit (if not already done) and rotate the coolant pump in the required direction to achieve the necessary reading on the gauge. Rotate the pump clockwise to increase the belt tension, or anti-clockwise to decrease the tension.

26 Lightly tighten the coolant pump securing bolts sufficiently to prevent the pump from moving.

27 Remove the tensioning gauge and turn the crankshaft through one complete revolution clockwise.

28 Recheck the belt tension as described in paragraphs 23 and 24.

29 If the tension is not as specified, repeat paragraphs 25 to 28 inclusive until the required reading is obtained.

30 On completion of adjustment, remove the checking gauge and tighten the coolant pump bolts to the specified torque.

31 Refit the timing belt covers and crankshaft pulley as described in Sections 7 and 9.

1.8 and 2.0 litre engines from 1993

Removal

32 Proceed as described previously for 1.4 and 1.6 litre engines, in paragraphs 1 to 4.

33 Slacken the timing belt tensioner securing bolt slightly then, insert a suitable Allen key or hexagon bit into the hole provided in the tensioner arm, and turn the tensioner arm clockwise until the tensioner pointer is at its left stop. Tighten the tensioner securing bolt.

34 Slide the timing belt from its sprockets and remove it from the engine. If the belt is to be re-used, use white paint or similar to mark the direction of rotation on the belt. **Do not** rotate the crankshaft until the timing belt has been refitted.

35 If signs of oil contamination are found, trace the source of the oil leak and rectify it, then wash down the engine timing belt area and all related components to remove all traces of oil.

Refitting

36 On reassembly, thoroughly clean the timing belt sprockets then check that the camshaft sprocket timing mark is still correctly aligned with the cover cut-out and the crankshaft sprocket mark is still aligned with the mark on the oil pump flange.

37 Check that the coolant pump is correctly positioned by checking that the lug on the coolant pump flange is aligned with the corresponding lug on the cylinder block. If this is not the case, slacken the coolant pump retaining bolts slightly, and move the pump until the lugs are aligned **(see illustration)**. Tighten the coolant pump bolts to the specified torque on completion.

38 Fit the timing belt over the crankshaft and camshaft sprockets, ensuring that the belt front run is taut (ie, all slack is on the tensioner pulley side of the belt), then fit the belt over the coolant pump sprocket and tensioner

4A

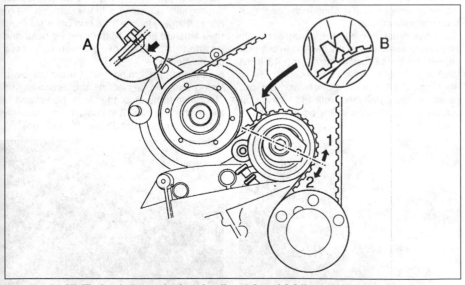

11.37 Timing belt tensioning details - 1.8 and 2.0 litre engines from 1993

A   *Alignment lugs on coolant pump and cylinder block*
B   *Tensioner pointer aligned with notch in tensioner bracket*
1   *Move the tensioner arm anti-clockwise to tension the belt*
2   *Move the tensioner arm clockwise to release the belt tension*

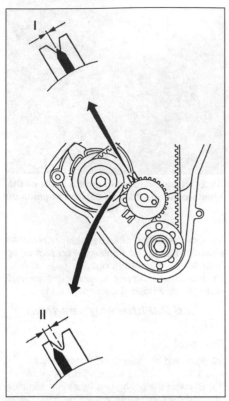

11.43 Timing belt adjustment for new and used timing belts - 1.8 and 2.0 litre engines from 1993

1   *Tensioner pointer alignment for new belts*
2   *Tensioner pointer alignment for used belts (approx 4.0 mm to the left of centre)*

pulley. Do not twist the belt sharply while refitting it. Ensure that the belt teeth are correctly seated centrally in the sprockets, and that the timing marks remain in alignment. If a used belt is being refitted, ensure that the running direction mark made on removal points in the normal direction of rotation.

39 Slacken the tensioner securing bolt and move the tensioner arm anti-clockwise, until the tensioner pointer lies at its stop, without exerting excess pressure on the timing belt. Tighten the tensioner securing bolt to hold the tensioner in this position.

40 Check that the sprocket timing marks are still correctly aligned. If adjustment is necessary, release the tensioner again, then disengage the belt from the sprockets and make any necessary adjustments.

41 Using a socket on the crankshaft pulley/sprocket bolt (as applicable), rotate the crankshaft smoothly through two complete turns (720°) in the normal direction of rotation to settle the timing belt in position.

42 Check that both the camshaft and crankshaft sprocket timing marks are still aligned (see Section 3), then slacken the tensioner bolt again.

43 If a new timing belt is being fitted, adjust the tensioner (turn it clockwise) so that the pointer is aligned with the centre of the V-

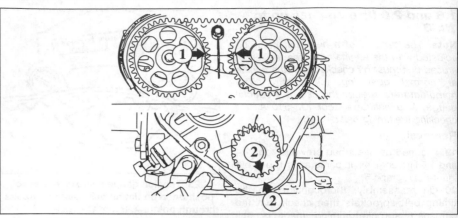

12.4a Camshaft and crankshaft sprocket timing marks - 1.6 litre engine

1   *Camshaft sprocket timing marks aligned with the cylinder head upper surface*
2   *Crankshaft sprocket timing mark aligned with mark on oil pump housing*

shaped cut-out on the tensioner backplate **(see illustration)**. Hold the tensioner in the correct position and tighten its retaining bolt to the specified torque. Rotate the crankshaft smoothly through another two complete turns in the normal direction of rotation, to bring the sprocket timing marks back into alignment. Check that the tensioner pointer is still aligned with the centre of the backplate cut-out.

44 If the original belt is being refitted, adjust the tensioner (turn it clockwise) so that the pointer is positioned 4 mm to the left of the centre of the V-shaped cut-out on the tensioner backplate. Hold the tensioner in the correct position and tighten its retaining bolt to the specified torque. Rotate the crankshaft smoothly through another two complete turns in the normal direction of rotation, to bring the sprocket timing marks back into alignment. Check that the tensioner pointer is still correctly positioned in relation to the centre of the backplate cut-out.

45 If the tensioner pointer is not correctly positioned in relation to the backplate cut-out, repeat the procedure in paragraph 43 (new belt) or 44 (original belt), as applicable.

46 Once the tensioner pointer and cut-out remain correctly aligned, refit the timing belt covers and crankshaft pulley as described in Sections 7 and 9.

12 Timing belt (DOHC) –
removal and refitting

***Note**: The timing belt must be removed and refitted with the engine cold.*

1.4 and 1.6 litre engines

Removal

1 Position No 1 cylinder at TDC on its compression stroke as described in Section 4.
2 Remove the crankshaft pulley as described in Section 8.
3 Unbolt the timing belt lower cover and remove it from the engine (see Section 10).
4 Check that the camshaft sprocket timing marks are correctly aligned with the cylinder head surface and the crankshaft sprocket timing mark is aligned with the mark on the oil pump flange. Unscrew the two bolts securing the camshaft sensor to the cylinder head and position it clear of the engine **(see illustrations)**.
5 Slacken the timing belt tensioner bolt. Using an Allen key, rotate the tensioner arm clockwise to its stop, to relieve the tension in the timing belt, hold it in position and securely tighten the retaining bolt **(see illustration)**.

12.4b On 1.6 litre engines unbolt the camshaft sensor and position it clear of the timing belt

12.5 Slacken the timing belt tensioner bolt (1) and rotate the tensioner clockwise using an Allen key in the arm cut-out (2)

12.6 Removing the timing belt

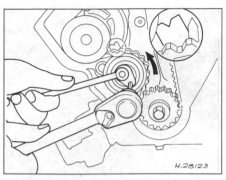

12.11 Tension the belt by rotating the tensioner arm fully anti-clockwise until the pointer is positioned as shown

12.15 If a new belt is being fitted, position the tensioner so that the pointer is aligned with the backplate cut-out

6 Slide the timing belt off from its sprockets and remove it from the engine **(see illustration)**. If the belt is to be re-used, use white paint or similar to mark the direction of rotation on the belt. **Do not** rotate the crankshaft or camshafts until the timing belt has been refitted.

7 If signs of oil contamination are found, trace the source of the oil leak and rectify it, then wash down the engine timing belt area and all related components to remove all traces of oil.

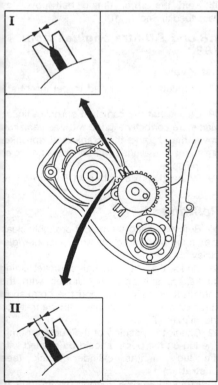

12.16 Timing belt tensioner pointer positions

I   Location if a new belt is being fitted

II Location if the original belt is being re-used (pointer should be 4 mm to the left of the backplate cut-out

Refitting

8 Before refitting the belt, thoroughly clean the timing belt sprockets and tensioner/idler pulleys.

9 Check that the camshaft sprocket timing marks are still correctly aligned with the cylinder head surface, and that the crankshaft sprocket mark is still aligned with the mark on the oil pump flange (see Section 4).

10 Fit the timing belt over the crankshaft and camshaft sprockets and around the idler pulleys, ensuring that the belt front run is taut (ie, all slack is on the tensioner side of the belt), then fit the belt over the coolant pump sprocket and tensioner pulley. Do not twist the belt sharply while refitting it. Ensure that the belt teeth are correctly seated centrally in the sprockets, and that the timing marks remain in alignment. If a used belt is being refitted, ensure that the arrow mark made on removal points in the normal direction of rotation.

11 Slacken the timing belt tensioner bolt to release the tensioner spring. Rotate the tensioner arm anti-clockwise until the tensioner pointer is fully over against its stop, without exerting any excess strain on the belt. Hold the tensioner in position and securely tighten its retaining bolt **(see illustration)**.

12 Check that the sprocket timing marks are still correctly aligned. If adjustment is necessary, release the tensioner again, then disengage the belt from the sprockets and make any necessary adjustments.

13 Using a socket on the crankshaft pulley bolt, rotate the crankshaft smoothly through two complete turns (720°) in the normal direction of rotation to settle the timing belt in position.

14 Check that both the camshaft and crankshaft sprocket timing marks are correctly aligned with the upper edge of the cylinder head and the timing mark on the rear belt cover respectively, then slacken the tensioner bolt again.

15 If a new timing belt is being fitted, adjust the tensioner so that the pointer is aligned with the centre of the V-shaped cut-out on the backplate **(see illustration)**. Hold the

tensioner in the correct position and tighten its retaining bolt to the specified torque. Rotate the crankshaft smoothly through another two complete turns in the normal direction of rotation, to bring the sprocket timing marks back into alignment. Check that the tensioner pointer is still aligned with the centre of the backplate cut-out.

16 If the original belt is being refitted, adjust the tensioner so that the pointer is positioned 4 mm to the left of the centre of the V-shaped cut-out on the backplate **(see illustration)**. Hold the tensioner in the correct position and tighten its retaining bolt to the specified torque. Rotate the crankshaft smoothly through another two complete turns in the normal direction of rotation, to bring the sprocket timing marks back into alignment. Check that the tensioner pointer is still correctly positioned in relation to the backplate cut-out.

17 If the tensioner pointer is not correctly positioned in relation to the backplate cut-out, repeat the procedure in paragraph 15 (new belt) or 16 (original belt) (as applicable).

18 Once the tensioner pointer and backplate cut-out remain correctly aligned, refit the timing belt covers and crankshaft pulley as described in Sections 8 and 10. Refit the camshaft sensor to the cylinder head, and tighten its retaining bolts to the specified torque, prior to refitting the upper cover.

Pre 1993 1.8 and 2.0 litre engines

Note: *The manufacturers specify the use of a special adjustment wrench, Vauxhall/Opel tool KM-666 for adjusting the timing belt tension. No checking of fitted (in-use) timing belt adjustment is specified, and the adjustment procedure applies only to a newly-fitted belt. The adjustment must be carried out with the engine cold.*

Removal

19 Proceed as described in paragraphs 1 and 2.

20 Remove the outer timing belt cover as described in Section 10.

21 Check that the timing marks are still

4A

12.21 On 1.8 and 2.0 litre engines ensure the camshaft sprocket marks are correctly aligned with the marks on the camshaft cover (arrowed)

12.22 Slackening the timing belt tensioner bolt - pre 1993 2.0 litre engine

12.26 Timing pointer on rear timing belt cover aligned with notch in crankshaft pulley (arrowed) - pre 1993 2.0 litre engine

aligned with the marks on the camshaft cover **(see illustration)**, then remove the timing belt as follows.

22 Slacken the timing belt tensioner bolt, then slide the timing belt off from its sprockets and remove it from the engine **(see illustration)**. If the belt is to be re-used, use white paint or similar to mark the direction of rotation on the belt. **Do not** rotate the crankshaft or camshafts until the timing belt has been refitted.

23 Proceed as described in paragraph 7.

Refitting

24 Remove the timing belt tensioner pulley bolt, then fit a new bolt, but do not fully tighten it at this stage.

25 Before refitting the belt, thoroughly clean the timing belt sprockets and tensioner/idler pulleys.

26 Check that the camshaft sprockets timing marks are still correctly aligned with the marks on the camshaft cover, then temporarily refit the crankshaft pulley and check that the timing mark on the crankshaft pulley is still aligned with the pointer on the rear timing belt cover (see Section 4) **(see illustration)**.

27 Fit the timing belt over the crankshaft and camshaft sprockets and around the idler pulley, ensuring that the belt front run is taut (ie, all slack is on the tensioner side of the belt), then fit the belt over the coolant pump sprocket and tensioner pulley. Do not twist the belt sharply while refitting it. Ensure that the belt teeth are correctly seated centrally in the sprockets, and that the timing marks remain in alignment. If a used belt is being refitted, ensure that the arrow mark made on removal points in the normal direction of rotation.

28 Refit the crankshaft pulley, and tighten the securing bolts to the specified torque. Do not allow the crankshaft to turn as the bolts are tightened.

29 Check that the timing marks are still aligned as described previously, then adjust the timing belt tension as follows.

Adjustment using Vauxhall/Opel tool KM-666

30 Fit the tool KM-666 to the belt tensioner pulley mounting plate in accordance with the tool manufacturer's instructions.

31 Working anti-clockwise from the TDC mark on the exhaust camshaft sprocket, mark the eighth tooth on the sprocket **(see illustration)**.

32 Using a socket or spanner on the crankshaft sprocket bolt, turn the crankshaft slowly and evenly clockwise through two complete turns. Continue to turn the crankshaft until the reference mark made in paragraph 31 is aligned with the timing notch on the cylinder head cover.

33 Tighten the **new** tensioner pulley bolt to the specified torque in the three stages given in the Specifications.

34 Remove tool KM-666.

35 Turn the crankshaft clockwise until the TDC marks on the camshaft sprockets are aligned with the timing notches in the cylinder head cover, and check that the TDC mark on the crankshaft pulley is aligned with the pointer on the rear timing belt cover.

36 Refit the outer timing belt cover as described in Section 10.

1.8 and 2.0 litre engines from 1993

Removal

37 Proceed as described in paragraphs 1 and 2.

38 Check that the camshaft sprocket timing marks are correctly aligned with the camshaft cover marks, and the crankshaft sprocket timing mark is aligned with the mark on the oil pump flange.

39 Proceed as described in paragraphs 5 to 7.

Refitting

40 Before refitting the belt, thoroughly clean the timing belt sprockets and tensioner/idler pulleys.

41 Check that the camshaft sprocket timing marks are still correctly aligned with the camshaft cover marks, and the crankshaft sprocket mark is still aligned with the mark on the oil pump flange.

42 Check the position of the coolant pump. The lug on the pump should be aligned with the lug on the cylinder block **(see illustration)**.

43 Proceed as described in paragraphs 10 to 17, but use a socket on the crankshaft sprocket bolt to turn the crankshaft.

44 Once the tensioner pointer and backplate cut-out remain correctly aligned, refit the timing belt cover and crankshaft pulley as described in Sections 8 and 10.

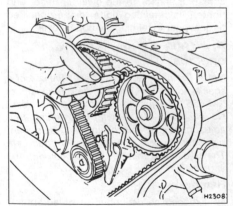

12.31 Working anti-clockwise from the TDC mark on the exhaust camshaft sprocket, mark the eighth tooth on the sprocket - pre 1993 2.0 litre engine

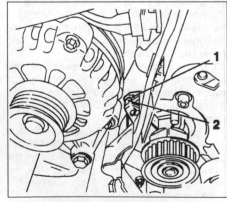

12.42 The lug (1) on the coolant pump should be aligned with the lug (2) on the cylinder block - 1.8 and 2.0 litre engines from 1993

13.2 Using a home-made sprocket holding tool to retain the camshaft sprocket whilst the bolt is slackened

13.5 Refit the camshaft sprocket making sure the locating pin (1) engages with the sprocket hole (2)

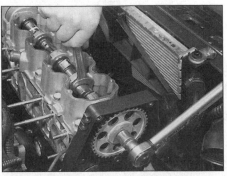

13.6 Using an open-ended spanner to hold the camshaft whilst the sprocket retaining bolt is tightened

13 Timing belt tensioner and sprockets (SOHC) - removal and refitting

Camshaft sprocket

Removal

1 Remove the timing belt as described in Section 11.
2 The camshaft must be prevented from turning as the sprocket bolt is unscrewed, and this can be achieved in one of two ways as follows.

a) *Make up a sprocket-holding tool using two lengths of steel strip (one long, the other short), and three nuts and bolts; one nut and bolt forms the pivot of a forked tool, with the remaining two nuts and bolts at the tips of the 'forks' to engage with the sprocket spokes as shown (see illustration).*

b) *Remove the camshaft cover as described in Section 5 and hold the camshaft with an open-ended spanner on the flats provided between Nos 3 and 4 cam lobes.*

3 Unscrew the retaining bolt and washer and remove the sprocket from the end of the camshaft.

Refitting

4 Prior to refitting check the camshaft front oil seal for signs of damage or leakage, if

necessary, renewing it as described in Section 9.
5 Refit the sprocket to the end of the camshaft, aligning the hole in the sprocket with the camshaft locating pin, then refit the retaining bolt and washer (**see illustration**).
6 Tighten the sprocket retaining bolt to the specified torque, whilst preventing rotation using the method employed on removal (**see illustration**).
7 Refit the timing belt as described in Section 11 then, where applicable, refit the camshaft cover as described in Section 5.

Crankshaft sprocket – 1.4 and 1.6 litre engines

Removal

8 Remove the timing belt as described in Section 11.
9 Slide the sprocket from the end of the crankshaft, noting which way around it is fitted. Where applicable, recover the Woodruff key from the end of the crankshaft.

Refitting

10 Where applicable, refit the Woodruff key to the end of the crankshaft, then slide the sprocket into position, making sure its timing mark is facing outwards (**see illustration**).
11 Refit the timing belt as described in Section 11.

Crankshaft sprocket – 1.8 and 2.0 litre engines

Note: *A suitable puller may be required to*

remove the sprocket. A new sprocket bolt should be used on refitting.

Removal

12 Remove the timing belt as described in Section 11.
13 Slacken the crankshaft sprocket retaining bolt. Do not allow the crankshaft to turn, as the timing belt has been removed, and there may be a danger of piston-to-valve contact on some engines if the crankshaft it turned. To prevent crankshaft rotation on manual transmission models, have an assistant select top gear and apply the brakes firmly. On automatic transmission models prevent rotation by removing one of the torque converter retaining bolts and bolting the driveplate to the transmission housing using a metal bar, spacers and suitable bolts.
14 Remove the sprocket bolt and washer, then remove the sprocket from the end of the crankshaft, using a suitable puller if necessary. Where applicable, recover the Woodruff key and the thrust washer from the end of the crankshaft (**see illustrations**).

Refitting

15 Where applicable, refit the thrust washer and the Woodruff key to the end of the crankshaft, then refit the crankshaft sprocket.
16 Fit a new sprocket securing bolt, ensuring that the washer is in place under the bolt head, and tighten the bolt to the specified torque in the two stages given in the Specifications. Prevent the crankshaft from

4A

13.10 Refit the crankshaft sprocket making sure its timing mark is facing outwards

13.14a Remove the crankshaft sprocket . . .

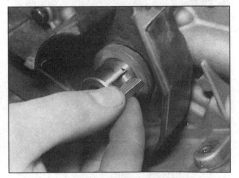

13.14b . . . then remove the Woodruff key . . .

13.14c . . . and the thrust washer - 1.8 and 2.0 litre engines

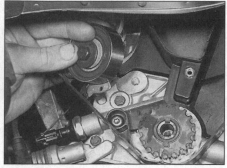

13.19 Slacken and remove the retaining bolt and remove the timing belt tensioner assembly

13.20 On refitting ensure the tensioner backplate lug (1) is correctly located in the oil pump housing hole (2) - 1.4 and 1.6 litre engines

turning using the method employed on removal.

17 Refit the timing belt as described in Section 11.

Tensioner assembly

Removal

18 Remove the timing belt as described in Section 11.

19 Slacken and remove the retaining bolt and remove the tensioner assembly from the engine **(see illustration)**.

Refitting

20 Fit the tensioner to the engine. On 1.4 and

14.2 Using an open-ended spanner to retain the camshaft whilst the sprocket retaining bolt is slackened

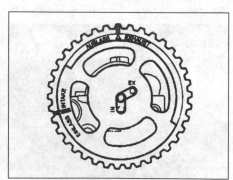

14.7 On 1.4 and 1.6 litre engines ensure the camshaft sprocket cut-out (arrowed) is correctly engaged with the locating pin

1.6 litre engines, make sure that the positioning lug on the tensioner backplate is correctly located in the oil pump housing hole **(see illustration)**. On 1.8 and 2.0 litre engines, make sure that the positioning lug on the tensioner backplate is correctly located between the two guide lugs on the oil pump.

21 Ensure that the tensioner is correctly seated, then refit the timing belt (Section 11).

---

14 Timing belt sprockets, tensioner and idler pulleys (DOHC) - removal and refitting

Camshaft sprockets

Note: *New sprocket retaining bolt(s) will be required on refitting.*

Removal

1 Remove the timing belt as described in Section 12.

2 The relevant camshaft must be prevented from turning as the sprocket bolt is unscrewed, and this can be achieved in one of two ways as follows.

a)   *Make up a sprocket-holding tool using two lengths of steel strip (one long, the other short), and three nuts and bolts; one nut and bolt forms the pivot of a forked*

14.8 On 1.8 and 2.0 litre engines ensure the locating pin is engaged in the correct sprocket hole on refitting (see text)

tool, with the remaining two nuts and bolts at the tips of the 'forks' to engage with the sprocket spokes (see illustration 13.2).

b)   *Remove the camshaft cover as described in Section 6 and hold the camshaft with an open-ended spanner on the flats provided (see illustration).*

3 Unscrew the retaining bolt and washer and remove the sprocket from the end of the camshaft. If the sprocket locating pin is a loose fit in the camshaft end, remove it and store it with the sprocket for safe-keeping.

4 If necessary, remove the remaining sprocket using the same method. On 1.4 and 1.6 litre engines the inlet and exhaust sprockets are different; the exhaust camshaft sprocket can be easily identified by the lugs which activate the camshaft position sensor. On 1.8 and 2.0 litre engines both sprockets are the same.

Refitting

5 Prior to refitting check the oil seal(s) for signs of damage or leakage. If necessary, renew them.

6 Ensure that the locating pin is in position in the camshaft end.

7 On 1.4 and 1.6 litre engines refit the sprocket to the camshaft end, aligning its cut-out with the locating pin, and fit the washer and **new** retaining bolt **(see illustration)**. If both sprockets have been removed, ensure that each sprocket is fitted to the correct camshaft; the exhaust camshaft sprocket can be identified by the lugs on the sprocket outer face which trigger the camshaft position sensor.

8 On 1.8 and 2.0 litre engines both inlet and exhaust camshaft sprockets are the same, but each one is equipped with two locating pin cut-outs. If the sprocket is being fitted to the inlet camshaft, engage the locating pin in the IN cut-out, and if the sprocket is being fitted to the exhaust camshaft engage the locating pin in the EX cut-out **(see illustration)**. Ensure that the camshaft locating pin is engaged in the correct sprocket cut-out, then fit the washer and **new** retaining bolt.

9 On all models, retain the sprocket by the

14.9 Using a spanner to prevent camshaft rotation

method used on removal, and tighten the pulley retaining bolt to the specified stage 1 torque setting, then angle-tighten the bolt through the specified stage 2 angle, using a socket and extension bar, and finally through the specified stage 3 angle **(see illustration)**. It is recommended that an angle-measuring gauge is used during the final stages of the tightening, to ensure accuracy. If a gauge is not available, use white paint to make alignment marks between the bolt head and pulley prior to tightening; the marks can then be used to check that the bolt has been rotated through the correct angle.

10 Refit the timing belt as described in Section 12, then (where applicable) refit the camshaft cover as described in Section 6.

Crankshaft sprocket – 1.4 and 1.6 litre engines

Removal

11 Remove the timing belt as described in Section 12.

12 Slide the sprocket off from the end of the crankshaft, noting which way around it is fitted.

Refitting

13 Align the sprocket locating key with the crankshaft groove, then slide the sprocket into position, making sure that its timing mark is facing outwards.

14 Refit the timing belt as described in Section 12.

Crankshaft sprocket - 1.8 and 2.0 litre engines

Note: *A new crankshaft sprocket retaining bolt will be required on refitting.*

Removal

15 Remove the timing belt as described in Section 12.

16 Slacken the crankshaft sprocket retaining bolt. To prevent crankshaft rotation on manual transmission models, have an assistant select top gear and apply the brakes firmly. On automatic transmission models prevent rotation by removing one of the torque converter retaining bolts and bolting the driveplate to the transmission housing using a metal bar, spacers and suitable bolts.

17 Unscrew the retaining bolt and washer and remove the crankshaft sprocket from the end of the crankshaft. Where applicable, recover the thrust washer and the Woodruff key from the end of the crankshaft.

Refitting

18 Where applicable, refit the Woodruff key and the thrust washer to the end of the crankshaft.

19 Align the sprocket location key with the crankshaft groove, or align the sprocket groove with the Woodruff key, as applicable, and slide the sprocket into position, ensuring its timing mark is facing outwards. Fit the washer and new retaining bolt.

20 Lock the crankshaft by the method used on removal, and tighten the sprocket retaining bolt to the specified stage 1 torque setting then angle-tighten the bolt through the specified stage 2 angle, using a socket and extension bar. It is recommended that an angle-measuring gauge is used during the final stages of the tightening, to ensure accuracy. If a gauge is not available, use white paint to make alignment marks between the bolt head and sprocket prior to tightening; the marks can then be used to check that the bolt has been rotated through the correct angle.

21 Refit the timing belt as described in Section 12.

Tensioner pulley assembly – all engines except pre 1993 2.0 litre

Removal

22 Remove the timing belt as described in Section 12.

23 Slacken and remove the retaining bolt and remove the tensioner pulley assembly from the engine. Where applicable, recover the spacer sleeve from the retaining bolt.

Refitting

24 Fit the tensioner to the engine, making sure that the lug on the backplate is correctly located in the oil pump housing hole. Ensure the tensioner is correctly seated then refit the retaining bolt. Using an Allen key, rotate the tensioner arm clockwise to its stop then securely tighten the retaining bolt.

25 Refit the timing belt as described in Section 12.

Tensioner pulley assembly – pre 1993 2.0 litre engines

Note: *A new tensioner pulley assembly securing bolt will be required on refitting.*

Removal

26 Remove the timing belt as described in Section 12.

27 Slacken and remove the retaining bolt and remove the tensioner pulley and mounting plate from the engine. Note the orientation of the mounting plate to aid refitting. Recover the spacer sleeve from the bolt.

Refitting

28 Refit the mounting plate and tensioner pulley using a new bolt, noting that the spacer sleeve should be fitted with the smaller diameter against the pulley.

29 Do not fully tighten the bolt until the timing belt has been refitted and tensioned as described in Section 12.

Idler pulleys – all engines except pre 1993 2.0 litre

Removal

30 Remove the timing belt as described in Section 12.

31 Slacken and remove the retaining bolt(s) and remove the idler pulley(s) from the engine. On 1.8 and 2.0 litre models, if necessary, unbolt the pulley mounting bracket and remove it from the cylinder block.

Refitting

32 On 1.8 and 2.0 litre models refit the pulley mounting bracket (where removed) to the cylinder block and tighten its retaining bolts to the specified torque.

33 On all models, refit the idler pulley(s) and tighten the retaining bolt(s) to the specified torque.

34 Refit the timing belt as described in Section 12.

Idler pulley – pre 1993 2.0 litre engines

Note: *A new idler pulley securing bolt will be required on refitting.*

Removal

35 Remove the timing belt as described in Section 12.

36 Slacken and remove the retaining bolt and remove the idler pulley from the engine. Recover the spacer sleeve from the bolt.

Refitting

37 Refit the idler pulley using a new bolt, noting that the spacer sleeve should be fitted with the smaller diameter against the pulley.

38 Tighten the new securing bolt to the specified torque in the three stages given in the Specifications.

15 Engine right-hand mounting - removal and refitting

Note: *Suitable thread-locking compound will be required to coat the threads of the mounting-to-body bolts on refitting.*

1 Apply the handbrake, then raise the front of the vehicle and support securely on axle stands.

2 Attach lifting tackle to the engine lifting brackets on the cylinder head and support the weight of the engine.

3 Working under the vehicle, unbolt the engine mounting bracket from the cylinder block and unbolt the mounting from the body,

4A

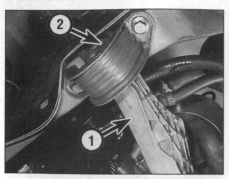

15.3 Right-hand engine mounting bracket (1) and mounting block (2) - C 16 SE model (viewed from underneath

then withdraw the bracket/mounting assembly **(see illustration)**.

4 Unbolt the mounting from the bracket.

5 Fit the new mounting to the bracket and tighten the securing bolts to the specified torque.

6 Refit the mounting bracket to the cylinder block and tighten the securing bolts to the specified torque.

7 Coat the threads of the mounting-to-body bolts with thread-locking compound, then refit them and tighten to the specified torque.

8 Disconnect the lifting tackle and hoist from the engine.

9 Lower the vehicle to the ground.

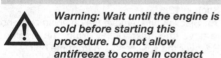

16 Cooling system - draining and refilling

> **Warning: Wait until the engine is cold before starting this procedure. Do not allow antifreeze to come in contact with your skin, or with the painted surfaces of the vehicle. Rinse off spills immediately with plenty of water. Never leave antifreeze lying around in an open container, or in a puddle in the driveway or garage floor. Children and pets are attracted by its sweet smell but antifreeze is fatal if ingested.**

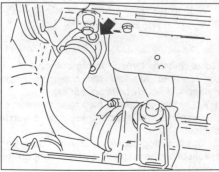

16.5b Location of the Allen key bolt for bleeding the cooling system - C 20 XE model

16.5a Bleeding the cooling system by removing the temperature sender unit - C 16 SE model

Draining

1 To drain the cooling system, carefully remove the expansion tank filler cap.

2 On DOHC models, remove the engine undershield. Refer to Section 18 for details.

3 Position a container beneath the radiator bottom hose connection. Then slacken the hose clip and ease the hose from the radiator stub. If the hose joint has not been disturbed for some time, it may be necessary to twist the hose to break the joint. Allow the coolant to drain into the container.

Refilling

4 Before attempting to fill the cooling system, make sure that all hoses and clips are in good condition, and that the clips are tight. Antifreeze must be used all year round, to prevent corrosion of the alloy engine components.

5 On 1.4 and 1.6 litre models, disconnect the wire and unscrew the coolant temperature sender from the inlet manifold. On X 16 XEL, C 18 XE, C 18 XEL and C 20 XE models, remove the Allen bolt in the thermostat housing cover **(see illustrations)**.

6 Remove the expansion tank cap, and fill the system by slowly pouring the coolant into the expansion tank to prevent airlocks from forming.

7 Refit the coolant temperature sender when coolant free of air bubbles emerges from the bore of the manifold (or thermostat housing). Where applicable, replace the Allen bolt with sealing compound (eg, Vauxhall P/N 90094714), when coolant flows free of

17.4 Withdrawing the coolant pump (O-ring arrowed) - C 16 NZ model

bubbles, and tighten the bolt securely.

8 Top-up the coolant level to the KALT (or COLD) mark on the expansion tank, then refit the expansion tank cap.

9 Start the engine and run it until it reaches normal operating temperature, then stop the engine and allow it to cool.

10 Check for leaks, particularly around disturbed components. Check the coolant level in the expansion tank, and top-up if necessary. Note that the system must be cold before an accurate level is indicated in the expansion tank.

11 On DOHC models, refit the engine undershield on completion.

17 Coolant pump - removal and refitting

Note: *A new pump O-ring will be required when refitting. Silicone grease (Vauxhall P/N 90167353, or equivalent) will be required to coat the pump mounting face in the cylinder block.*

Removal

1 Drain the cooling system, detailed in Section 16.

2 Remove the timing belt and rear cover. Where applicable, remove the timing belt automatic tensioner after belt removal.

3 Unscrew and remove the three coolant pump securing bolts.

4 Withdraw the coolant pump from the cylinder block, and recover the O-ring **(see illustration)**. It may be necessary to tap the pump lightly with a soft-faced hammer to free it from the cylinder block.

Refitting

5 If the original pump is being refitted, ensure that the sealing surfaces are clean. Smear the pump mounting face in the cylinder block with a suitable silicone grease.

6 Fit the pump using a new O-ring. Ensure that the lugs on the pump and the cylinder block are aligned before tightening the pump securing bolts to the specified torque setting **(see illustration)**. Do not tighten the pump

17.6 Lugs (arrowed) on coolant pump and cylinder block must be aligned - C 20 XE model

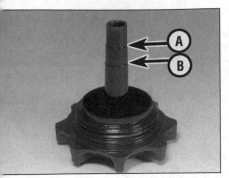

19.1 Power steering fluid level dipstick markings

A MIN   B MIN

19.2 Topping-up the power steering fluid

20.3 Removing the power steering pump pulley - C 16 SE model

securing bolts until the timing belt has been fitted and tensioned.
7 Refit the rear timing belt cover, timing belt and tension roller (as applicable).
8 Refill the cooling system as described in Section 16.

18 Engine undershield - removal and refitting

Removal

1 Apply the handbrake, then jack up the front of the vehicle, and support securely on axle stands.
2 Release the two securing clips, and remove the oil filter access panel.
3 Working around the edges of the undershield, remove the self-tapping screws that secure the shield to the underbody, noting that some of the screws may also secure the wheelarch liners **(see illustration)**.
4 With the help of an assistant, pull the shield from the vehicle, and place it to one side to avoid damage.

Refitting

5 Refitting is a reversal of removal.

19 Power steering hydraulic system - bleeding

1 With the engine stopped, initially fill the reservoir to the level of the MAX mark on the dipstick attached to the reservoir filler cap **(see illustration)**.
2 Start the engine, and immediately top-up the fluid level to the MIN mark on the dipstick **(see illustration)**. **Do not** allow the reservoir to run dry at any time. The help of an assistant will ease this operation.
3 With the engine running at idle speed, turn the steering wheel slowly two or three times approximately 45° to the left and right of the

centre, then turn the wheel twice from lock to lock. Do not hold the wheel on either lock, as this imposes strain on the hydraulic system.
4 Stop the engine, and check the fluid level. With the fluid at operating temperature (80°C), the level should be on the MAX mark, and with the fluid cold (20°C), the level should be on the MIN mark. Top-up if necessary.

20 Power steering pump - removal and refitting

Note: *A new fluid pipe union O-ring must be used on refitting.*

1.4 and 1.6 litre models, with V-belt
Removal

1 For improved access, remove the air cleaner casing from the right-hand front wing, as described in Section 2.
2 Remove the alternator/power steering pump drivebelt, as described in Section 1.
3 Counterhold the power steering pump pulley, using an old drivebelt, then unscrew the three pulley securing bolts, and remove the pulley **(see illustration)**.
4 To improve access, remove the upper outer timing belt cover.

5 Disconnect the fluid pipe union and the flexible fluid hose from the pump. Be prepared for fluid spillage, and plug or cover the open ends of the pump, pipe and hose, to prevent dirt ingress and further fluid loss **(see illustrations)**.
6 Unscrew and remove the pump securing bolts and carefully manipulate the pump from its bracket. Take care not to damage the bodywork, as there is very little clearance to withdraw the pump **(see illustration)**.

Refitting

7 Refitting is a reversal of removal, but renew the O-ring when reconnecting the fluid pipe

20.5a Unscrewing the power steering pump fluid pipe union (arrowed) - C 16 NZ model

4A

20.5b Power steering pump fluid pipe and hose ends covered to prevent dirt ingress and fluid loss

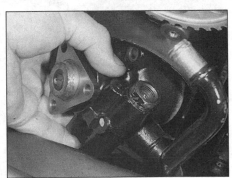

20.6 Removing the power steering pump - C 16 NZ model

20.7 Renew the power steering pump fluid pipe O-ring (arrowed) on refitting

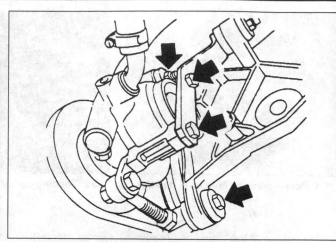

20.11 Power steering pump mounting bolts (arrowed) - SOHC ribbed V-belt model

union **(see illustration)**, and tension the alternator/power steering pump drivebelt, as described in Section 1. Tighten the pump and pulley securing bolts to the specified torque setting.

8 On completion, top-up the fluid level, and bleed the fluid circuit as described in Section 19.

Ribbed V-belt models

Removal

9 Remove the power steering pump drivebelt, as described in Section 1. On DOHC models remove the air cleaner box.

10 Disconnect the fluid pipe union and the flexible fluid hose from the pump. Be prepared for fluid spillage, and plug the open ends of the pump, pipe and hose, to prevent dirt ingress and further fluid loss.

11 Unscrew and remove the four mounting bolts shown **(see illustration)**. Recover the nuts, and take care not to lose the rubber insulators that fit into the mounting bracket.

12 Withdraw the pump from the vehicle.

13 No overhaul of the pump is possible, and if faulty, a new unit must be fitted.

Refitting

14 Refitting is a reversal of removal, but renew the O-ring when reconnecting the fluid pipe union, and before finally tightening the pump mounting bolts, tension the drivebelt, as described in Section 1.

15 On completion, top-up the fluid level, and bleed the fluid circuit as described in Section 19.

Chapter 4B
Vauxhall/Opel Astra diesel 1991 to 1996

Contents

Specifications

Timing belt renewal interval . . . . Every 36 000 miles (60 000 km) or 4 years - whichever comes first
Note: *Although the interval for timing belt renewal is increased for later models, it is strongly recommended that this shorter interval is applied to vehicles which are subjected to intensive use, ie, mainly short journeys or a lot of stop-start driving. The actual belt renewal interval is therefore very much up to the individual owner. That being said, it is highly recommended to err on the side of safety, and renew the belt at this earlier interval, bearing in mind the drastic consequences resulting from belt failure.*

Auxiliary drivebelts

17D, 17DR and 17DTL engines

Tension (using gauge KM-128-A):
   Alternator:
      New . . . . 450 N
      Used . . . . 250 to 400 N
   Power steering pump:
      New . . . . 450 N
      Used . . . . 250 to 300 N

17DT engine

Tension (using gauge KM-128-A):
   Alternator:
      New . . . . 440 to 540 N
      Used . . . . 320 to 390 N
   Power steering pump:
      New . . . . 450 N
      Used . . . . 250 to 300 N

Timing belt tension

17D engine (using tension gauge KM-510-A):

New belt, warm	7.5
New belt, cold	9.5
Run-in belt, warm	5.0
Run-in belt, cold	9.0
17DR,17DTL and 17DT engines	Automatic tensioner

Injection pump timing setting

17D, 17DR and 17DTL engines:

Bosch	0.80 + 0.05 mm
Lucas/CAV	x – 0.15 mm (where x = manufacturer's calibration marked on pump)
17DT engine	0.50 to 0.60 mm

Torque wrench settings

	Nm	lbf ft
17D, 17DR and 17DTL engines		
Alternator:		
Adjuster strap nuts and bolts	25	18
Pivot bolt	25	18
Coolant pump bolts	25	18
Camshaft sprocket bolt:*		
Stage 1	75	55
Stage 2	Angle tighten a further 60°	
Stage 3	Angle tighten a further 5°	
Crankcase pulley to sprocket	20	15
Engine mountings:		
Left-hand:		
Flexible mounting to bracket	60	44
Flexible mounting to sidemember	65	48
Mounting bracket to transmission	60	44
Right-hand:		
Flexible mounting to bracket	35	26
Flexible mounting to sidemember	65	48
Mounting bracket to cylinder block	60	44
Rear:		
Flexible mounting to bracket	45	33
Flexible mounting to sidemember	40	30
Mounting bracket to transmission	60	44
Fuel injection pump:		
Fuel lines to pump	25	18
Hub to pump	25	18
Pump to bracket(s)	25	18
Pump to support - M6 bolts	12	9
Sprocket to hub	25	18
Vent bolt to pump	25	18
Power steering pump:		
Drivebelt tensioner to pump	40	30
Timing belt:		
Guide roller to cylinder block	40	30
Tension roller to cylinder block	25	18
Vacuum pump to camshaft housing	28	21
Wheel bolts	90	66
17DT engine		
Alternator to mounting bracket:		
M8 bolt	24	18
M10 bolt	48	35
Camshaft sprocket bolts	10	7
Crankshaft:		
Pulley-to-sprocket bolts	20	15
Sprocket centre bolt	196	145
Fuel injection pump:		
Central vent bolt	20	15
Fuel lines to pump	25	18
Pump to bracket	40	30
Pump to cylinder block/flange	23	17
Sprocket to pump	70	52

Torque wrench settings

	Nm	lbf ft
17DT engine (continued)		
Mountings:		
Left-hand damping block to bracket	60	44
Left and right-hand damping blocks to sidemember	65	48
Rear damping block:		
To bracket	45	33
To crossmember	40	30
Right-hand damping block to bracket	35	26
Right-hand mounting bracket:		
To cylinder block	40	30
To mounting	45	33
Power steering pump:		
Drivebelt tensioner to bracket	25	18
Drivebelt tensioner to pump	18	13
Pressure line to pump connections	28	21
Pump mounting bracket to cylinder block	60	44
Pump support to mounting bracket	25	18
Pump to support	25	18
Timing belt:		
Cover to cylinder block	8	6
Guide roller to cylinder block	76	56
Tension roller to cylinder block	19	14
Wheel bolts	110	81

* Bolts must be renewed every time

<table>
<tr><td>

1 Auxiliary drivebelts - removal, refitting and adjustment

</td></tr>
</table>

Alternator

17D, 17DR and 17DTL engines

1 Gain full access to the drivebelt by raising the car, supporting it on axle stands and removing the right-hand front roadwheel. Remove the air cleaner housing assembly.

2 To remove the drivebelt, first slacken the alternator pivot and adjuster strap nuts and bolts **(see illustration)**.

3 Where fitted, remove the power steering pump drivebelt.

4 Move the alternator towards the engine and slip the drivebelt off its pulleys.

5 Fit the new drivebelt in position over the pulleys and adjust it as follows:

6 Tighten the alternator fastening slightly, so that the alternator can just be moved by hand.

7 Move the alternator away from the engine until the belt tension is correct.

8 Vauxhall recommend the use of a special tool (KM-128-A) for tensioning the belt to the specified amount **(see illustration)**. In the absence of this tool, aim for a tension such that the belt can be deflected about 12 mm by firm finger pressure in the middle of its run. The belt tension must, however, be checked with the special tool as soon as possible. If using a lever to move the alternator, only use a wooden or plastic one and only lever at the pulley end.

9 Tighten the alternator fastenings to the specified torque setting once the belt tension is correct.

10 Where applicable, refit and tension the steering pump drivebelt.

11 Refit the air cleaner housing assembly.

17DT engine

12 Gain full access to the alternator by jacking up the front right-hand side of the vehicle and supporting it on axle stands.

13 To remove the drivebelt, first slacken the alternator pivot and adjuster bolts.

14 Where fitted, remove the power steering pump drivebelt.

15 Move the alternator towards the engine and slip the drivebelt off its pulleys.

16 Fit the new drivebelt in position over the pulleys and adjust it as follows:

17 Tighten the alternator fastenings slightly, so that the alternator can just be moved by hand.

18 Insert a socket drive in the end of the

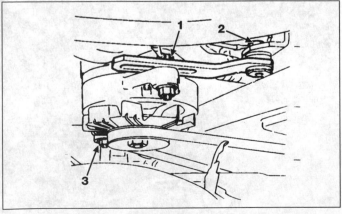

1.2 Alternator drivebelt adjustment points

1 *Alternator to adjuster strap bolt*
2 *Adjuster strap pivot bolt*
3 *Alternator pivot bolt*

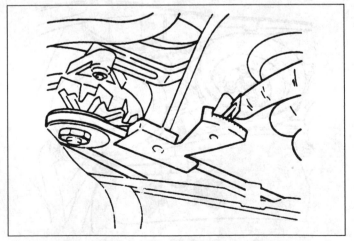

1.8 Using special tool KM-128-A to tension the alternator drivebelt

1.18 Tensioning the alternator drivebelt

A Socket drive in end of adjuster arm
B Adjuster strap bolt
C Pivot bolt

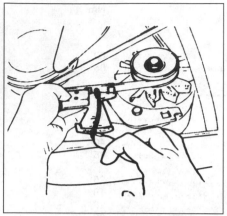

1.19 Using special tool KM-128-A to tension the alternator drivebelt

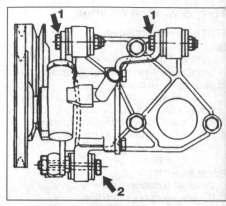

1.25a Power steering pump drivebelt adjustment points

1 Pump mounting bolts
2 Tensioner bolt

adjuster arm and use it as a lever to move the alternator away from the engine until the belt tension is correct. Nip the adjuster bolt tight whilst checking the belt tension **(see illustration)**.

19 Vauxhall recommend the use of a special tool (KM-128-A) for tensioning the belt to the specified amount **(see illustration)**. In the absence of this tool, aim for a tension such that the belt can be deflected about 12 mm by firm finger pressure in the middle of its run. The belt tension must, however, be checked with the special tool as soon as possible.

20 Tighten the alternator fastenings to the specified torque setting once the belt tension is correct.

21 Where applicable, refit and tension the steering pump drivebelt.

22 Lower the front of the vehicle, removing the axle stands and jack.

23 The tension of a new drivebelt should be rechecked after a few hundred miles.

Power steering pump

17D, 17DR and 17DTL engines

24 Gain full access to the drivebelt by jacking up the front right-hand side of the vehicle and supporting it on axle stands.

25 To remove the drivebelt, first loosen the pump mounting and tensioner bolts shown **(see illustration)**. Release the tensioner screw locknuts and rotate them to allow the drivebelt to slacken **(see illustration)**. Slip the drivebelt off its pulleys.

26 Fit the new drivebelt in position over the pulleys and adjust it as follows:

27 Rotate the tensioner screw locknuts until the belt tension is correct.

28 Vauxhall recommend the use of a special tool (KM-128-A) for tensioning the belt to the specified amount. In the absence of this tool, aim for a tension such that the belt can be deflected approximately 12 mm by firm finger pressure in the middle of its run. The belt

tension must, however, be checked with the special tool as soon as possible.

29 Once belt tension is correct, tighten the tensioner screw locknuts and lower the vehicle.

17DT engine

30 Gain access to the drivebelt by removing the air cleaner housing assembly.

31 To remove the drivebelt, first loosen the pump pivot and adjuster bolts.

32 Move the pump towards the engine and slip the drivebelt off its pulleys.

33 Fit the new drivebelt in position over the pulleys and adjust it as follows:

34 Tighten the pump fastenings slightly, so that the pump can just be moved by hand.

35 Insert a socket drive in the end of the adjuster arm and use it as a lever to move the pump away from the engine until the belt tension is correct. Nip the adjuster bolt tight whilst checking the belt tension **(see illustration)**.

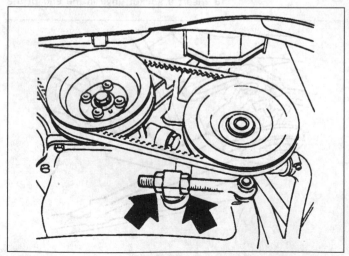

1.25b Rotate the tensioner screw locknuts (arrowed) to adjust drivebelt tension

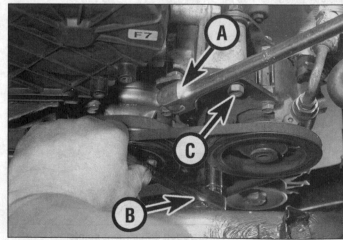

1.35 Tensioning the power steering pump drivebelt

A Socket drive in end of adjuster arm
B Adjuster strap bolt
C Pivot bolt

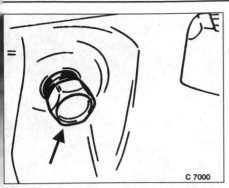

2.4 The cylinder block coolant drain plug (arrowed) - 17DT engine

36 Vauxhall recommend the use of a special tool (KM-128-A) for tensioning the belt to the specified amount. In the absence of this tool, aim for a tension such that the belt can be deflected approximately 12 mm by firm finger pressure in the middle of its run. The belt tension must, however, be checked with the special tool as soon as possible.

37 Once belt tension is correct, tighten the pump fastenings to the specified torque setting.

38 Refit the air cleaner housing assembly.

39 The tension of a new drivebelt should be rechecked after a few hundred miles.

2 Coolant - draining and refilling

> ⚠ **Warning: Take care to avoid scalding when removing the cooling system expansion tank cap. Place a thick cloth over the cap before turning it anti-clockwise.**
> **Caution: Never operate the vehicle with plain water in the cooling system, except in an emergency. Apart from the risk of freezing in winter weather, serious corrosion and rust and scale formation may occur.**
> **Warning: Antifreeze is poisonous and must be handled with due care.**

Draining

1 The system should only be drained when it is cool. If it must be drained hot, take great care to avoid scalding.

2 Remove the expansion tank cap. If the system is hot, place a thick cloth over the cap before turning it anti-clockwise.

3 Place a container underneath the radiator bottom hose. Disconnect the hose from the radiator and allow the system to drain.

4 A cylinder block drain plug is only provided on 17DT engines, making it possible to drain the cooling system completely if necessary **(see illustration)**.

Filling

5 Make sure that all hoses and clips are in good condition. Refit any disturbed hoses and see that their clips are tight. Before refitting

the cylinder block drain plug (if applicable), coat its threads with sealing compound (to GM spec. 15 03 166).

6 Fill the system via the expansion tank cap. If new coolant is being put in, start by pouring in the required quantity of neat antifreeze and follow it up with the water.

7 Massage the large coolant hoses to help displace air pockets during filling.

8 Most vehicles will be fitted with a self-venting cooling system this can be recognised by the two small vent hoses which enter the top of the expansion tank. If the system is not self-venting, open the bleed screw on the thermostat elbow during filling and close it when coolant runs out at the bleed screw.

9 When the system appears full, refit the expansion tank cap. Run the engine up to operating temperature, keeping a look-out for coolant leaks, then stop it and allow it to cool. Recheck the coolant level and top-up if necessary.

10 Recheck the tightness of all hose clips when the engine has cooled, and again after a few hundred miles.

3 Timing belt - removal and refitting

> **Caution: A timing belt which is damaged, oil-soaked or fuel soaked must be renewed**

3.2a Removing the timing belt upper cover

3.3 The crankshaft pulley viewed through the front wheel arch

or it will fail, resulting in serious engine damage.

17D engine

Removal

1 Remove the alternator drivebelt (Section 1).

2 Remove the air filter housing. Remove the timing belt covers. Two versions of the moulded plastic timing belt covers have been used since the introduction of this engine, the later version being identified by the squared-off top surface of the outer belt cover. On the earlier version, a screwdriver blade can be used to release the outer cover retaining clips and the cover sections can then be removed as required to gain access to the timing belt. On the later version, the method of retention is by bolts instead of clips. This arrangement is, in fact, the same as used on the 17DR engine **(see illustrations)**.

3 Remove the crankshaft pulley - it is secured to the sprocket by four Allen screws **(see illustration)**.

4 Disconnect the battery earth lead.

5 Remove the clutch/flywheel access cover from the bottom of the gearbox bellhousing **(see illustration)**.

6 Turn the crankshaft in the normal direction of rotation, using a spanner on the sprocket bolt, until the timing mark on the injection pump sprocket aligns with the reference mark on the pump bracket. In this position No 1 piston is at TDC on the firing stroke.

4B

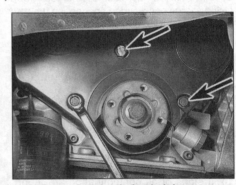

3.2b Removing the timing belt lower cover retaining bolts

3.5 Removing the clutch/flywheel access cover

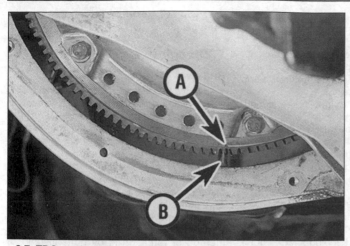

3.7 TDC mark on flywheel (A) and pointer on clutch housing (B)

3.10 Undoing a coolant pump bolt - other two arrowed (engine removed)

7 Check that the TDC mark on the flywheel and the pointer on the clutch housing are aligned (see illustration).

8 If a suitable tool is available, remove the vacuum pump and lock the camshaft in position by fitting the tool. If a tool is not available, make alignment marks between the camshaft sprocket and its backplate for use when refitting.

9 Drain the coolant.

10 Slacken the three bolts which secure the coolant pump to the block (see illustration). Using a large open-ended spanner on the flats of the pump, pivot it to release the tension on the belt.

11 Separate the right-hand front engine mounting by undoing the two bolts which are accessible from the top (see illustration).

12 Mark the running direction of the belt if it is to be re-used. Also take care not to kink the belt, nor get oil, grease etc. on it.

13 Slip the belt off the sprockets and jockey wheel. Remove the belt by feeding it through the engine mounting.

14 If signs of oil contamination are found, trace the source of the oil leak and rectify it,

then wash down the engine timing belt area and all related components to remove all traces of oil.

Refitting

15 Commence refitting by threading the belt through the engine mounting. Refit and tighten the engine mounting bolts.

16 Place the belt over the sprockets and the jockey wheel (see illustration). Make sure that No 1 piston is still at TDC, the injection pump sprocket mark is aligned and the camshaft position is still correct.

17 Move the coolant pump so as to put some tension on the timing belt. Nip up the pump securing bolts, but do not tighten them fully yet.

18 Remove the camshaft locking tool, if used, and refit and secure the crankshaft pulley.

19 Belt tension can only be adjusted accurately using tension gauge KM-510-A or equivalent (see illustration). A belt which is too tight will usually hum when running and a belt which is too slack will wear rapidly and may jump teeth.

20 Settle the belt by rotating the crankshaft

through half a turn in the normal direction of rotation. Fit the tension gauge to the slack side of the belt (the alternator side) and read the tension. Desired values are given in the *Specifications*.

21 If adjustment is necessary, slacken the coolant pump bolts and pivot the pump to increase or decrease the tension. Nip up the coolant pump bolts.

22 Turn the crankshaft through one full turn, then recheck the tension. Keep adjusting the belt tension until a stable value is obtained.

23 Tighten the coolant pump bolts to the specified torque. Refill the cooling system (Section 2).

24 Check the injection pump timing (Section 6).

25 Refit the belt covers, clutch/flywheel cover and other disturbed components.

26 Refit the roadwheel, lower the vehicle and tighten the wheel bolts.

17DR and 17DTL engines

Removal and refitting

27 The procedure for these engines with an automatic timing belt tensioner is essentially the same as described for the 17D engine,

3.11 Right-hand front engine mounting-to-side chassis member securing bolts (arrowed)

3.16 Timing belt correctly fitted

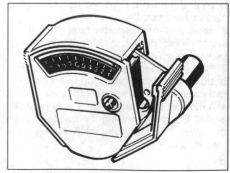

3.19 Timing belt tension gauge

3.28 Release the drivebelt tensioner securing bolt, then turn the tensioner arm with an Allen key until the belt is slack

except that it is not necessary to drain the coolant, remove the engine mounting, nor to slacken the coolant pump mounting bolts and move the pump to adjust the belt tension. Instead, belt adjustment is catered for by means of the automatic tensioner, as follows.

28 To release the belt tension prior to removal, unscrew the timing belt tensioner securing bolt slightly then, with a suitable Allen key inserted in the slot on the tensioner arm, turn the tensioner arm until the timing belt is slack (see illustration). Tighten the securing bolt slightly to hold the tensioner in this position. The timing belt can now be removed.

29 Prior to fitting the timing belt, first ensure that the coolant pump is correctly positioned by checking that the lug on the pump flange is aligned with the corresponding lug on the cylinder block. If this is not the case, slacken the pump mounting bolts slightly and move the pump accordingly. Tighten the bolts to the specified torque on completion.

30 Initially refit the timing belt as described above, ensuring that No 1 piston is still at TDC, that the injection pump sprocket mark is still aligned and the camshaft position is still correct (see illustration). On 17DTL engines, flywheel position for TDC must be determined by the use of a setting tool (Adjuster KM-851) fitted next to the flywheel as shown (see illustration).

31 Tension the timing belt by first slackening the automatic tensioner securing bolt and moving the tensioner arm anti-clockwise until the tensioner pointer is at its stop. Tighten the tensioner securing bolt to hold the tensioner in this position.

32 Turn the crankshaft through two complete revolutions in the normal direction of rotation until No 1 piston is once again at the TDC position. Check that the injection pump sprocket and camshaft sprocket positions are still correct.

33 Slacken the automatic tensioner securing bolt once again and move the tensioner arm until the tensioner pointer and tensioner bracket notch coincide (see

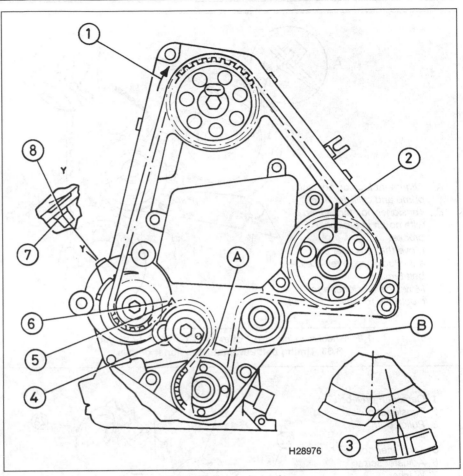

3.30a Timing belt routing

A To tension drivebelt
B To loosen drivebelt
1 Direction of rotation
2 Fuel injection pump marking - No.1 cylinder TDC
3 Flywheel marking - No.1 cylinder TDC
4 Tensioning roller
5 Tensioning roller pointer
6 Alignment mark - tensioning roller
7 Alignment mark - coolant pump
8 Alignment mark -

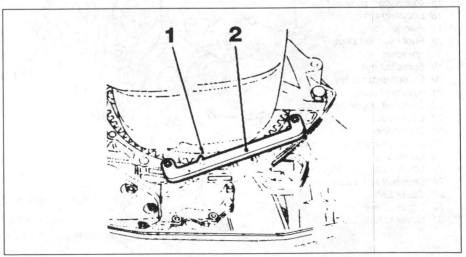

cylinder block
3.30b On 17DTL engines, flywheel position for TDC must be determined by the use of a setting tool (Adjuster KM-851)

4B

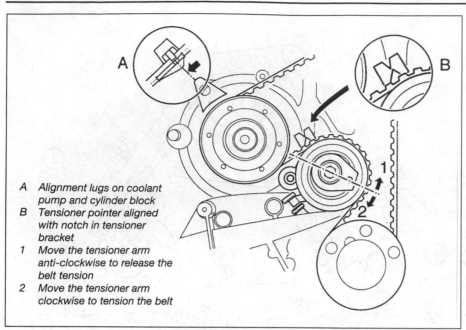

A Alignment lugs on coolant pump and cylinder block
B Tensioner pointer aligned with notch in tensioner bracket
1 Move the tensioner arm anti-clockwise to release the belt tension
2 Move the tensioner arm clockwise to tension the belt

1 Flywheel marking - No.1 cylinder TDC   2 Setting tool
3.33 Timing belt automatic tensioner details

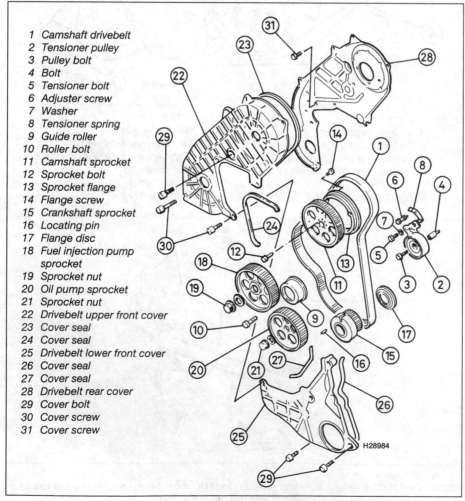

1 Camshaft drivebelt
2 Tensioner pulley
3 Pulley bolt
4 Bolt
5 Tensioner bolt
6 Adjuster screw
7 Washer
8 Tensioner spring
9 Guide roller
10 Roller bolt
11 Camshaft sprocket
12 Sprocket bolt
13 Sprocket flange
14 Flange screw
15 Crankshaft sprocket
16 Locating pin
17 Flange disc
18 Fuel injection pump sprocket
19 Sprocket nut
20 Oil pump sprocket
21 Sprocket nut
22 Drivebelt upper front cover
23 Cover seal
24 Cover seal
25 Drivebelt lower front cover
26 Cover seal
27 Cover seal
28 Drivebelt rear cover
29 Cover bolt
30 Cover screw
31 Cover screw

3.36 Camshaft drivebelt and associated components

illustration). Tighten the tensioner securing bolt securely.
34 Check the valve timing and injection pump timing.
35 Refitting the remainder of the components is the reversal of removal.

17DT engine

36 The timing belt also drives the oil pump and fuel injection pump (see illustration).

Removal

37 Disconnect the battery earth lead.
38 Gain access to the timing belt cover by first removing the air inlet collector box from its mounting on the right-hand side of the engine bay.
39 Release the box inlet scoop from the vehicle front crossmember by removing its two securing screws and then pull it clear of the box inlet stub. Unclip the cable loom from the inlet stub (see illustration). Release the outlet tube retaining clamp at the engine air filter box. Release the box mounting nuts at its base and lift the box from the vehicle.
40 Release the brake servo vacuum line retaining clamp and pull the line from the servo unit (see illustrations).
41 Remove the upper part of the timing belt cover by undoing its nine securing bolts (noting their respective lengths) and lifting it from position.

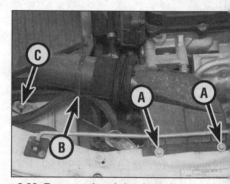

3.39 Remove the air intake collector box inlet scoop securing screws (A) unclip the cable loom (B) and release the box front mounting nut (C)

3.40a Release the brake servo vacuum line retaining clamp (arrowed) . . .

3.40b . . . and pull the line from the servo unit

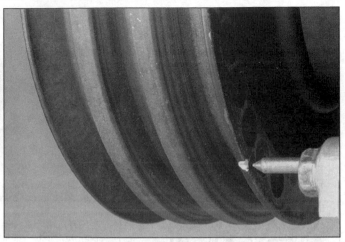

3.47 Align the timing mark on the crankshaft pulley with the reference pointer on the engine block to bring No 1 piston to TDC on the firing stroke

42 Turn the steering wheel so that access to the side of the engine can be gained through the right-hand wheelarch, in front of the roadwheel.

43 Support the engine by positioning a jack beneath its sump and raising it slightly. Protect the sump by placing a piece of thick wood between it and the jack.

44 Remove the engine right-hand mounting by first removing its two centre bolts. Remove the two mounting-to-vehicle body retaining bolts and then the three mounting-to-engine bolts to allow the complete mounting assembly to be withdrawn.

45 Slacken the power steering pump upper and lower retaining bolts to allow the pump to be moved towards the engine, see Section 1. With the V-belt slackened, detach it from the crankshaft, coolant pump and power steering pump pulleys.

46 Slacken the alternator pivot and retaining bolts and move it towards the engine. With the V-belt slackened, detach it from the crankshaft, coolant pump and alternator pulleys.

47 Turn the crankshaft in the normal direction of rotation until the timing mark on its pulley aligns with the reference pointer on the engine block **(see illustration)**. In this position No 1 piston is at TDC on the firing stroke.

48 Now check that the locking bolt holes in the camshaft and fuel injection pump sprockets are aligned with their respective threaded holes in the engine casing before inserting the locking bolts (bolt sizes M6 x 1.00 for camshaft and M8 x 1.25 for injection pump) **(see illustrations)**.

49 Mark the fitted position of the crankshaft pulley. Remove the four pulley retaining bolts and detach the pulley, gently tapping its rim to free it if necessary.

50 Undo the three bolts and remove the lower part of the timing belt cover from the engine.

51 Release the timing belt tensioner by loosening the pulley centre bolt, the upper spring bracket securing bolt and the lower pivot securing nut. Push the tensioner spring towards the front of the engine to release belt tension and then nip tight the bracket securing bolt.

52 Mark the running direction of the timing belt if it is to be re-used. Also take care not to kink the belt, nor get oil, grease etc. on it.

53 Slip the belt off the injection pump sprocket first and then the remaining sprockets to remove it from the engine.

54 If signs of oil contamination are found, trace the source of the oil leak and rectify it, then wash down the engine timing belt area and all related components to remove all traces of oil.

Refitting

55 Commence refitting by first placing the timing belt over the camshaft sprocket and then the injection pump sprocket etc. until it is

4B

3.48a Insert the locking bolt (arrowed) through the camshaft sprocket . . .

3.48b . . . and insert the locking bolt through the injection pump sprocket

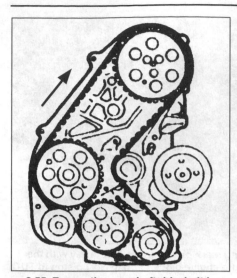

3.55 Ensure the camshaft drivebelt is correctly routed

Arrow denotes direction of belt travel

correctly routed **(see illustration)**. The crankshaft must not be disturbed and the camshaft and fuel injection pump sprockets should still be locked in alignment.

56 Remove the camshaft and fuel injection pump sprocket alignment bolts.

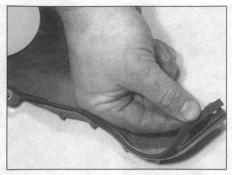

3.58 Checking the sealing strip in the lower front section of camshaft drivebelt cover

57 Release the tensioner spring bracket securing bolt to allow the tensioner to act upon the timing belt. Turn the crankshaft against the normal direction of rotation by approximately 60 degrees to automatically tension the timing belt and then tighten the tensioner pulley centre bolt, the upper spring bracket securing bolt and the lower pivot securing nut to the specified torque settings (where given).

58 Refit the lower part of the timing belt cover to the engine, renewing any damaged sealing strips and tightening the retaining bolts to the specified torque setting **(see illustration)**.

59 Refit the crankshaft pulley in its previously noted position, tightening the retaining bolts to the specified torque setting.

60 Check the injection pump timing (Section 6).

61 Refit and tension both auxiliary drivebelts referring to Section 1.

62 Refit the engine right-hand mounting in the reverse sequence to removal, tightening all retaining bolts to the specified torque settings, see Section 4.

63 Refit the upper part of the timing belt cover, renewing any damaged sealing strips and tightening the retaining bolts to the specified torque setting.

64 Refit all other removed components.

65 Remove the jack from beneath the engine and reconnect the battery earth lead.

4 Engine/transmission mountings (17DT engine) - removal and refitting

Note: *Only remove and refit one engine mounting at a time*

1 The flexible mountings can be renewed if they have deteriorated. To facilitate removal take the weight of the engine/transmission on a hoist, or use a jack with a protective wooden block from below. Only remove and refit one mounting at a time.

2 Unbolt the mounting brackets from the engine/transmission and from the bodyframe **(see illustrations)**. Separate the flexible component from the brackets.

3 Fit the new flexible component and refit the mounting. Only nip up the retaining bolts at first, then tighten them to the specified torque.

4 Lower the hoist or jack and check that the mounting is not under strain. Slacken and retighten the bolts as necessary.

5 Valve timing - checking and adjustment

17D, 17DR and 17DTL engines

1 Valve timing on these engines is more complicated than on the petrol equivalents

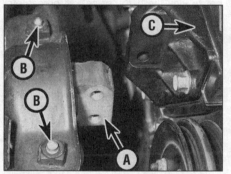

4.2a Engine/transmission right-hand mounting assembly

A *Flexible mounting to engine bracket bolt location*
B *Flexible mounting to vehicle body bolts*
C *Engine bracket*

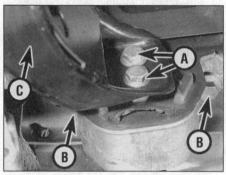

4.2b Engine/transmission left-hand mounting assembly

A *Flexible mounting to engine bracket bolts*
B *Flexible mounting to vehicle body bolts*
C *Engine bracket*

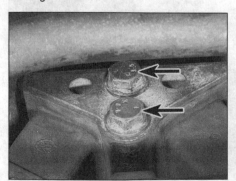

4.2c Engine/transmission rear flexible mounting to engine bracket bolts

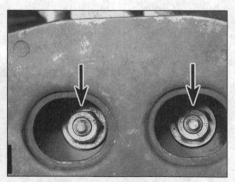

4.2d Engine/transmission rear flexible mounting to vehicle body nuts

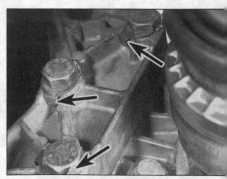

4.2e Engine/transmission rear mounting engine bracket bolts. Note locking washer tabs (arrowed)

because there are no timing marks as such on the camshaft or sprocket, neither is the sprocket keyed or pegged to the camshaft.

2 Note that the camshaft sprocket bolt should be renewed whenever it has been slackened.

3 If the valve timing has been lost completely, be careful when turning the crankshaft or camshaft in case piston/valve contact occurs.

4 The valve timing on this engine is checked using a dial test indicator. Before starting work, it is necessary to make sure that the drivebelt tension is set correctly.

5 Bring the engine to TDC, No 1 firing, by turning the crankshaft in the normal direction of rotation, using a spanner on the sprocket bolt, until the timing mark on the injection pump sprocket aligns with the reference mark on the belt cover (see illustration 6.4). Check that the TDC mark on the flywheel and the pointer on the clutch housing are aligned (see illustration 3.7).

6 Remove the air cleaner. Disconnect the breather hose and remove the camshaft cover (see illustration). If necessary, also remove the vacuum pump.

7 You will need a dial test indicator (DTI) with a 10 mm diameter measuring foot. Special tool KM-661-1 should ideally be available. This is a support bar which rests on the top face of the camshaft carrier and positions the DTI above the camshaft (see illustration). A home-made support can be used if tool KM-661-1 is not available.

8 An additional tool (KM-661-2) is prescribed by the manufacturer. This comprises a slotted steel plate with a stop screw which is secured by bolts to the camshaft carrier, immediately above the flats on the camshaft. The second part of the tool is effectively an open-jawed spanner which fits over the flats on the camshaft and passes up through the slotted plate. The stop screw bears on the spanner handle, allowing precise positioning of the camshaft (see illustrations). In the absence of the manufacturer's tool, it should not prove difficult to make up an equivalent device at home.

Checking

9 To check the valve timing, turn the crankshaft in the normal direction of rotation and stop when the crankshaft is approximately 90° BTDC, with No 1 cylinder on the compression stroke. Fit the DTI to the support bar and position the foot of the gauge over the base circle of the second cam from the sprocket end (No 1 cylinder inlet cam). Set the DTI to zero.

10 Carefully move the DTI and the support bar (without disturbing the position of the DTI in the support bar) exactly 10 mm to the left, as viewed from the camshaft sprocket end of the engine (ie. towards the peak of the cam lobe). Turn the crankshaft to the TDC position for No 1 cylinder (see Section 3). In this position, the DTI should show a lift of 0.55 ± 0.03 mm. If so, the valve timing is correct.

Adjustment

11 If adjustment is necessary, slacken the camshaft sprocket bolt, noting that since this must be renewed each time it is disturbed. It is as well to fit a new bolt loosely at this stage. Release the taper between the sprocket and the camshaft, if necessary by tapping the sprocket with a wooden or plastic mallet.

12 Using the flats on the camshaft, turn it until the DTI reads approximately 0.80 mm of lift. Check that the crankshaft is still set to TDC.

13 Assemble and fit the holding tool, KM-661-2 or equivalent. Using the stop screw, gradually set the cam lift to 0.60 to 0.64 mm. Tighten the camshaft sprocket bolt tight enough for the camshaft taper to lock the sprocket, then remove the holding tool.

14 Carefully lift away the DTI and its support bar, taking care not to disturb the DTI position in the bar. Turn the crankshaft through two complete revolutions, then position the DTI once more and check that a lift figure of 0.55 ± 0.03 mm is shown at TDC. If the correct figure is not shown, repeat the adjustment sequence. If the figure is correct, tighten the (new) camshaft sprocket bolt to the specified torque, check the valve timing once more, then remove the tools.

15 Remember that the injection pump timing must be checked after any change in the valve timing setting. Refit the various covers removed during the checking operation.

17DT engine

Checking

16 Disconnect the battery earth lead.

17 Gain access to the timing belt upper cover by first removing the air inlet collector box from its mounting on the right-hand side of the engine bay - see Section 3.

18 Release the brake servo vacuum line retaining clamp and pull the line from the servo unit.

19 Remove the upper part of the cover by undoing its nine securing bolts (noting their respective lengths) and lifting it from position.

20 Turn the crankshaft in the normal direction of rotation until the timing mark on its pulley aligns with the reference pointer on the engine block. In this position No 1 piston is at TDC on the firing stroke.

21 Now check that the valve timing is correct by ensuring that the locking bolt holes in the camshaft and fuel injection pump sprockets are aligned with their respective threaded holes in the engine casing before inserting the locking bolts (bolt sizes M6 x 1.00 for camshaft and M8 x 1.25 for injection pump). The mark on the crankshaft pulley should align with the pointer on the engine block.

Adjustment

22 If the locking bolt holes in the camshaft and fuel injection pump sprockets are not in alignment with their respective threaded holes in the engine casing, then the valve timing must be adjusted as follows.

23 Turn the steering wheel so that access to the side of the engine can be gained through the right-hand wheelarch, in front of the roadwheel.

4B

5.6 **Removing the camshaft cover**

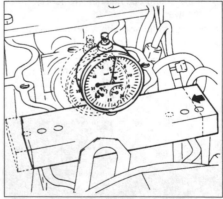

5.7 **Dial test indicator (DTI) in position above camshaft**
Note dotted lines indicating the two base positions during the test procedure

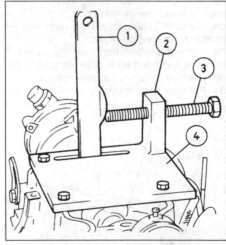

5.8 **Service tool KM-661-2 in use**

1 *Open-jawed spanner*
2 *Stop screw bracket welded to baseplate*
3 *Stop screw*
4 *Baseplate located by camshaft cover bolts*

6.4 Fuel injection pump sprocket timing mark aligned with moulded mark on drivebelt inner cover

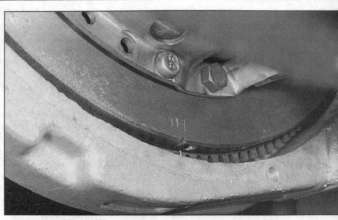

6.5 Flywheel timing marks are visible through clutch housing inspection cover - 17D and 17DR engines

24 Support the engine by positioning a jack beneath its sump and raising it slightly. Protect the sump by placing a piece of thick wood between it and the jack.

25 Remove the engine right-hand mounting by first removing its two centre bolts. Remove the two mounting-to-vehicle body retaining bolts and then the three mounting-to-engine bolts to allow the complete mounting assembly to be withdrawn. This will expose the timing belt tensioner assembly.

26 Release the tensioner by loosening the pulley centre bolt, the upper spring bracket securing bolt and the lower pivot securing nut. Push the tensioner spring towards the front of the engine to release belt tension and then nip tight the bracket securing bolt.

27 Slip the belt off the camshaft and injection pump sprockets.

28 Rotate the camshaft and fuel injection pump sprockets by the least amount until the locking bolt holes are aligned with their respective threaded holes in the engine casing. Insert the locking bolts. The mark on the crankshaft pulley should still align with the pointer on the engine block.

29 Place the timing belt over the camshaft sprocket and then the injection pump sprocket.

30 Remove the sprocket locking bolts.

31 Release the tensioner spring bracket securing bolt to allow the tensioner to act upon the drivebelt. Turn the crankshaft against the normal direction of rotation by approximately 60 degrees to automatically tension the belt and then tighten the tensioner pulley centre bolt, the upper spring bracket securing bolt and the lower pivot securing nut to the specified torque settings (where given).

32 Confirm valve timing by turning the crankshaft in the normal direction of rotation two full turns and rechecking that all timing marks are in correct alignment.

33 With valve timing correct, reassemble all disturbed components whilst noting the specified torque settings.

6 Fuel injection pump timing - checking and adjustment

17D, 17DR and 17DTL engines
Bosch pump

1 Timing of the injection pump should only be necessary in the following circumstances:

a) *When fitting a new or overhauled pump*
b) *If the timing is suspected of being wrong*
c) *If the timing belt has been re-tensioned or renewed*

A dial test indicator with a long probe and a suitable support will be needed.

2 The procedure as shown here was carried out during engine rebuilding. With the engine in the vehicle, it will be necessary to remove the timing belt covers, the air cleaner snorkel and the clutch/flywheel cover.

3 Check the valve timing (Section 5).

4 Bring the engine to TDC, No 1 firing. The timing mark on the pump sprocket must be aligned with the moulded mark on the timing belt inner cover **(see illustration)**.

5 On 17D and 17DR engines, remove the clutch housing cover plate. With No 1 piston set to TDC on the firing stroke, the TDC mark on the flywheel and the pointer on the clutch housing will be aligned **(see illustration)**.

6 On 17DTL engines, remove the flywheel cover plate. Flywheel position for TDC must be determined by the use of a setting tool (Adjuster KM-851) fitted next to the flywheel as shown **(see illustration)**. With No 1 piston set to TDC on the firing stroke, the TDC mark on the flywheel and the pointer on the setting tool will be aligned.

7 Turn the engine against the normal direction of rotation so that the flywheel TDC mark is approximately 5.0 cm away from the TDC pointer.

8 Remove the central plug from the rear of the injection pump **(see illustration)**.

9 Mount the dial test indicator with its probe entering the central plug hole. Zero the indicator **(see illustration)**.

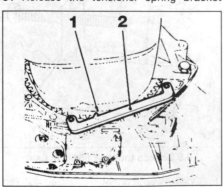

6.6 Determining flywheel position for TDC by the use of a setting tool (Adjuster KM-851) - 17DTL engines

1 Flywheel TDC mark   2 Setting tool

6.8 Removing the plug from the rear of the injection pump

6.9 Dial test indicator mounted with its probe in the plug hole

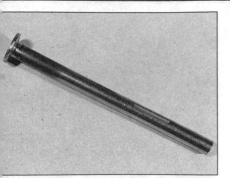

6.19a Home-made probe used for checking Lucas/CAV pump timing

0 Be prepared for fuel spillage during subsequent operations. The manufacturers specify the use of a probe which screws into, and presumably seals, the plug hole.

1 Bring the engine back to TDC, No 1 firing. When the timing marks are aligned, the dial test indicator should show a lift corresponding to the desired timing setting - see *Specifications*.

2 If adjustment is necessary, slacken the three bolts which clamp together the two halves of the pump sprocket. Turn the inner part of the sprocket anti-clockwise (against the normal direction of rotation) as far as the slots will allow. The fit between the two parts of the sprocket is tight and a rod or soft metal drift may be needed to encourage the inner part to move.

3 With the sprocket positioned as just described and the engine still at TDC, No 1 firing, the dial test indicator should again read zero. Reset it if necessary.

4 Turn the inner part of the sprocket clockwise until the dial test indicator shows the desired lift, then tighten the sprocket clamp bolts.

5 Repeat the checking procedure from paragraph 7.

6 When the injection timing is correct, remove the test gear and refit the plug to the rear of the pump.

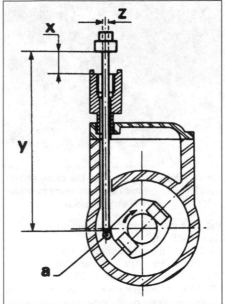

6.19b Special DTI probe shown in position during pump timing check - Lucas/CAV injection pump

a Timing piece
x Timing value (as shown on plate)
y 95.5 ± 0.01 mm
z 7.00 mm shank diameter

17 Refit the timing belt covers and other disturbed components.

Lucas/CAV pump

18 There are some slight changes from the timing procedure above when dealing with the Lucas/CAV injection pump as detailed below.

19 Note that the closing plug is located on the upper surface of the pump rather than at the end of the pump casing as on the Bosch pump. In the absence of the measuring tool KM-690-A and the dial test indicator KM-571-B, you will need a standard dial test indicator (DTI), together with some method of mounting it above the timing hole at the

appropriate height. Also required is a headed probe made to the dimensions shown, this being placed in the timing hole before the DTI is mounted in position **(see illustrations)**.

20 Check the amount of lift indicated on the DTI when the crankshaft timing marks are brought into alignment. There is no standard specified lift figure for Lucas/CAV pumps. Each pump is calibrated during manufacture and the lift figure marked on a plate which is fitted to the pump lever **(see illustration)**. If the lift figure shown on the DTI does not correspond with that given on the plate, adjust the pump sprocket as described in above. Once adjustment is complete, remove the DTI with probe and refit the closing plug.

17DT engine

Note: *The following procedure was carried out with the engine removed from the vehicle. Should the engine be in the vehicle, then access to the injection pump will be restricted. Depending on vehicle type, remove the inlet manifold and/or the starter motor for access to the pump.*

Note: *Ensure that valve timing is correct before checking fuel injection pump timing (see Section 6).*

21 Timing of the injection pump should only be necessary in the following circumstances:

a) *When fitting a new or overhauled pump*
b) *If the timing is suspected of being wrong*
c) *If the timing belt has been re-tensioned or renewed*

22 Obtain a dial test indicator (DTI) and adapter **(see illustration)**. The manufacturer specifies the use of an adapter which screws into, and seals, the plug hole.

23 Disconnect the battery earth lead.

24 Clean around the injection pipe unions to the pump and cylinder head.

25 Disconnect Nos 1 and 2 injection pipes from the injectors and the pump and remove them from the engine. Be prepared for fuel spillage during subsequent operations.

4B

6.20 Lucas/CAV pump showing DTI set up for timing check. Individual value for each pump is stamped on plate (arrowed)

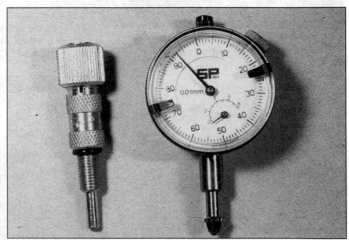

6.22 The dial test indicator and adapter required to set fuel injection pump timing

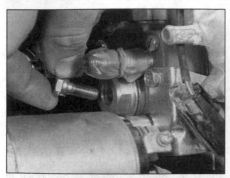

6.27 Removing the central plug from the injection pump

6.28 The timing mark on the crankshaft pulley aligned with the reference pointer on the engine block

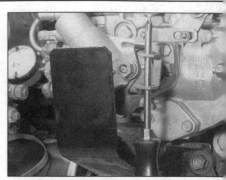

6.29 Deactivating the cold start lever with a screwdriver

26 Blank off all exposed pipe connections to prevent the ingress of dirt and moisture.

27 Remove the central plug from the injection pump **(see illustration)**.

28 Turn the crankshaft in the normal direction of rotation until the timing mark on its pulley aligns with the reference pointer on the engine block **(see illustration)**. In this position No 1 piston is at TDC on the firing stroke.

29 Deactivate the cold start lever by using a screwdriver as shown **(see illustration)**.

30 Fit the adapter and dial test indicator with the indicator probe entering the central plug hole and contacting the pump piston **(see illustration)**.

31 Turn the crankshaft in the normal direction of rotation to approximately 60° before TDC (No 1 firing) **(see illustration)**. At this point,

the injection pump piston will be at bottom dead centre (BDC).

32 Zero the indicator, checking its adjustment by rotating the crankshaft slightly in either direction to ensure BDC.

33 Bring the engine back to TDC (No 1 firing). When the timing mark on the pulley is aligned with the reference pointer, the dial test indicator should show a lift corresponding to the desired timing setting - see the *Specifications* at the start of this Chapter.

34 If adjustment is necessary, loosen the two nuts which secure the injection pump and the two bolts which secure the pump bracket **(see illustration)**.

35 Loosen Nos 3 and 4 injection pipes at the injectors and pump.

36 Rotate the pump until the dial test

indicator shows the desired lift, then tighten the loosened nuts and bolts to the specified torque settings. Rotating the top of the pump towards the engine will lower the lift value whereas rotating the pump in the opposite direction will raise the lift value.

37 Repeat the checking procedure.

38 With the pump timing correct, remove the DTI and adapter then refit the plug to the pump.

39 Remove any blanking materials and reconnect all injection pipe unions, working in the reverse sequence to removal and tightening them to the specified torque settings.

40 Refit any other disturbed components, start the engine and check for fuel leaks.

---

7 Vacuum pump (17D, 17DR and 17DTL engines) - removal and refitting

Removal

1 Disconnect the servo vacuum pipe from the pump. Do this by counterholding the large union nut and unscrewing the small one **(see illustration)**.

2 On 17DR and 17DTL engines, disconnect the EGR system vacuum supply hose from the pump **(see illustration)**.

6.30 The adapter and dial test indicator fitted to the injection pump

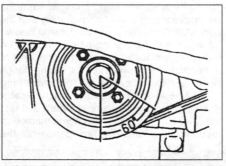

6.31 Turn the crankshaft in the normal direction of rotation to approximately 60° before TDC (No 1 firing)

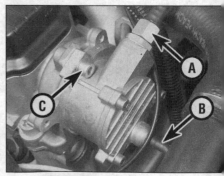

7.2 Vacuum pump connections - 17DR and 17DTL engines
A Servo vacuum pipe
B EGR system vacuum supply hose
C Pump securing screws (2 off)

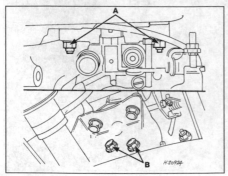

6.34 The fuel injection pump securing nuts (A) and pump bracket bolts (B)

7.1 Disconnecting the servo vacuum pipe from the vacuum pump

7.3a Remove the two pump securing screws . . .

7.3b . . . and withdraw the vacuum pump from the camshaft housing

3 Remove the two pump securing screws and withdraw the pump from the camshaft housing **(see illustrations)**. Be prepared for some oil spillage.

4 Recover the small central oil pipe and the driving dog.

5 Discard the two O-rings fitted to the central oil pipe and also the pump body to camshaft housing seal **(see illustration)**.

Refitting

6 Fit new sealing rings to the pump assembly.

7 Refit the central oil pipe and the driving dog to the pump **(see illustration)**.

8 Offer the pump to the camshaft housing, making sure that the teeth of the driving dog engage with the slot in the camshaft end. Fit the pump securing screws and tighten them to the specified torque.

9 Reconnect and secure the vacuum pipe connection(s).

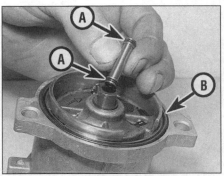

7.5 Renew the O-rings fitted to the central oil pipe (A) and the pump body to camshaft housing seal (B)

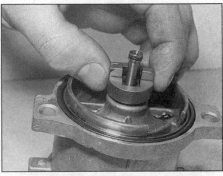

7.7 Refitting the central oil pipe with driving dog to the vacuum pump

Notes

Chapter 5
Vauxhall/Opel Calibra 1990 to 1998

Contents

Specifications

Timing belt renewal interval . . . . Every 36 000 miles (60 000 km) or 4 years - whichever comes first

Auxiliary drivebelt tension
Power steering drivebelt (measured with Vauxhall gauge KM-128-A):
  New belt . . . . 250 to 300 N
  Used belt . . . . 450 N

Timing belt (SOHC engines without automatic tension roller)
Tension, using Vauxhall gauge KM-510-A (see Section 2):
  New belt, cold 4.5
  New belt, warm 7.5
  Used belt, cold 2.5
  Used belt, warm 7.0

Torque wrench settings	Nm	lbf ft
Coolant pump bolts (M8)	25	18
Engine mounting, left:		
Bracket to transmission	60	44
Mounting bush to bracket	60	44
Mounting bush to bodywork (use locking compound) *	65	48
Engine mounting, rear:		
Bracket to transmission (use new locking plates)	60	44
Mounting bush to bracket	45	33
Mounting bush to front subframe	40	30
Engine mounting, right:		
Bracket to engine block	60	44
Mounting bush to bracket	35	26
Mounting bush to bodywork (use locking compound) *	65	48
Power steering pump mounting (refer to Section 1):		
Models with V-belts:		
Bolts A and C	25	18
Bolt B	40	30
SOHC models with serpentine belts:		
Bolts 1, 2, 3 and 4	20	15
DOHC models with serpentine belts:		
Bolts 1 and 2	25	18
Bolts 3 and 4	18	13
Roadwheel bolts	110	81

5

Torque wrench settings (continued)

	Nm	lbf ft
SOHC engine		
Alternator and inlet manifold to brackets	18	13
Alternator to bracket:		
M8	30	22
M10	40	30
Alternator to shackle	25	18
Auxiliary drivebelt tensioner to cylinder block	20	15
Auxiliary drivebelt tensioner to support	18	13
Camshaft cover	8	6
Camshaft sprocket	45	33
Crankshaft pulley	20	15
Crankshaft sprocket:*		
Stage 1	130	96
Stage 2	Angle tighten by between 40° to 50°	
Timing belt cover to oil pump/camshaft housing	6	4
DOHC engine		
Alternator to cylinder block bracket	35	26
Camshaft cover:		
M6 bolts	9	7
M8 bolts	22	16
Crankshaft pulley	20	15
Camshaft sprocket:*		
Stage 1	50	37
Stage 2	Angle tighten by 60°	
Stage 3	Angle tighten by 15°	
Crankshaft sprocket: *		
Stage 1	250	185
Stage 2	Angle tighten by between 40° and 50°	
Spark plug lead cover:		
C20XE	8	6
X20 XEV	6	4
Timing belt cover	8	6
Timing belt guide roller bracket to block	25	18
Timing belt guide roller to bracket	25	18
Timing belt guide roller to cylinder block:		
Engines up to 1993:*		
Stage 1	25	18
Stage 2	Angle tighten by 45°	
Stage 3	Angle tighten by 15°	
1993-on engines	25	18
Timing belt tensioner pulley bolt	20	15

* **Note:** *Use new bolts or nuts*

1 Auxiliary drivebelts -
removal and refitting

1 Early Calibra models, up to 1993, are fitted with twin V-belts, one for the alternator and one for the power steering pump. From 1993 onwards, these were replaced by a single serpentine belt, driving the alternator, power steering pump, and also the air conditioning pump if fitted. The serpentine belt is tensioned by an automatic tensioning roller and needs no adjustment.

Power steering pump V-belt

Removal

2 Slacken the pump mounting and adjuster bolts.
3 Slacken the adjuster nuts and adjust the length of the threaded rod to remove the belt **(see illustration)**.

1.3 Adjusting the length of the power steering pump threaded rod - models with V-belts

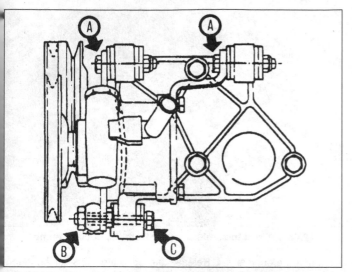

1.6a Mounting and adjuster bolts (arrowed) must be loosened to adjust drivebelt tension - models with V-belts

For A, B and C tightening torques see Specifications

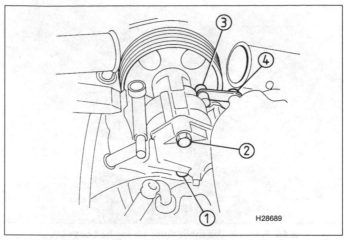

1.6b Power steering pump mounting (tightening torques shown in Specifications) - models with serpentine belts

1	Pump to support	3	Shackle to pump*
2	Pump to support	4	Shackle to engine*

* The shackle is not present on some models

Refitting and adjustment

4 Refitting is the reverse of removal, noting the following points.

5 A special gauge is available for measuring the belt tension, and the values for use with this gauge are given in the Specifications. If the gauge is not available, a good approximation is achieved with a belt deflection of approximately 10.0 mm (0.4 in) under moderate thumb pressure at the midpoint of the belt run between the pulleys. If in doubt, err on the slack side, as an excessively tight belt may cause pump damage.

6 Tighten the adjuster nuts, and the adjuster and mounting bolts to the specified torque on completion **(see illustrations)**.

Alternator V-belt

Removal

7 Disconnect the air inlet trunking from the air cleaner, and the air box or throttle body, as applicable, and remove it for improved access.

8 Remove the power steering pump V-belt as described in paragraphs 2 and 3.

9 Slacken the two alternator mounting nuts and bolts sufficiently to allow the alternator to be pivoted in towards the engine, then slide the belt from the pulleys.

Refitting and adjustment

10 Refitting is the reverse of removal, noting the following points.

11 Although special tools are available for measuring the belt tension, a good approximation can be achieved with approximately 13.0 mm (0.5 in) of free movement under firm thumb pressure at the mid-point of the longest run between pulleys. Make sure the belt is not too tight as this can cause excessive wear in the alternator.

12 With the mounting bolts just holding the unit, lever the alternator away from the engine using a wooden lever at the mounting bracket end until the correct tension is achieved. Then tighten the mounting nuts and bolts. On no account lever at the free end of the alternator, as serious internal damage could be caused.

Serpentine-belt (models without air conditioning)

13 On these models, a single auxiliary drivebelt passes round the crankshaft, alternator and power steering pump pulleys, and is tensioned by an automatic tensioner pulley **(see illustration)**. The belt passes through the right-hand engine mounting, on its way from the power steering pump to the crankshaft pulley. To remove the drivebelt, you have to remove the engine mounting and drivebelt as a complete assembly, as described in Section 10.

Serpentine-belt (models with air conditioning)

14 The routing of this auxiliary drivebelt is the same as in paragraph 13, except that there is an additional pulley for the air conditioning pump, below the power steering pump. The drivebelt passes underneath the engine mounting, instead of going through it, so you can disengage the mounting bush from the bodywork and feed the belt through the gap.

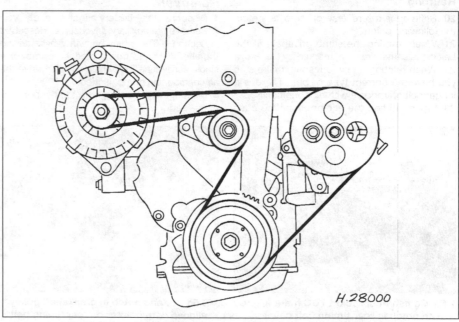

1.13 Routing of serpentine belt on models without air conditioning

5

2.4a Remove the main outer timing belt cover . . .

2.4b . . . and the smaller cover from the coolant pump

Removal

15 For improved access, remove the air cleaner assembly and air inlet trunking.

16 If the original drivebelt is to be refitted, mark the rotational direction on the belt with chalk.

17 Using a spanner or socket on the automatic tensioning roller hexagon, turn the tensioning roller clockwise (as viewed from the right-hand side of the car) and hold it in this position. With the drivebelt tension released, slip the drivebelt off the pulleys, then allow the tensioner to return to its original position.

18 Support the engine under the sump with a jack, and place a block of wood on top of the front subframe, under the sump.

19 Undo the bolts connecting the mounting bush to the bodywork, but leave the bush and bracket assembly attached to the engine. Then lower the engine just enough to allow the drivebelt to be withdrawn from between the mounting bush and the body.

Refitting

20 Refitting is the reverse of removal, noting the following points.

21 When refitting the same drivebelt, fit the belt in the same direction, marked by the arrow.

22 When refitting a new drivebelt, make sure you have the correct type of belt. There is a longer belt on models with air conditioning.

23 When refitting the engine mounting bush

to the bodywork, first check that the original bolts turn freely in their threaded bores and are not fouled by the old locking fluid. If necessary, re-cut the threaded bores using an M10 x 1.25 mm tap. Then use new bolts, coated with locking fluid, and tighten them to the specified torque.

24 You will need an assistant to help you refit the drivebelt around the pulleys. Slacken the tensioner from underneath the car and feed the belt round the power steering pump pulley, while your assistant, working above the car, feeds the belt over the alternator pulley. Then release the tensioner.

| 2 | **Timing belt and sprockets (manual tensioning) (SOHC models)** - removal and refitting |

Note: *A two-legged puller may be required to remove the crankshaft sprocket.*

Removal

1 Disconnect the battery negative lead.

2 Remove the auxiliary drivebelts as described in Section 1. There may be twin V-belts driving the alternator and power steering pump, or a single serpentine belt which will also drive the air conditioning pump, if fitted.

3 Disconnect the wiring from the temperature gauge sender.

4 Release the securing clips (or hexagon-headed screws, if fitted), and remove the main outer timing belt cover, then unclip the smaller outer timing belt cover from the coolant pump **(see illustrations)**.

5 Turn the crankshaft using a socket or spanner on the crankshaft sprocket bolt, until the timing mark on the camshaft sprocket is aligned with the notch in the rear timing belt cover, and the notch in the crankshaft pulley is aligned with the pointer on the rear timing belt cover **(see illustrations)**.

6 Loosen the three coolant pump securing bolts **(see illustration)**, and turn the pump to relieve the tension in the timing belt, then slide the belt from the camshaft sprocket.

7 The crankshaft pulley must now be removed. The pulley is secured by four bolts which must be unscrewed using an Allen key or hexagon bit. On manual transmission models, the crankshaft can be prevented from turning by having an assistant engage first gear and depress the brake pedal. Alternatively, the flywheel ring gear teeth can be jammed using a large screwdriver or similar tool.

8 With the crankshaft pulley removed, the timing belt can be withdrawn.

9 If desired, the sprockets and the rear timing belt cover can be removed as follows, otherwise go on to paragraph 19.

2.5a Camshaft sprocket TDC mark aligned with notch in rear timing belt cover . . .

2.5b . . . and notch in crankshaft pulley aligned with pointer on rear timing belt cover

2.6 Loosening a coolant pump securing bolt

2.14 Loosening the main rear timing belt cover lower securing bolt

2.15 Unscrewing the coolant pump rear belt cover securing bolt

10 To remove the camshaft sprocket, first disconnect the breather hose(s) from the camshaft cover, then unscrew the securing bolts noting the locations of the HT lead brackets and any other wiring brackets, and remove the camshaft cover.

11 Recover the gasket. Prevent the camshaft from turning by holding it with a spanner on the flats provided between Nos 3 and 4 camshaft lobes, and unscrew the camshaft sprocket bolt.

12 Withdraw the sprocket from the end of the camshaft.

13 To remove the crankshaft sprocket, it will be necessary to prevent the crankshaft from turning, as described in paragraph 7. Take care when unscrewing the sprocket bolt, as it

is very tight. If necessary, use a two-legged puller to remove the sprocket. Recover the Woodruff key and the thrustwasher from the end of the crankshaft.

14 To remove the main rear timing belt cover, disconnect the TDC sensor wiring plug and unclip the wiring from the belt cover. Then unscrew the two upper securing bolts and the lower securing bolt. Withdraw the cover, manipulating it from the smaller rear belt cover on the coolant pump **(see illustration)**.

15 If desired, the smaller rear belt cover can be removed from the coolant pump, after unscrewing the securing bolt **(see illustration)**, by rotating it to disengage it from the retaining flange on the pump.

Refitting

16 Refit the rear timing belt covers using a reversal of the removal procedure, ensuring that the main cover engages correctly with the smaller cover on the coolant pump, and reconnect the TDC sensor.

17 Refit the thrustwasher and the Woodruff key to the end of the crankshaft. Then refit the crankshaft sprocket, and tighten the securing bolt to the specified torque in the two stages given in the Specifications. Ensure that the washer is in place under the bolt head, and prevent the crankshaft from turning as during removal **(see illustrations)**.

18 Refit the camshaft sprocket, ensuring that

2.17a Refit the thrustwasher . . .

2.17b . . . the Woodruff key . . .

2.17c . . . the crankshaft sprocket . . .

2.17d . . . and the washer and bolt

2.17e Tighten the bolt to the specified torque . . .

2.17f . . . then through the specified angle

5

2.18a Refit the camshaft sprocket . . .

2.18b . . . and tighten the securing bolt to the specified torque

2.18c Fit the camshaft cover gasket . . .

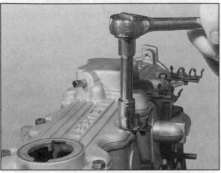

2.18d . . . fit the cover and tighten the bolts. Note position of HT lead brackets

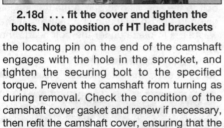

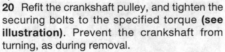

2.19 Refitting the timing belt

the locating pin on the end of the camshaft engages with the hole in the sprocket, and tighten the securing bolt to the specified torque. Prevent the camshaft from turning as during removal. Check the condition of the camshaft cover gasket and renew if necessary, then refit the camshaft cover, ensuring that the HT lead brackets and any other wiring bracket are correctly located, and reconnect the breather hose(s) **(see illustrations)**.

19 Temporarily refit the crankshaft pulley and ensure that the crankshaft pulley and camshaft sprocket timing marks are still

aligned as described in paragraph 5, then refit the timing belt around the sprockets **(see illustration)**, starting at the crankshaft sprocket.

20 Refit the crankshaft pulley, and tighten the securing bolts to the specified torque **(see illustration)**. Prevent the crankshaft from turning, as during removal.

21 Adjust the timing belt tension (go to paragraph 25).

22 Refit the outer timing belt covers and reconnect the temperature gauge sender wiring.

23 Refit the auxiliary drivebelts as described in Section 1.

24 Reconnect the battery negative lead.

Adjustment

Note: *The manufacturers specify the use of special gauge Vauxhall tool No KM-510-A for checking the timing belt tension.*

25 The tension of a used timing belt should be checked with the engine at normal operating temperature. The tension of a new timing belt should be checked with the engine cold.

26 Release the securing clips and remove the main outer timing belt cover, then unclip the smaller outer timing belt cover from the coolant pump.

27 Turn the crankshaft through at least quarter of a turn clockwise using a socket or spanner on the crankshaft sprocket bolt.

28 Place the locked gauge at the centre of the belt run between the coolant pump and the camshaft sprocket. The gauge should locate on the timing belt **(see illustration)**.

29 Slowly release the operating lever on the gauge, then lightly tap the gauge two or three times, and note the reading on the scale.

30 If the reading is not as specified, loosen the three coolant pump securing bolts, and

2.20 Tightening a crankshaft pulley securing bolt

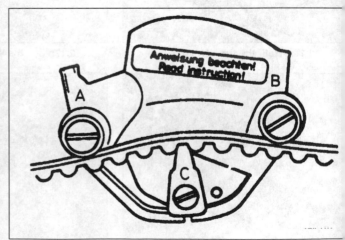

2.28 Tension blade KM-510-A correctly positioned on timing belt. Belt must pass through points A, B and C - SOHC engines

rotate the pump in the required direction to achieve the desired reading on the gauge. Rotate the pump clockwise to increase the belt tension, or anti-clockwise to decrease the tension.

31 Lightly tighten the coolant pump securing bolts.

32 Remove the tensioning gauge, and turn the crankshaft through one full turn clockwise.

33 Re-check the belt tension as described in paragraphs 28 and 29.

34 If the tension is not as specified, repeat paragraphs 30 to 33 inclusive until the desired reading is obtained.

35 On completion of adjustment, remove the checking gauge, tighten the coolant pump bolts to the specified torque, and refit the outer timing belt covers.

3 Timing belt and automatic tensioner (SOHC models) - removal and refitting

Note: *Removal and refitting of the timing belt sprockets and covers are as described in Section 2.*

Removal

1 A spring-loaded automatic timing belt tensioner is fitted from 1993 onward **(see illustration)**.

2 Remove the auxiliary drivebelts and timing belt main outer cover, as described in Section 2, paragraphs 1 to 4.

3 Unscrew the timing belt tensioner securing bolt slightly. Insert a tool in the slot on the tensioner arm, and turn the tensioner arm until the timing belt is slack. The belt can then be removed.

4 With the timing belt slackened or removed, check that the tensioner roller rotates smoothly and easily, with no noises or signs of free play, roughness or notchy movement. Undo the securing bolt and remove the tensioner, and check that there is no sign of physical wear or damage. If the tensioner is faulty in any way, or if there is any reason to doubt the continued efficiency of its spring, the complete assembly must be renewed.

Refitting

5 Refit the tensioner into position and tighten the securing bolt slightly.

6 Ensure that the coolant pump is correctly positioned by checking that the lug on the coolant pump flange is aligned with the corresponding lug on the cylinder block. If this is not the case, slacken the coolant pump mounting bolts slightly and move the pump accordingly (see Section 7). Tighten the bolts to the specified torque on completion.

7 Refit the timing belt around the sprockets, then tension it as follows.

Adjustment

8 Slacken the automatic tensioner securing bolt and move the tensioner arm anti-clockwise, until the tensioner pointer lies at its stop. Tighten the tensioner securing bolt to hold the tensioner in this position.

9 Turn the crankshaft through two complete revolutions in the normal direction of rotation, and check that with the crankshaft pulley TDC mark aligned with the pointer on the rear timing belt cover, the TDC mark on the camshaft sprocket is still aligned with the notch in the timing belt rear cover. Slacken the automatic tensioner securing bolt again and move the tensioner arm clockwise, until the tensioner pointer is aligned with the notch in the tensioner bracket. In the first few hours of operation a new belt will be subjected to settling-in, if you are refitting a used belt (one that has been run-in), align the pointer to approximately 4 mm to the left of the notch **(see illustration)**.

10 Tighten the tensioner securing bolt securely. Turn the crankshaft through one complete revolution, in the normal direction of rotation, and check that the crankshaft and camshaft timing marks still align. Then refit the remainder of the components as described in Section 2.

11 With the timing belt adjustment set in this way, correct tension will always be maintained by the automatic tensioner and no further checking or adjustment will be necessary.

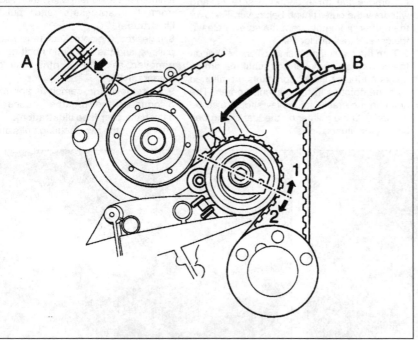

3.1 Timing belt automatic tensioner

A Alignment lugs on coolant pump and cylinder block
B Tensioner pointer aligned with notch in tensioner bracket
1 Move the tensioner arm anti-clockwise to release the belt tension
2 Move the tensioner arm clockwise to tension the belt

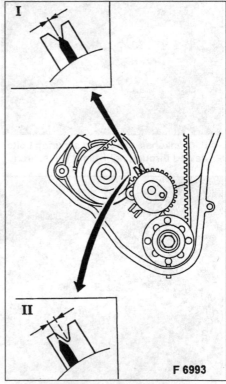

F 6993

3.9 Timing belt adjustment

I   Alignment for new belts
II Alignment for run-in belts (gap is approximately 4 mm to the left of centre)

5

4.5a Camshaft sprocket TDC mark aligned with notch in camshaft cover

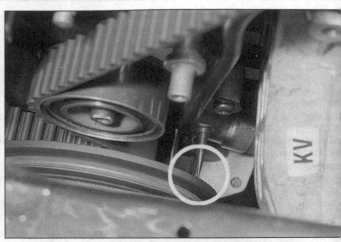

4.5b . . . and notch in crankshaft pulley aligned with pointer on rear timing belt cover (circled)

4 Timing belt and sprockets (manual tensioning) (DOHC models) - removal and refitting

Note: *The timing belt should be renewed on refitting. A two-legged puller may be required to remove the crankshaft sprocket.*

4.6 Crankshaft pulley and securing bolts viewed through right-hand wheel arch

Removal

1 Disconnect the battery negative lead.
2 Disconnect the air cleaner trunking from the airflow meter, then remove the cover and the air cleaner element from the air cleaner. If desired, for improved access, the complete air cleaner assembly can be removed, as described in Section 8.
3 Remove the auxiliary drivebelts as described in Section 1. There may be twin V-belts driving the alternator and power steering pump, or a single serpentine belt which will also drive the air conditioning pump, if fitted.
4 Remove the three securing screws, and withdraw the outer timing belt cover. Recover the rubber grommets from the screw holes in the cover if they are loose.
5 Turn the crankshaft, using a Torx socket on the crankshaft sprocket bolt, until the timing marks on the camshaft sprockets are aligned with the notches in the camshaft cover. The notch in the crankshaft pulley should also be aligned with the pointer on the rear timing belt cover (**see illustrations**).

6 Extract the securing bolts using a splined bit, and withdraw the crankshaft pulley (**see illustration**). If necessary, counterhold the crankshaft using a socket on the crankshaft sprocket bolt. The crankshaft can be prevented from turning by having an assistant engage first gear and depress the brake pedal. Alternatively, the flywheel ring gear teeth can be jammed using a large screwdriver or similar tool. Before removing the pulley, check that the timing marks are still aligned.
7 Loosen the securing bolt and release the timing belt tensioner pulley, then slide the belt from the sprockets and pulleys (**see illustration**).
8 If desired, the sprockets, tensioner and idler pulleys, and the rear timing belt cover can be removed as follows, otherwise go on to paragraph 26.
9 To remove the camshaft sprockets, first disconnect the breather hoses from the camshaft cover (**see illustration**).
10 Extract the two securing bolts and remove

4.7 Timing belt tensioner pulley securing bolt (arrowed)

4.9 Disconnecting a breather hose from the rear of the camshaft cover

4.10 Removing the spark plug cover

4.11 Unscrewing a camshaft cover securing bolt

the spark plug cover **(see illustration)**, then disconnect the HT leads from the spark plugs, and unclip them from the end of the camshaft cover. If necessary, mark the HT leads for position, to avoid confusion when refitting.

11 Unscrew the twenty securing bolts and withdraw the camshaft cover **(see illustration)**.

12 Recover the one-piece rubber gasket **(see illustration)**.

13 Prevent the relevant camshaft from turning by holding it with a spanner on the flats provided in front of No 1 cam lobe, and unscrew the camshaft sprocket bolt **(see illustration)**.

14 Withdraw the sprocket from the end of the camshaft, then repeat the procedure for the remaining camshaft sprocket.

15 Remove the crankshaft sprocket. It will be necessary to prevent the crankshaft from turning by bolting a metal bar to the sprocket using two of the crankshaft pulley bolts, or by jamming the flywheel ring gear teeth. A Torx socket will be required to unscrew the sprocket bolt - take care, as the bolt is very

tight. If necessary, use a two-legged puller to remove the sprocket. Recover the thrustwashers from the end of the crankshaft, and from under the bolt head.

16 To remove the belt tensioner pulley,

simply unscrew the securing bolt from the centre of the pulley, then withdraw the pulley complete with mounting plate **(see illustration)**. Recover the spacer sleeve from the pulley bolt.

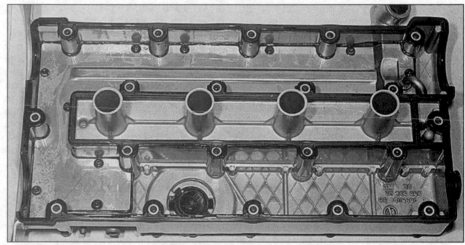

4.12 Camshaft cover removed to show one-piece rubber gasket

4.13 Spanner positioned to counterhold exhaust camshaft

4.16 Timing belt tensioner pulley securing bolt (1), tensioner pulley mounting plate (2), and idler pulley securing bolt (3)

5

4.18a Timing belt outer cover screw upper stud (1) and rear belt cover upper securing bolts (2)

4.18b Rear timing belt cover lower right-hand securing bolt

17 To remove the belt idler pulley, unscrew the securing bolt from the centre of the pulley, then withdraw the pulley and recover the spacer sleeve from the pulley bolt.

18 The rear timing belt cover can now be removed after unscrewing the upper and middle studs for the timing belt outer cover screws. Note that the upper stud simply unscrews from the cylinder head, but the middle stud is secured by a bolt. Unscrew the two upper and single lower right-hand rear belt cover securing bolts, and withdraw the rear belt cover (see illustrations).

Refitting

19 Refit the rear timing belt cover using a reversal of the removal procedure.

20 Refit the belt idler and tensioner pulleys, noting that the spacer sleeves should be fitted with their smaller diameters against the pulleys (see illustration). Do not fully tighten the tensioner pulley bolt at this stage.

21 Refit the thrustwasher to the end of the crankshaft, then refit the crankshaft sprocket.

Apply a little grease to the threads of the securing bolt, and tighten it to the specified torque in the two stages given in the Specifications. Ensure that the thrustwasher is in place under the bolt head, and prevent the crankshaft from turning as during removal.

22 Refit the camshaft sprockets. Ensure that the locating pins on the ends of the camshafts engage with the holes in the sprockets, and with the sprocket timing marks facing forwards. Then tighten the securing bolts to the specified torque in the stages given in the Specifications. Prevent the camshafts from turning as during removal.

23 Check the condition of the camshaft cover rubber gasket and renew if necessary, then refit the camshaft cover and tighten the securing bolts (see illustration).

24 Refit the HT leads to the spark plugs (ensuring that they are refitted to their correct cylinders), then clip the leads to the end of the camshaft cover. Refit the spark plug cover and tighten the securing bolts.

25 Reconnect the breather hose to th camshaft cover.

26 Temporarily refit the crankshaft pulley and ensure that the crankshaft pulley an camshaft sprocket timing marks are sti aligned as described in paragraph 5. Then fit new timing belt around the sprocket and pulleys, starting at the crankshaf sprocket.

27 Refit the crankshaft pulley, and tighten th securing bolts to the specified torque. necessary, prevent the crankshaft from turning as during removal.

28 Adjust the timing belt tension, a described from paragraph 33 onwards.

29 Refit the outer timing belt cover, ensurin that the rubber grommets are in place in th screw holes, and tighten the securing screw

30 Refit the auxiliary drivebelt(s), a described in Section 1.

31 Refit the air cleaner components a applicable, referring to Section 8, necessary.

32 Reconnect the battery negative lead.

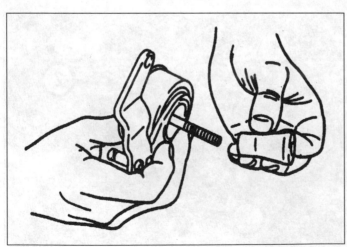

4.20 Belt tensioner pulley and spacer sleeve. Note that smaller diameter of spacer sleeve fits against pulley

4.23 Tightening a camshaft cover securing bolt

Adjustment

Note: *The manufacturers specify the use of special adjustment wrench Vauxhall tool No KM-666 for adjusting the timing belt tension.*

33 No checking of timing belt adjustment is specified, and the following adjustment procedure applies to a newly fitted belt. The adjustment must be carried out with the engine cold.

34 With the timing belt cover removed and the tensioner pulley bolt slackened, ensure that the TDC marks on the camshaft sprockets and the crankshaft pulley are aligned as described in paragraph 5. If necessary, turn the crankshaft to achieve alignment.

35 Fit the special tool KM-666 to the belt tensioner pulley mounting plate, in accordance with the tool manufacturer's instructions.

36 Working anti-clockwise from the TDC mark on the exhaust camshaft sprocket, mark the eighth tooth on the sprocket **(see illustration)**.

37 Turn the crankshaft clockwise until this tooth is aligned with the TDC notch in the camshaft cover. The crankshaft must be turned evenly, and without jerking, to prevent the timing belt from jumping off the sprockets and pulleys.

38 Tighten the tensioner pulley bolt to the specified torque.

39 Remove the special tool.

40 Turn the crankshaft clockwise until the TDC marks on the camshaft sprockets are aligned with the notches in the camshaft cover, and check that the crankshaft pulley TDC mark is aligned with the pointer on the rear timing belt cover.

41 Proceed as described in paragraphs 29 to 32 inclusive.

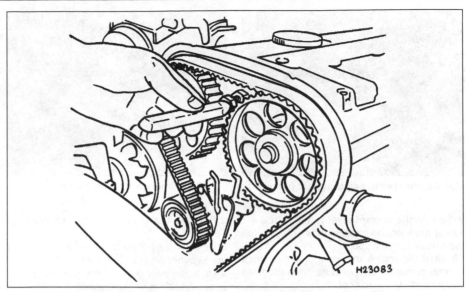

4.36 Working anti-clockwise from the TDC mark on the exhaust camshaft sprocket, mark the eighth tooth on the sprocket

---

5 Timing belt and automatic tensioner (DOHC models) - removal and refitting

Removal

1 The operations are essentially the same as described in Section 4, except that the tensioner pulley incorporates an automatic adjuster that simplifies the procedure as follows.

2 To release the belt tension before removal, unscrew the timing belt tensioner pulley securing bolt slightly, then with a large screwdriver (or similar tool) inserted in the slot on the tensioner arm, turn the tensioner arm until the timing belt is slack. Tighten the securing bolt slightly to hold the tensioner in this position.

Refitting

3 To refit the timing belt, first ensure that the coolant pump is correctly positioned by checking that the lug on the coolant pump flange is aligned with the corresponding lug on the cylinder block. If this is not the case, slacken the coolant pump mounting bolts slightly and move the pump accordingly. Tighten the bolts to the specified torque on completion.

4 Refit the timing belt as described in Section 4, then tension it as follows.

Adjustment

5 Slacken the tensioner pulley securing bolt and move the tensioner arm anti-clockwise, until the tensioner pointer lies at its stop. Tighten the tensioner pulley securing bolt to hold the tensioner in this position.

6 Turn the crankshaft through two complete revolutions in the normal direction of rotation and check that with the crankshaft pulley TDC mark aligned with the pointer on the rear timing belt cover, the TDC marks on the camshaft sprockets are still aligned with the notches in the camshaft cover.

7 Slacken the tensioner pulley securing bolt once again and move the tensioner arm clockwise, until the tensioner pointer is aligned with the notch in the tensioner. In the first few hours of operation a new belt will be subjected to settling-in, if you are refitting a used belt (one that has been run-in), align the pointer to approximately 4 mm to the left of the notch, refer to Section 3. Tighten the tensioner pulley securing bolt to the specified torque. Turn the crankshaft through one complete revolution in the normal direction of rotation and check that the crankshaft and camshaft timing marks still align, then refit the remainder of the components as described in Section 4.

8 With the timing belt adjustment set in this way, correct tension will always be maintained by the automatic tensioner and no further checking or adjustment will be necessary.

---

6 Coolant - draining and refilling

Draining

1 With the vehicle parked on level ground, remove the expansion tank filler cap. If the engine is warm, cover the filler cap with a thick cloth, and unscrew the cap slowly, to gradually relieve the system pressure. Take care to avoid scalding by steam or coolant escaping from the pressurised system.

2 On DOHC models, remove the engine undershield, with reference to Section 9.

3 Position a container beneath the radiator bottom hose connection, then slacken the hose clip and ease the hose from the radiator stub. If the hose joint has not been disturbed for some time, it will be necessary to manipulate the hose to break the joint. Allow the coolant to drain into the container.

4 As no cylinder block drain plug is fitted, and the radiator bottom hose may be situated halfway up the radiator, the system cannot be drained completely. Care should therefore be taken when refilling the system to maintain antifreeze strength.

5 If the coolant has been drained for a reason other than renewal, then provided it is clean and less than two years old, it can be re-used.

Refilling

6 Before attempting to fill the cooling system, make sure that all hoses and clips are in good condition, and that the clips are tight.

7 Remove the expansion tank cap, and fill the system by slowly pouring the coolant into the expansion tank to prevent air locks from forming.

8 If the coolant is being renewed, begin by pouring in a couple of pints of water, followed by the correct quantity of antifreeze, then top-up with more water.

5

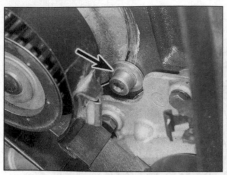

7.4 Coolant pump securing bolt (arrowed)

7.5a Withdraw the coolant pump . . .

7.5b . . . and recover the O-ring

9 Top-up the coolant level to the COLD (or KALT) mark on the expansion tank, then refit the expansion tank cap.

10 Start the engine and run it until it reaches normal operating temperature, then stop the engine and allow it to cool.

11 Check for leaks, particularly around disturbed components. Check the coolant level in the expansion tank, and top-up if necessary. Note that the system must be cold before an accurate level is indicated in the expansion tank. If the expansion tank cap is removed while the engine is still warm, cover the cap with a thick cloth and unscrew the cap slowly, to gradually relieve the system pressure. Take care to avoid scalding by steam or coolant escaping from the pressurised system.

12 On DOHC models, refit the engine undershield on completion (see Section 9).

7 Coolant pump (SOHC models) - removal and refitting

Removal

1 Drain the cooling system as described in Section 6.

2 Remove the timing belt as described in Section 2.

3 Remove the timing belt tension roller from the oil pump, where applicable.

4 Unscrew and remove the coolant pump securing bolts (see illustration).

5 Withdraw the coolant pump from the cylinder block, and recover the O-ring (see illustrations). It may be necessary to tap the pump lightly with a plastic-faced hammer to free it from the cylinder block.

6 If desired, the rear timing belt cover can be removed from the pump by rotating the cover to release it from the flange on the pump.

Refitting

7 Refitting is a reversal of removal, bearing in mind the following points.

8 Use a new O-ring when refitting the pump. Before refitting the pump, smear the pump mounting face in the cylinder block and the O-ring with a silicone grease or petroleum jelly.

9 Do not fully tighten the pump securing bolts until the timing belt has been fitted and tensioned.

10 Refit and tension the timing belt, as described in Section 2.

11 Refill the cooling system, as described in Section 6.

8 Air cleaner housing - removal and refitting

Removal

1 Unclip the coolant expansion tank hose from the air cleaner cover, and move it to one side out of the way.

2 On SOHC models, there is a vane-type airflow meter connected directly to the air cleaner cover, so that the cover and meter have to be removed together. Disconnect the battery negative lead, then disconnect the wiring plug from the meter. Loosen the clamp screw and disconnect the meter from the air trunking at the downstream end (see illustration).

3 On DOHC models, there is a mass airflow meter, separated from the air cleaner cover by a length of air trunking. Loosen the clamp screw and disconnect the air trunking from the air cleaner cover (see illustration).

4 Release the two securing clips from the left-hand side of the air cleaner cover, and undo the two captive securing screws from the right-hand side, then lift off the cover. On SOHC models, lift off the cover and airflow meter as a complete assembly.

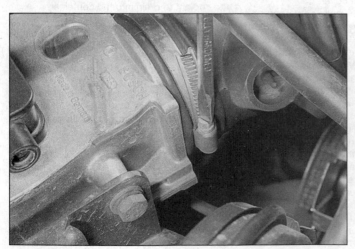

8.2 Disconnect the air trunking from the airflow meter - SOHC models

8.3 Disconnect the air trunking from the air cleaner cover - DOHC models

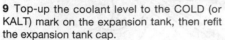

5 Lift out the air cleaner element.
6 Slacken the three rubber mounting nuts on the air cleaner housing.
7 Lift up the air cleaner housing to release it from the air intake pipe, then remove it from the vehicle (see illustration).

Refitting

8 Refitting is the reverse of removal.

9 Engine undershield (DOHC models) - removal and refitting

Removal

1 Apply the handbrake, then jack up the front of the vehicle, and support on axle stands.
2 Extract the two securing screws, and remove the oil filter access panel.
3 Working around the edges of the splash shield, remove the self tapping screws that secure the shield to the body, noting that some of the screws also secure the wheel arch liners.
4 With the help of an assistant, pull the shield from the vehicle, and place it to one side to avoid damage.

Refitting

5 Refitting is the reverse of removal.

10 Right-hand mounting - removal and refitting

Note: When refitting engine/transmission mounting bushes, first check that the original

8.7 Remove the air cleaner housing

bolts which secured the mounting bush to the body rotate freely in their threaded bores and are not fouled by old locking fluid. If necessary, re-cut the threaded bores using an M10 x 1.25 mm tap. Then use new bolts, coated with locking fluid, to secure the mounting bush to the bodywork.

Models with serpentine belts, without air conditioning

Removal

1 For improved access, remove the air cleaner assembly and air inlet trunking (see Section 8).
2 If the original drivebelt is to be removed and refitted, mark the rotational direction of the belt with chalk.
3 Using a spanner or socket on the automatic tensioning roller hexagon, turn the tensioning roller clockwise (as viewed from the right-hand side of the car) and hold it in this position. With the drivebelt tension released, slip the drivebelt off the pulleys, then allow the tensioner to return to its original position.
4 If not already done, apply the handbrake,

then raise the front of the vehicle, and support securely on axle stands.
5 Attach lifting tackle and a hoist to the engine lifting brackets on the cylinder head, and support the weight of the engine.
6 Undo the three bolts on the mounting bracket and two bolts on the mounting bush, then withdraw the bracket and bush assembly, complete with the drivebelt (see illustration).
7 Undo the bolt and separate the mounting bush from the bracket (see illustration).
8 If the drivebelt is to be removed, undo the three bolts and separate the two halves of the bracket. Alternatively, undo two bolts and slacken one, then rotate the two halves against each other to open up the gap (see illustration).

Refitting

9 Refitting is the reverse of removal, noting the following points.
10 When refitting the same drivebelt, fit the belt in the same direction, marked by the arrow.
11 When refitting a new drivebelt, make sure you have the correct type of belt. There is a longer belt on models with air conditioning.
12 Clean out the threaded bores in the bodywork, then fit new mounting bush-to-body bolts, coated with locking fluid (see the note at the beginning of this Section). Tighten the bolts to the specified torque.
13 You will need an assistant to help you refit the drivebelt around the pulleys. Slacken the tensioner from underneath the car and feed the belt round the power steering pump pulley, while your assistant, working above the car, feeds the belt over the alternator pulley. Then release the tensioner.
14 Disconnect the lifting tackle and lower the vehicle to the ground.

5

10.6 Right-hand mounting bracket and bush with drivebelt. The arrow on the belt gives the direction of travel

10.7 Undo the bolt and separate the mounting bush from the bracket

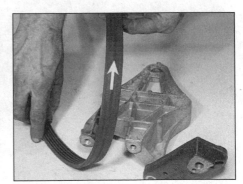

10.18 Remove the drivebelt from the mounting bracket

Notes

Chapter 6 Vauxhall Carlton & Opel Rekord petrol 1978 to 1986

Contents

Specifications

Timing belt renewal interval . . . . Every 36 000 miles (60 000 km) or 4 years - whichever comes first

Ignition timing . . . . 10° BTDC at idle

Torque wrench settings	Nm	lbf ft
Alternator bracket bolts	40	30
Camshaft sprocket bolt	45	33
Coolant pump bolts	25	18
Torsional damper bolt	60	44
Wheel nuts	90	66

1 Auxiliary drivebelt - removal, refitting and adjustment

Power-assisted steering

1 Remove the air cleaner pre-heating hose.

2 Slacken off the pump-to-bracket front mounting bolt and the rear upper mounting bolt and nut **(see illustration)**.

3 Push the pump body inwards as far as it will go then lift the drivebelt off the pump and crankshaft pulleys.

4 Place a new belt in position over the two pulleys.

5 Using a stout bar as a lever move the pump away from the engine until there is approximately 13 mm (0.5 in) deflection using light finger pressure on the belt midway between the two pulleys **(see illustration)**.

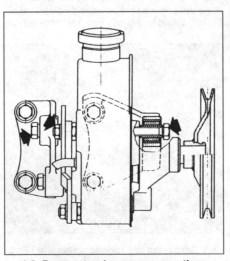

1.2 Power steering pump mountings

1.5 Adjusting the power steering belt tension using bar (arrowed) as lever

1.9 Alternator mounting and adjusting bolts

1 Lower mounting bolt
2 Adjusting arm bolt
3 Upper mounting bolt (where fitted)

6 Holding the pump in this position tighten the three mountings and recheck the belt tension.
7 Refit the air cleaner pre-heating hose.

Alternator

8 If the vehicle is fitted with power steering, it will be necessary to remove the power steering drivebelt.
9 Loosen the alternator adjusting and mounting bolts **(see illustration)**, then move the alternator toward the engine as far as possible.
10 Slip the belt over the edge of the alternator pulley, then remove it from the fan and crankshaft pulleys.
11 Pass the new belt around the crankshaft and fan pulley, then ease it over the edge of the alternator pulley.
12 Carefully lever the alternator away from the engine until the belt can be deflected by

2.6 Cooling system bleed plug located in the thermostat cover

1.11 Checking the alternator drivebelt tension

finger pressure approximately 13 mm (0.5 in) at a point midway between the alternator and water pump pulleys **(see illustration)**.
13 With the alternator held in this position, tighten the mounting and adjusting bolts, then recheck the tension.
14 With the fanbelt refitted and correctly tensioned, the power steering drivebelt, where applicable, should be refitted and tensioned.

2 Cooling system - draining and filling

Draining

1 If possible, ensure the engine is cold before draining the coolant to avoid the risk of scalding.
2 Remove the radiator filler cap. If the engine is hot, this must be done very cautiously, because a sudden release of pressure can result in the coolant boiling and blowing out. On a hot engine, place a cloth over the cap and turn it very gently to release the pressure slowly.
3 Place a suitable container beneath the radiator, disconnect the bottom hose and allow the coolant to drain **(see illustration)**.
4 The cylinder block may be drained by

3.5 Removing the radiator retaining clips

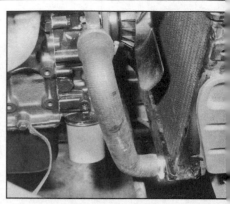

2.3 Radiator bottom hose connections

removing the drain plug located at the rear right-hand side of the engine.

Filling

5 Ensure the cylinder block drain plug is screwed in firmly and all cooling system hoses are in position and secured with hose clips.
6 Unscrew the small bleed plug on the top of the thermostat housing to allow air trapped in the cylinder block to escape as the system is filled **(see illustration)**.
7 Fill the cooling system slowly to minimise air-locks. Ensure the heater control is in the HOT position otherwise an air-lock may form in the heater.
8 Do not fill the system higher than 40 mm (1.5 in) from the top of the filler neck, because the coolant expands when heated and overfilling will result in coolant overflowing.
9 When the system is full, refit the bleed plug and radiator filler cap, then run the engine until normal temperature has been reached. Allow the engine to cool, then check and top-up the coolant level, if necessary.

3 Radiator - removal and refitting

Removal

1 Drain the cooling system as described in Section 2.
2 On automatic transmission models, place a tray beneath the oil cooler unions at the base of the radiator, wipe the unions clean and undo them. Quickly plug the pipe ends and the oil cooler unions, to prevent the loss of fluid and the ingress of dirt.
3 Remove the radiator top hose and the bottom hose also (if not already removed as part of the radiator draining operation).
4 If a radiator cowl is fitted, remove the securing screws and lift the cowl rearwards over the fan.
5 Using a pair of pliers, compress the two retaining clips, one on each side of the radiator, and lift them out of their mounting brackets **(see illustration)**.

3.6 Radiator removal

3.7 Location of radiator lower mounting

6 Lift out the radiator, taking care not to damage the radiator core or the fan blades **(see illustration)**.

Refitting

7 Refitting the radiator is the reverse sequence to removal **(see illustration)**. If any new hoses have been fitted, it will be found easier to position them onto the radiator outlets if their bores are first smeared with soap or rubber grease.

8 After refitting the radiator and hoses, tighten the hose clips and refill the cooling system.

4.5 Removing coolant pump

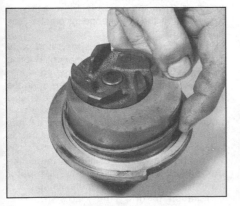

4.6a Coolant pump O-ring seal

9 On automatic transmission models, reconnect the oil cooler pipes and top-up the transmission with the recommended grade of fluid. If necessary, refer to Section 5.

4 Coolant pump - removal and refitting

Removal

1 Disconnect the battery earth cable.
2 Refer to Section 3 and remove the fan cowl and radiator. Begin this operation by unclipping the power cable from the cowl and disconnecting it from the battery positive terminal.
3 Remove the timing belt (see Section 6). Unless the drivebelt is to be renewed it can be left on the camshaft sprocket.
4 Remove the drivebelt backplate.
5 Unbolt the pump and remove it from the block **(see illustration)**.

Refitting

6 Before fitting the pump, clean its mounting in the engine block and fit a new O-ring seal to the pump body **(see illustration)**. Install the pump in the block and fit the three retaining bolts and washers, but only hand tighten them at this stage **(see illustration)**. The cut-out in

4.6b Coolant pump correctly fitted. Rotational stops (timing belt tension) arrowed

the pump flange must be positioned as shown to act as the timing belt adjustment limit stop when the pump is rotated to tension the timing belt. Refit the belt cover backplate.
7 Refit and tension the timing belt.
8 Refit the remaining components in the reverse order to removal.
9 Refill the cooling system, run the engine and check for leaks.

5 Automatic transmission - fluid level checking

1 If the dipstick is marked + 20°C on one side and +90°C on the other the fluid level may be checked with the engine and transmission hot or cold.
2 With the vehicle standing on level ground, leave the engine running and place the selector lever in P or N.
3 Withdraw the transmission dipstick, wipe it clean, re-insert it, withdraw it a second time and read off the level.
4 If necessary, top-up with the specified fluid to the F mark. The distance between ADD and F on the dipstick is 0.56 litre (1 pint)

6 Timing belt - removal and refitting

Removal

1 Unscrew and remove the drivebelt cover, removing cooling system components as necessary.
2 Using a socket spanner on the crankshaft pulley bolt, turn the crankshaft until No 1 piston is rising on its compression stroke. The notch in the rim of the crankshaft pulley should be aligned with the timing pointer and represents ignition timing at the specified degrees BTDC, not TDC which is not marked on these engines. The camshaft sprocket mark will be in alignment with the mark on the belt cover backplate **(see illustration)**.

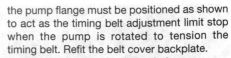

6.2 Camshaft sprocket timing marks

6

6.10a Checking timing belt tension

6.10b Adjusting timing belt tension

6.10c Tightening a coolant pump bolt after tensioning the drivebelt

3 Remove the auxiliary drivebelt, the crankshaft torsional damper and the distributor (see Section 7). Remove the distributor drivebelt.
4 Drain the cooling system.
5 Release the coolant pump mounting bolts just enough to be able to swivel the pump and to release the tension of the drivebelt.
6 If the drivebelt is to be used again, note its running direction before removing it.
7 Take the belt off the sprockets and fit the new one without moving the set position of the camshaft or crankshaft.

Refitting

8 Engage the new belt over the sprockets and apply some tension by moving the coolant pump.
9 Refit the torsional damper and then check that the pulley notch is still in alignment with the timing pointer and that the camshaft sprocket mark is aligned with the groove in the plate behind it. If not, release the belt tension and readjust the position of the sprockets as necessary.
10 The belt tension should now be adjusted in the following way. Partially tighten the clamping screws on the coolant pump and, using the thumb and forefinger, twist the belt through 90°. If with moderate effort, the belt twists too easily or will not reach the full 90°,

increase or decrease the tension as necessary by moving the coolant pump; a hexagon is moulded into the pump to turn it with a spanner. If the belt is overtightened, it will usually be heard to hum when the engine is running. Fully tighten the coolant pump bolts (see illustrations).
11 Refit the remaining components in the reverse order to removal. Refill the cooling system and reset the ignition timing on completion.

---

7 Distributor - removal and refitting

Removal

1 The distributor is mounted on the left-hand side of the cylinder head and is belt-driven from the front of the camshaft.
2 Gain access to the distributor drive cover securing bolts by removing the appropriate cooling system components (fan cowl, etc). Remove the cover. Mark the distributor body-to-engine alignment.
3 Ensure the marks on the distributor gear and camshaft sprocket align with those on the housing (see illustration). These marks must

remain aligned during the removal and refitting procedure.
4 Detach the distributor cap.
5 Unbolt the distributor body steady strut from the cylinder head. Disconnect the feed pipe from the vacuum advance unit.
6 Remove the two distributor securing nuts and the steady strut. Pull the distributor carefully away from its mounting so that its drivegear slips free of the toothed belt. Remove the distributor.

Refitting

7 Refitting the distributor is a reversal of the removal procedure. Ensure that the distributor gear and camshaft sprocket are correctly aligned and that the distributor body is placed in its previously noted position before nipping tight the two securing nuts and fully tightening the steady strut-to-cylinder head bolt.
8 On completion of refitting, check the ignition timing

---

8 Ignition timing - checking

1 Obtain a strobe light and connect it into the No 1 cylinder HT circuit, following the manufacturer's instructions. Dab a spot of white paint on the notch in the crankshaft pulley and on the corresponding pointer (see illustration).
2 Run the engine at idling speed and point the strobe light at the timing marks. At idling speed the white paint marks should appear to be immediately opposite each other; open the throttle slightly and check that as the engine revolutions rise the spot on the crankshaft will move away from the pointer. This indicates the centrifugal advance mechanism is operating correctly.
3 If timing marks do not line up under the strobe light, slightly slacken the distributor clamp nuts and carefully turn the distributor in its location to bring the marks into line. Retighten the clamp nuts.

7.3 Camshaft sprocket (A) and distributor drivegear (B) alignment marks

8.1 Ignition timing marks

Chapter 7
Vauxhall Carlton & Opel Omega petrol 1986 to 1994

Contents

Specifications

Timing belt renewal interval .... Every 36 000 miles (60 000 km) or 4 years - whichever comes first

Timing belt

Timing belt tension (using gauge KM-510-A) - early (pre 1993) models:

New belt, cold	4.5
New belt, warm	7.5
Used belt, cold	2.5
Used belt, warm	7.0

Torque wrench settings	**Nm**	**lbf ft**
Automatic transmission fluid coolant lines	35	26
Cooling fan pulley	8	6
Camshaft sprocket	45	33
Crankshaft sprocket bolt:		
Stage 1	130	96
Stage 2	Angle tighten a further 40 to 50°	
Crankshaft pulley to sprocket	20	15
Water pump bolts	25	18
Roadwheel bolts	90	66

7

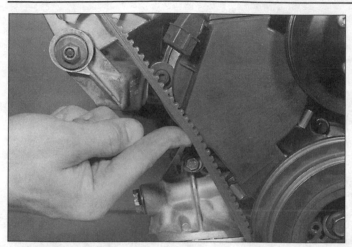

1.3 Checking the tension of the drivebelt

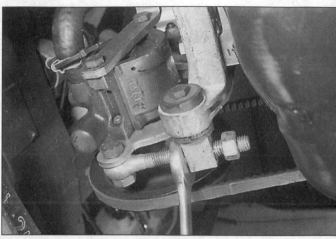

1.6a Slackening the power steering pump adjustment nut

1 Auxiliary drivebelt(s) - removal, refitting and adjustment

Alternator

Manually adjusted belt

1 To remove the belt, simply loosen the mounting nuts and bolts, and the bolt securing the adjuster bracket and slacken the belt sufficiently to slip it from the pulleys. On models with power steering it will first be necessary to remove the power steering pump drivebelt as described below.
2 Locate the belt on the pulleys and tension it as follows.
3 Although special tools are available for measuring the belt tension, a good approximation can be achieved if the belt is tensioned so that there is approximately 13.0 mm of free movement under firm thumb pressure at the mid-point of the longest run between pulleys (see illustration). If in doubt, err on the slack side, as an excessively-tight belt may cause damage to the alternator or other components.

4 Lever the alternator away from the engine using a wooden lever at the mounting bracket until the correct tension is achieved, then tighten the bolt securing the adjuster bracket, and the alternator mounting nuts and bolts. On no account lever at the free end of the alternator, as serious internal damage could be caused to the alternator.

Power steering pump

Manually adjusted belt

5 Loosen the power steering pump pivot bolts.
6 Loosen the adjustment rod locknut and unscrew the adjustment nut sufficiently until the drivebelt can be released from the pulleys and removed (see illustrations).
7 Locate the belt on the pulleys and tension as follows.
8 Although special tools are available for measuring the belt tension, a good approximation can be achieved if the belt is tensioned so that there is approximately 13.0 mm of free movement under firm thumb pressure at the mid-point of the longest run between pulleys (see illustration 1.3). If in doubt, err on the slack side, as an

excessively-tight belt may cause damage to the alternator or other components.
9 Using the adjustment nut, position the power steering pump so that the correct belt tension is achieved. Once the pump is correctly positioned, securely tighten the adjustment rod locknut and the pump pivot bolts.

Models with a spring loaded belt tensioner

10 If necessary, to improve access remove the cooling fan as described in Section 7.
11 Using a suitable socket and extension bar fitted to the spring loaded tensioner arm pulley bolt, pivot the tensioner arm downwards to release the belt tension and slip the belt off the pulleys. Slowly release the tensioner arm and remove the belt from the engine, noting its correct routing.
12 Locate the new belt on all except the power steering pump pulley, making sure it is correctly routed (see illustration).
13 Rotate the tensioner arm again and slip the belt onto the final pulley. Make sure the belt is correctly located on all pulleys then slowly release the tensioner arm. No further adjustment of the tension is required.

1.6b Removing the power steering pump drivebelt

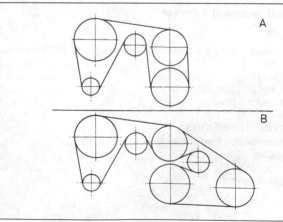

1.12 Drivebelt routing - models with a spring loaded tensioner

A Models without air conditioning   *B Models with air conditioning*

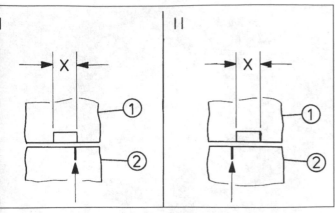

1.14 On models with a spring loaded belt tensioner, mark on tensioner arm (2) must be within mark/recess (X) on tensioner body (1) - illustration I. If mark is as shown in illustration II, the belt must be renewed

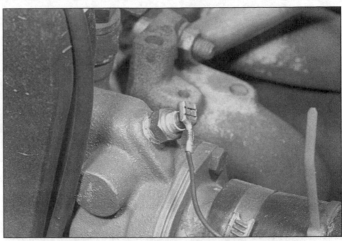

2.7 Temperature sensor on thermostat housing

14 Looking down on the tensioner, check the position of the tensioner arm mark in relation to the recess/mark on the tensioner body. The mark should be positioned within the recess/mark. If the mark is outside the recess/mark, or approaching its outer limit the belt should be renewed **(see illustration)**.

2 Cooling system - draining and refilling

Draining

1 Unscrew the filler cap from the expansion tank or radiator (as applicable). If the engine is hot, place a thick cloth over the cap before removing it slowly, otherwise there is a danger of scalding.
2 Place a suitable container beneath the right-hand side of the radiator.
3 Loosen the clip and disconnect the bottom hose from the radiator. Drain the coolant into the container.

Refilling

4 Reconnect the hoses and tighten the clips.
5 On carburettor engines, disconnect the

warm air duct to provide access to the thermostat housing.
6 Disconnect the wiring and unscrew the temperature sensor from the top of the thermostat housing **(see illustration)**.
7 On fuel injection engines, also disconnect the coolant hose from the bottom of the throttle housing.
8 Pour the coolant into the radiator or expansion tank (as applicable) until it flows from the temperature sensor hole, then refit and tighten the sensor and reconnect the wiring.
9 Refit the warm air duct on carburettor engines.
10 On fuel injection engines, continue to add coolant until it runs out of the throttle housing hose, then reconnect the hose.
11 On all engines, continue to add coolant until it reaches the cold level mark. On the radiator this is either indicated by a level plate in the filler neck or by being 50.0 mm (2.0 in) below the top edge of the filler neck. On the remote expansion tank, a cold level mark is provided.
12 Refit the filler cap.
13 Start the engine and run it at a fast idle speed until it reaches normal operating temperature, indicated by the thermostat

opening and the top hose becoming hotter when touched. Watch for any signs of overheating, and check for leaks.
14 Stop the engine and allow it to cool for two or three hours, then recheck the coolant level and if necessary top-up to the COLD level. Refit the filler cap.

3 Water pump - removal and refitting

Removal

1 Remove the thermo-viscous cooling fan (Section 8) and auxiliary drivebelt (Section 1).
2 Remove the radiator (Section 6).
3 Remove the screws and lift auxiliary drivebelt pulley from the cooling fan hub.
4 Unclip and remove the timing belt covers.
5 Turn the engine with a spanner on the crankshaft pulley bolt until the mark on the camshaft sprocket is aligned with the pointer on the top of the rear timing belt cover. Also align the notch in the crankshaft pulley with the pointer on the lower part of the rear timing belt cover.
6 Using an Allen key loosen the three bolts securing the water pump to the block.
7 Unscrew and remove the bolt securing the water pump section of the timing cover to the oil pump housing.
8 Rotate the water pump body anti-clockwise. Release the timing belt from the water pump sprocket and tie it loosely to one side.
9 Unscrew and remove the three securing bolts and washers, and withdraw the water pump from the block **(see illustration)**.
10 Prise the rubber O-ring from the groove in the water pump **(see illustration)**.
11 If a new water pump is being fitted, transfer the timing cover section to the new pump. To do this, engage the two cut-outs

7

3.9 Removing the water pump

3.10 Prise the rubber O-ring from groove in the water pump

3.11a Twisting the timing cover section from the plate (arrowed) on the water pump

3.11b Water pump with timing cover section removed

and twist off the timing cover section **(see illustrations)**. Similarly fit the cover to the new water pump.

Refitting

12 Commence refitting by smearing silicon grease or equivalent to the surfaces of the water pump in contact with the block. If this precaution is not taken the water pump may seize in the block.

13 Apply the grease to the rubber O-ring and locate it in the groove.

14 Locate the water pump in the block with the timing cover projections correctly seated. Insert the securing bolts and washers loosely.

15 Engage the timing belt with the water pump sprocket. Turn the water pump clockwise to tension it. Complete the tensioning procedure with reference to Section 4, making sure that the timing marks are correctly aligned. Tighten the water pump securing bolts to the specified torque.

16 Insert and tighten the bolt securing the timing cover to the oil pump housing.

17 Refit the timing belt covers.

18 Refit the drivebelt pulley to the cooling fan hub and tighten the screws.

19 Refit the radiator (Section 6).

20 Refit the alternator/fan drivebelt (see Section 1) and the thermo-viscous cooling fan (see Section 8).

4 Timing belt - removal and refitting

Removal

1 Disconnect the battery negative lead.

2 Remove the spark plugs.

3 Remove the thermo-viscous cooling fan, drivebelt, and fan cowling. If applicable, remove the power steering pump and air conditioning compressor drivebelts (Sections 8 and 1).

4 Drain the cooling system (Section 2).

5 Unclip and remove the timing belt covers.

6 Turn the engine with a spanner on the crankshaft pulley bolt until the mark on the camshaft sprocket is aligned with the pointer on the top of the rear timing belt cover. Also align the notch in the crankshaft pulley with the pointer on the lower part of the rear timing belt cover.

7 Unbolt the crankshaft pulley from the timing belt sprocket.

8 On early (pre 1993) models, loosen the three bolts securing the water pump to the block. Rotate the water pump body anti-clockwise and remove the timing belt from the sprockets.

9 On later (1993 on) models with a spring loaded timing belt tensioner, slacken the tensioner securing bolt slightly. Pivot the tensioner away from the belt and slip the belt off the sprockets.

Refitting

10 Locate the new timing belt temporarily on the sprockets.

11 Locate the crankshaft pulley on the crankshaft sprocket and tighten its retaining bolts.

12 Disconnect the timing belt and align the timing marks on the camshaft sprocket and crankshaft pulley with the pointers on the rear cover and reconnect the belt without disturbing the sprockets.

Early (pre 1993) models

13 Apply some tension to the belt by moving the water pump clockwise.

14 Using the special tensioning gauge (KM-510-A), turn the water pump clockwise to apply moderate tension to the belt then tighten the bolts. Rotate the crankshaft half a turn clockwise to tension the belt between the camshaft and crankshaft sprockets. Fit the tension gauge between the camshaft and water pump sprockets and check that the reading is as given in the Specifications **(see illustration)**. If adjustment is necessary move the water pump clockwise to increase or anti-clockwise to decrease the tension.

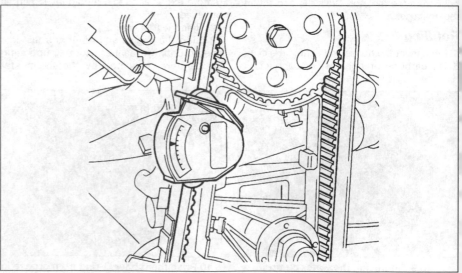

4.14 Checking the timing belt tension with a tension gauge - early (pre 1993) models

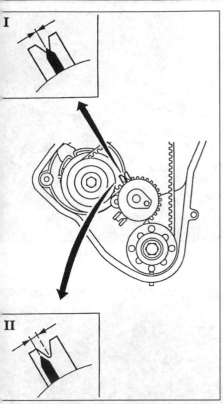

4.18 On later (1993 on) models with a spring loaded timing belt tensioner position the tensioner pointer as shown

New belt - align pointer with the centre of the tensioner bracket notch

Used belt - position pointer about 4 mm to the left of the centre of the tensioner bracket notch

Rotate the crankshaft through one full turn and repeat the test.

15 Once the belt is correctly tensioned, tighten the water pump bolts to the specified torque and recheck the timing mark alignment.

Later (1993 on) models with spring-loaded belt tensioner

16 Slacken the automatic tensioner securing bolt and move the tensioner arm anti-clockwise, until the tensioner pointer lies at its stop. Tighten the tensioner securing bolt to hold the tensioner in this position.

17 Turn the crankshaft through two complete turns clockwise, and check that the crankshaft pulley and camshaft sprocket timing marks are correctly aligned.

18 Slacken the automatic tensioner securing bolt and move the tensioner arm clockwise. If a new belt is being fitted, align the tensioner pointer with the notch in the tensioner bracket and if a used belt is fitted, align the pointer to approximately 4 mm to the left of the notch **(see illustration)**. Hold the tensioner arm in the correct position and securely tighten its securing bolt. Turn the crankshaft through one complete revolution, in the normal direction of rotation, and check that the crankshaft and camshaft timing marks still align.

All models

19 Refit the timing belt covers.
20 Refit and tension the drivebelt(s) (Section 1).
21 Refit the cooling fan and fan cowling.
22 Refit the spark plugs.
23 Refill the cooling system (Section 2)
24 Reconnect the battery negative lead.

---

5 Automatic transmission fluid level check

1.8 and early (pre 1990) 2.0 litre models - AW03-71L and AW03-71LE transmission

1 Ensure that the vehicle is on level ground. With the engine running and the brakes applied, move the selector lever through all the gear positions, finishing in P (Park).

2 With the engine still idling and the transmission in P, withdraw the transmission dipstick, wipe it clean, then re-insert it and withdraw it again. Read the fluid level.

3 With the engine and transmission hot (after at least 20 km/13 miles running) the fluid level should be between the MIN and MAX marks on the side of the dipstick marked 90°C **(see illustration)**. The quantity of fluid required to raise the level from MIN to MAX is about 0.6 litre. With the engine and transmission cold, the fluid level should be up to the line on the side of the dipstick marked 20°C.

4 If necessary top-up the level with suitable fluid through the dipstick tube **(see illustration)**. Take care not to allow any dust or dirt to enter the tube.

5 Refit the dipstick and switch off the engine.

Later (1990 on) 2.0 litre models - AR25 and AR35 transmission

6 To check the automatic transmission fluid level, first take the vehicle on a run of approximately 12 miles/20 km to warm the transmission up to its normal operating temperature. On your return, ensure that the vehicle is parked on level ground. With the engine running and the brakes applied, move the selector lever slowly from the P position to the 1 position, and then return it to P.

7 With the engine still idling and the selector lever in the P position, withdraw the transmission dipstick, wipe it clean, then re-insert it fully into the tube. Withdraw the dipstick and note the level of the fluid. Repeat this procedure three times, and take the average reading as the true transmission fluid level.

8 With the engine and transmission at normal operating temperature, at air temperatures above 0°C (32°F), the fluid level should be within the HOT portion of the dipstick (approximately 42 mm up from the base of the dipstick) **(see illustration)**. At ambient

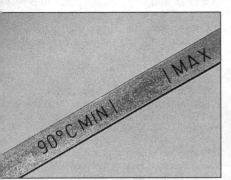

5.3 Automatic transmission fluid level dipstick markings - AW03-71L and AW03-71LE transmission

5.4 Topping up the automatic transmission

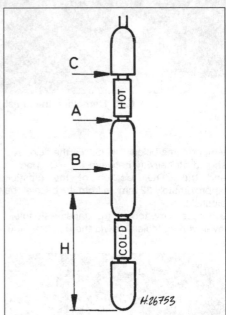

5.8 Automatic transmission dipstick level markings - AR25 and AR35 transmission

A Fill level when air temperature is above 0°C
B Fill level when air temperature is below 0°C
C Filling level after transmission overhaul (transmission completely dry)
H Fluid level from base of dipstick

7

6.2 Radiator top hose connection

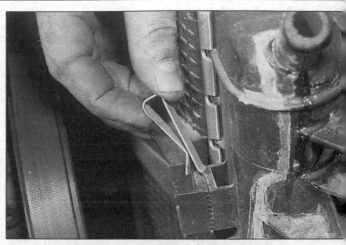

6.3a Removing a fan shroud spring clip

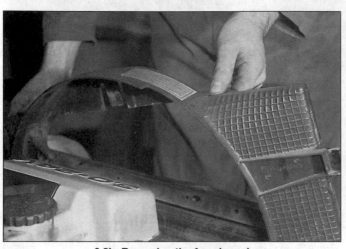

6.3b Removing the fan shroud

6.4 Unscrew the union nuts and detach the transmission fluid cooler pipes

temperatures below 0°C (32°F), the fluid level should be halfway between the HOT portion and the COLD portion of the dipstick (approximately 32 mm up from the base of the dipstick).

9 If necessary, top-up the transmission fluid level with suitable fluid via the dipstick tube,

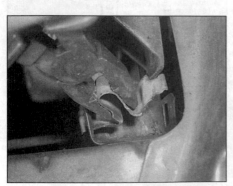

6.6 Radiator spring clip mountings

and recheck the fluid level as described above. Take great care not to allow any dust or dirt to enter the tube.

10 Once the level is correct, refit the dipstick and switch off the engine.

6 Radiator - removal and refitting

Removal

1 Where applicable, remove the engine undertray.

2 Drain the cooling system as desscribed in Section 2. Disconnect and remove the radiator top hose from the radiator and thermostat housing (see illustration).

3 Pull out the upper clips and release the cooling fan shroud from the slots in the bottom of the radiator. The shroud may now be positioned over the cooling fan blades, however for additional working room unclip

the engine wiring harness and completely remove the shroud (see illustrations).

4 On automatic transmission models, place a container beneath the radiator, then unscrew the union nuts and disconnect the fluid cooler pipes from the radiator (see illustration). Drain the fluid and plug the pipes to prevent entry of dust and dirt.

5 Where applicable disconnect the expansion tank hose from the right-hand side of the radiator.

6 Squeeze together and remove the spring clips retaining the rubber mountings on each side of the radiator (see illustration).

7 Lift the radiator straight up from the side and bottom mountings and withdraw it from the engine compartment.

Refitting

8 Refitting is a reversal of removal. Refill the cooling system as described in Section 2. On automatic transmission models, tighten the fluid cooler unions to the specified torque, and also top-up the transmission fluid level.

8.3 Removing the thermo-viscous fan

7 Electric auxiliary fan - removal and refitting

Removal

1 Refer to Section 6 and remove the radiator.

2 Unplug the fan supply cabling at the connector.
3 Remove the three screws that secure the auxiliary fan assembly to its mounting bracket.
4 Lift the auxiliary fan out of the engine bay, taking care not to damage the cooling fins of air conditioning heat exchanger radiator (where fitted).

Refitting

5 Refit the fan by following the removal procedure in reverse, noting the following points (where applicable):
  a) *On completion, refill the engine with the correct quantity and concentration of coolant.*
  b) *On engines fitted wth an oil cooler, refill the engine with correct grade and quantity of oil.*
  c) *On vehicles fitted with an automatic transmission fluid cooler, refer to Section 5 and, if necessary, replenish the automatic transmission fluid.*

8 Thermo-viscous cooling fan - removal and refitting

Removal

1 On carburettor engines disconnect the warm air duct and move it to one side.
2 If required, the cooling fan shroud may be moved out of the way. Pull out the upper clips, unclip the wiring harness, and lift the shroud towards the cylinder head, over the fan blades.
3 Using two open-ended spanners hold the hub stationary then unscrew the fan nut noting that it has a left-hand thread. Remove the cooling fan **(see illustration)**. **Note:** *Spanners specifically designed for the removal of viscous-coupled fans are available.*

Refitting

4 Refitting is a reversal of removal.

7

Notes

Chapter 8A
Vauxhall Cavalier &
Opel Ascona Petrol 1981 to 1988

Contents

Specifications

Timing belt renewal interval	Every 36 000 miles (60 000 km) or 4 years, whichever comes first

Torque wrench settings	Nm	lbf ft
Alternator bracket to block	40	30
Camshaft sprocket bolt	45	33
Coolant pump bolts:		
1.3 litre engine	8	6
1.6, 1.8 and 2.0 litre engines	25	18
Crankshaft pulley bolt:		
1.3 litre engine	55	41
1.6, 1.8 and 2.0 litre engine	20	15
Crankshaft sprocket bolt - 1.6, 1.8 and 2.0 litre engines:		
Stage 1	130	96
Stage 2	Angle tighten a further 40° to 50°	
Roadwheel bolts	90	66
Spark plugs	20	15

1.2 Alternator pivot mounting and adjustment link bolt

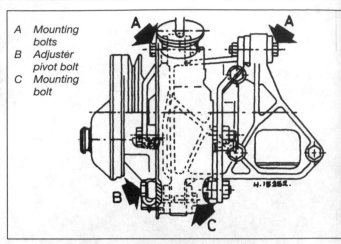

A Mounting
   bolts
B Adjuster
   pivot bolt
C Mounting
   bolt

1.6 Power steering pump mountings

1 Auxiliary drivebelt - removal, refitting and adjustment

Alternator

Adjustment

1 Although special tools are available for measuring the belt tension, a good approximation can be achieved if the belt is tensioned so that there is approximately 13.0 mm of free movement under firm thumb pressure at the mid-point of the longest run between pulleys. If in doubt, err on the slack side, as an excessively-tight belt may cause damage to the alternator or other components.

2 If adjustment is required, loosen the alternator upper mounting nut and bolt - use two spanners, one to counterhold the bolt. Lever the alternator away from the engine using a wooden lever at the mounting bracket until the correct tension is achieved, then tighten the bolt securing the adjuster bracket, and the alternator mounting nuts and bolts **(see illustration)**. On no account lever at the free end of the alternator, as serious internal damage could be caused to the alternator.

Removal and refitting

3 To remove the belt, simply loosen the mounting nuts and bolts, and the bolt securing the adjuster bracket, as described previously, and slacken the belt sufficiently to slip it from the pulleys. On models with power steering it will first be necessary to remove the power steering pump drivebelt as described below.

4 Refit the belt, and tension it as described previously.

Power steering pump

Adjustment

5 Refer to the information given in para-

graph 1, noting that there should be approximately 8 mm of free movement in the belt.

6 If adjustment is required, slacken the adjuster bolt locknut (situated on the base of the pump) and rotate the adjuster nut as necessary to tension the belt **(see illustration)**. Once the belt tension is correct, securely tighten the locknut.

Removal and refitting

7 To remove the belt, simply loosen the locknut and fully slacken the adjuster nut sufficiently to slip the drivebelt from the pulleys.

8 Refit the belt, and tension it as described previously.

2 Coolant - draining and refilling

> ⚠️ *Warning: Wait until the engine is cold before starting this procedure. Do not allow antifreeze to come in contact with your skin or painted surfaces of the vehicle. Rinse off spills immediately with plenty of water. Never leave antifreeze lying around in an open container or in a puddle in the driveway or on the garage floor. Children and pets are attracted by its sweet smell. Antifreeze is fatal if ingested.*

Draining

1 To drain the cooling system, remove the expansion tank filler cap. Turn the cap anti-clockwise until it reaches the first stop. Wait until any pressure remaining in the system is released then push the cap down, turn it anti-clockwise to the second stop and lift off.

2 Position a suitable container beneath the radiator bottom hose union.

3 Slacken the hose clip and ease the hose from the radiator stub. If the hose joint has not been disturbed for some time, it will be necessary to gently manipulate the hose to break the joint. Do not use excessive force, or

the radiator stub could be damaged. Allow the coolant to drain into the container.

4 Reconnect the hose and securely tighten its retaining clip on completion of draining.

Refilling

5 Before attempting to fill the cooling system, make sure that all hoses and clips are in good condition, and that the clips are tight.

6 Remove the expansion tank filler cap.

7 On 1.3 litre engines models, disconnect the wire and unscrew the coolant temperature sender from the inlet manifold **(see illustration)**. On larger-engine models, unscrew the bleed screw which is situated in the thermostat housing cover.

8 Fill the system by slowly pouring the coolant into the expansion tank to prevent airlocks from forming.

9 When coolant free of air bubbles emerges from the orifice, refit the coolant temperature sender and tighten it securely (1.3 litre engines), or refit the bleed screw and tighten it securely (larger engines).

10 Top-up the coolant level to the KALT (or COLD) mark on the expansion tank, then refit the expansion tank cap.

11 Start the engine and run it until it reaches normal operating temperature, then stop the engine and allow it to cool.

2.7 Coolant temperature sender (1.3 litre model)

3.4a Removing the coolant pump (early model)

3.4b On later models, remove the toothed belt cover from the pump as described

12 Check for leaks, particularly around disturbed components. Check the coolant level in the expansion tank, and top-up if necessary. Note that the system must be cold before an accurate level is indicated in the expansion tank.

3 Coolant pump -
removal and refitting

Removal

1 Drain the cooling system as described in Section 2.
2 Remove the timing belt as described in Section 4.
3 On early models unbolt and remove timing belt cover backplate from the block.
4 Unbolt and remove the coolant pump from the engine block. On later modes, to separate the pump and plate, apply sideways pressure to it whilst rotating it around the pump body (see illustrations).

Refitting

5 Before fitting the coolant pump, clean its mounting in the engine block and fit a new O-ring seal to the pump body (see illustration). Apply silicone grease to the seal, and to the sealing surface in the block. On later models, if necessary, refit the timing belt backplate to the pump body, making sure it is fitted the correct way around.
6 Install the pump in the block and fit the three retaining bolts and washers, but only hand tighten them at this stage. The cut-out in the pump flange must be positioned as shown to act as the timing belt adjustment limit stop when the pump is rotated to tension the timing belt (see illustration). On early models, refit the belt cover backplate.
7 Refit the timing belt as described in Section 4 and tighten the pump securing bolts to the specified torque.
8 Refill the cooling system as described in Section 2.

4 Timing belt -
removal and refitting

Note: Accurate adjustment of the timing belt entails the use of a tension checking gauge, which is Vauxhall special tool KM 510A.

1.3 litre and early 1.6 (16S) & 1.8 (18E) litre engines

Removal

1 Release the alternator adjustment link and mounting bolts, push the alternator in towards the engine and slip the drivebelt from the pulleys.
2 Unscrew the bolts and remove the timing belt cover. Remove the air cleaner unit for improved access on fuel injection models (Section 5).
3 Using a socket spanner on the crankshaft pulley bolt, turn the crankshaft until No 1 piston is rising on its compression stroke. To

8A

3.5 Coolant pump O-ring seal

3.6 Coolant pump correctly fitted with rotational stops arrowed

4.3a Crankshaft pulley timing mark

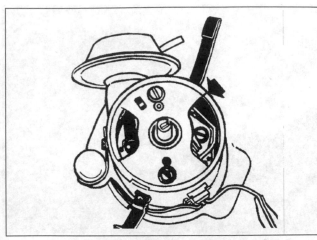

4.3b Distributor rotor alignment mark

check that this is the compression stroke, either remove No 1 spark plug and place a finger over the plug hole to feel the compression being generated or remove the distributor cap and check that the rotor is aligned with No 1 spark plug contact in the cap. The notch in the rim of the crankshaft pulley should be aligned with the timing pointer, and represents ignition timing at the specified degrees BTDC **not** TDC which is not marked on these engines. The camshaft sprocket mark will be in alignment with the mark on the belt cover backplate **(see illustrations)**.

4 On 1.3 litre engines, unscrew the crankshaft pulley bolt without disturbing the previously set position of the crankshaft. On larger engine models, undo and remove the four bolts which secure the pulley to the crankshaft drive sprocket. To prevent the crankshaft rotating as the bolt(s) are removed, either engage a gear and apply the brakes, or remove the flywheel

housing lower cover and jam the flywheel ring gear with a suitable tool. Withdraw the pulley from the crankshaft or drive sprocket (as applicable) **(see illustration)**.

5 Drain the cooling system (Section 2).

6 Release the coolant pump mounting bolts just enough to be able to swivel the pump and to release the tension of the timing belt. Flats are provided on the pump body behind the sprocket, and if necessary a large thin spanner can be used to turn the eccentrically-mounted pump. Alternatively, working under the car, the pump can be turned by carefully tapping it with a hammer and long drift.

7 If the timing belt is to be used again, note its running direction before removing it.

Refitting

8 Fit the new belt without moving the set position of the camshaft or crankshaft.

9 Engage the new belt over the sprockets and apply some tension by moving the coolant pump.

10 Refit the crankshaft pulley int position and then check that the pulle notch is still in alignment with the timing pointer and that the camshaft sprocke mark is aligned with the groove in the plat behind it. If not, release the belt tension an readjust the position of the sprockets a necessary.

11 The belt tension should now be adjuste using the official tool (KM 510A). Adjust the tension as necessary by moving the wate pump. If the belt is overtight, it will be heard t hum when the engine is running. Gaug readings are:

	New belt	Used belt
1.3 litre	6.0	5.0
1.6 litre	4.5	2.5
1.8 litre	4.5	2.5

When the adjustment is correct, tighten th coolant pump bolts, turn the crankshaf through one full turn, and check the tensio again. Repeat this procedure until the correc

4.3c Camshaft sprocket timing mark

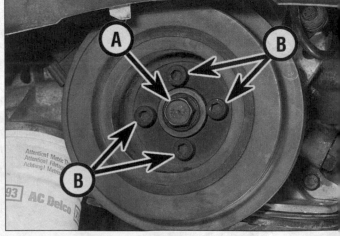

4.4 Crankshaft pulley on a 1.6 engine

A   *Torsional damper and crankshaft sprocket retaining bolt*
B   *Pulley retaining bolts (fillister type)*

4.11a Adjusting the timing belt tension

4.11b Tightening the coolant pump bolt after tightening the timing belt

tension is obtained. Fully tighten the coolant pump bolts **(see illustrations)**.

12 Remove the crankshaft pulley, then fit the timing belt cover into position.

13 Refit the crankshaft pulley.

14 Refit the alternator drivebelt and adjust the tension as described in Section 1.

Later 1.6 (16SH) & 1.8 (18SE) litre engines and all 2.0 litre engines

Removal

15 Disconnect the battery earth lead, and for improved access, remove the air cleaner assembly, as described in Section 5.

16 Drain the cooling system (Section 2).

17 Slacken the alternator adjustment link and mounting bolts **(see illustration)**, push the alternator in towards the engine, and slip the drivebelt off the pulleys.

18 Release the retaining clips, and remove the timing belt upper cover **(see illustration)**.

19 Using a socket or spanner on the crankshaft pulley bolt, turn the crankshaft until No 1 piston is at its firing point. This is indicated by the notch in the crankshaft pulley being in line with the pointer on the oil pump housing, and the notch on the camshaft sprocket being in line with the pip on the inner

circumference of the timing belt inner cover **(see illustrations)**.

20 Raise and support the front of the car, then remove the right-hand front roadwheel.

21 Using a suitable Allen key, unscrew four bolts securing the crankshaft pulley to the timing belt sprocket, and remove the pulley

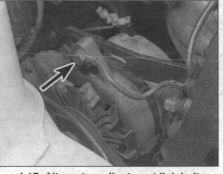

4.17 Alternator adjustment link bolt (arrowed)

4.18 Removing the toothed belt upper cover

4.19a Align the timing notch on the camshaft sprocket (arrowed) . . .

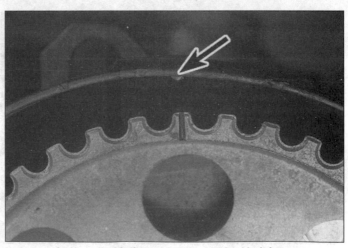

4.19b . . . with the pip on the toothed belt inner cover (arrowed)

4.21a Unscrew the four crankshaft pulley retaining bolts . . .

4.21b . . . and remove the pulley

4.22 Removing the toothed belt intermediate cover

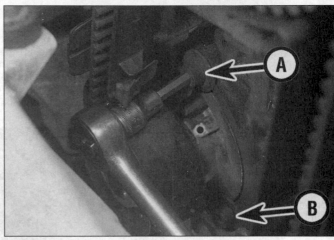

4.23a Slacken the coolant pump upper bolt (A), front bolt (B) . . .

(see illustrations). To prevent the crankshaft rotating as the bolts are removed, either engage a gear and apply the brakes, or remove the flywheel housing lower cover and jam the flywheel ring gear with a suitable tool.
22 Release the retaining clips, and remove the timing belt intermediate cover from the vicinity of the coolant pump (see illustration).
23 Using a suitable Allen key or socket bit, slacken the three coolant pump securing bolts, then swivel the pump to release the tension on the timing belt. The pump can be moved using the cast projection on the side of the pump body (see illustrations).
24 If the belt is to be re-used, mark it running direction using chalk, then ease the belt off the three sprockets (see illustration).
25 If signs of oil contamination are found

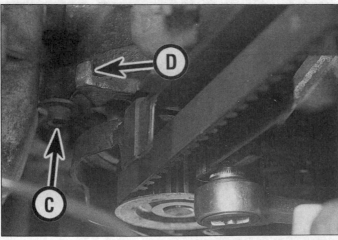

4.23b . . . and rear bolt (C), then move the pump by means of the cast projection (D)

4.24 Slip the toothed belt off the sprockets

5.1 On carburettor models, undo the retaining nut (or screws) . . .

5.2a Disconnect the breather hose at the air cleaner . . .

ace the source of the oil leak and rectify it, hen wash down the engine timing belt area nd all related components to remove all aces of oil.

Refitting

6 Without disturbing the set position of the rankshaft and camshaft, locate the new belt ver the sprockets. Apply some tension to the elt by moving the coolant pump, then emporarily tighten the coolant pump bolts.

7 Place the crankshaft pulley in position without the retaining bolts), and check that he timing marks are still aligned as described n paragraph 19. Now turn the crankshaft hrough two complete revolutions, in the ormal direction of rotation, and check that he marks can be re-aligned with their espective pointers. If not, release the belt ension, and alter the position of the belt on he camshaft sprocket until the marks can be correctly aligned.

8 The belt tension should now be adjusted sing the official tool (KM 510A). Adjust the ension as necessary by moving the water

pump. If the belt is overtight, it will be heard to hum when the engine is running. Gauge readings are:

New belt   4.5
Used belt   2.5

When the adjustment is correct, tighten the coolant pump bolts, turn the crankshaft through one full turn, and check the tension again. Repeat this procedure until the correct tension is obtained.

29 Refit the timing belt intermediate cover to the coolant pump.

30 Refit the crankshaft pulley, and secure with the four bolts tightened to the specified torque.

31 Place the timing belt upper cover in position, and secure with the retaining clips.

32 Refit the alternator drivebelt and adjust its tension as described in Section 1.

33 Refit the roadwheel and lower the car to the ground.

34 Refit the air cleaner as described in Section 5, refill the cooling system as described in Section 2, then reconnect the battery earth lead.

5 Air cleaner housing - removal and refitting

Carburettor models
Removal

1 Remove the centre retaining nut or bolt or the three screws from the air cleaner cover (see illustration).

2 Lift the air cleaner off the carburettor, disengaging the hot air pick-up from the manifold shroud, together with the breather and vacuum hoses (see illustrations).

Refitting

3 Refit by reversing the removal operations, making sure that the gasket or sealing ring is in place on the carburettor.

Fuel injection models
Removal

4 Release the locking clip, and disconnect the plug from the airflow sensor (see illustration). Disconnect the air trunking.

5.2b . . . and the vacuum hose (arrowed) at the carburettor

5.4 On fuel-injected models disconnect the airflow sensor wiring connector . . .

8A

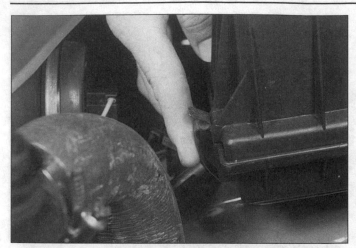

5.5a . . . then release the retaining clips . . .

5.5b . . . and remove the housing cover, complete with the filter element

5 Release the spring clips, and lift off the air cleaner cover with airflow sensor attached. The element will probably come away with the cover **(see illustrations)**. Do not drop or jar the airflow sensor.

6 Disconnect the air inlet tube then undo the retaining screws and remove the housing from the engine compartment.

Refitting

7 Refit by reversing the removal operations.

Chapter 8B
Vauxhall Cavalier & Opel Ascona diesel 1981 to 1988

Contents

Specifications

Timing belt renewal interval . . . . Every 36 000 miles (60 000 km) or 4 years - whichever comes first

Auxiliary drivebelts
Tension (using gauge KM-128-A):
    Alternator:
        New . . . . 450 N
        Used . . . . 250 to 400 N
    Power steering pump:
        New . . . . 450 N
        Used . . . . 250 to 300 N

Timing belt tension
Using tension gauge KM-510-A:
    New belt, warm 9.0
    New belt, cold 6.5
    Run-in belt, warm 8.0
    Run-in belt, cold 4.0

Injection pump
Timing setting . . . . 1.0 ± 0.05 mm

Torque wrench settings

	Nm	lbf ft
Alternator:		
Adjuster strap nuts and bolts	25	18
Pivot bolt	25	18
Camshaft sprocket bolt:*		
Stage 1	75	55
Stage 2	Angle-tighten a further 60°	
Coolant pump to cylinder block	25	18
Crankshaft pulley-to-sprocket bolt	20	15
Crankshaft sprocket centre bolt	155	114
Engine mountings:		
Except right-hand bracket to cylinder block	40	30
Right-hand mounting bracket to cylinder block	50	37
Fuel injection pump and brackets:		
Main bracket to block	25	18
Pump sprockets bolts	25	18
Subsidiary brackets:		
M6 bolts	14	10
M8 bolts	25	18
Power steering pump:		
Drivebelt tensioner to pump	40	30
Vacuum pump to camshaft housing	28	21
Wheel bolts	90	66

* Bolts tightened by the angular method must be renewed every time.

8B

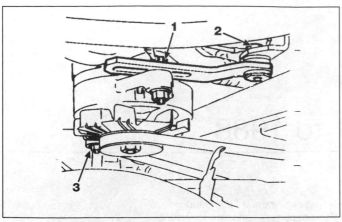

1.2 Alternator drivebelt adjustment points

1 *Alternator to adjuster strap bolt*
2 *Adjuster strap pivot bolt*
3 *Alternator pivot bolt*

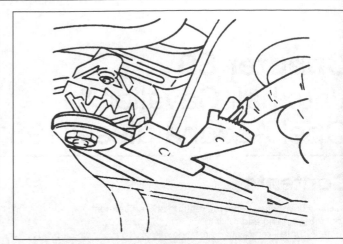

1.8 Using special tool KM-128-A to tension the alternator drivebelt

1 Auxiliary drivebelts - removal, refitting and adjustment

Alternator

Removal and refitting

1 Gain full access to the drivebelt by raising the car, supporting it on axle stands and removing the right-hand front roadwheel. Remove the air cleaner housing assembly.
2 To remove the drivebelt, first slacken the alternator pivot and adjuster strap nuts and bolts **(see illustration)**.
3 Where fitted, remove the power steering pump drivebelt.
4 Move the alternator towards the engine and slip the drivebelt off its pulleys.
5 Fit the new drivebelt in position over the pulleys and adjust it as follows:

Adjustment

6 Tighten the alternator fastening slightly, so that the alternator can just be moved by hand.
7 Move the alternator away from the engine until the belt tension is correct.
8 Vauxhall recommend the use of a special tool (KM-128-A) for tensioning the belt to the specified amount **(see illustration)**. In the absence of this tool, aim for a tension such that the belt can be deflected about 12 mm by firm finger pressure in the middle of its run. The belt tension must, however, be checked with the special tool as soon as possible. If using a lever to move the alternator, only use a wooden or plastic one and only lever at the pulley end.
9 Tighten the alternator fastenings to the specified torque setting once the belt tension is correct.
10 Where applicable, refit and tension the steering pump drivebelt.
11 Refit the air cleaner housing assembly.

Power steering pump

Removal and refitting

12 Gain full access to the drivebelt by jacking up the front right-hand side of the vehicle and supporting it on axle stands.
13 To remove the drivebelt, first loosen the pump mounting and tensioner bolts shown **(see illustration)**. Release the tensioner screw locknuts and rotate them to allow the drivebelt to slacken **(see illustration)**. Slip the drivebelt off its pulleys.
14 Fit the new drivebelt in position over the pulleys and adjust it as follows:

Adjustment

15 Rotate the tensioner screw locknuts until the belt tension is correct.
16 Vauxhall recommend the use of a special tool (KM-128-A) for tensioning the belt to the specified amount. In the absence of this tool, aim for a tension such that the belt can be deflected approximately 12 mm by firm finger pressure in the middle of its run. The belt tension must, however, be checked with the special tool as soon as possible.
17 Once belt tension is correct, tighten the tensioner screw locknuts and lower the vehicle.

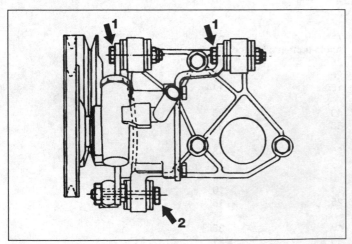

1.13a Power steering pump drivebelt adjustment points

1 Pump mounting bolts   2 Tensioner bolt

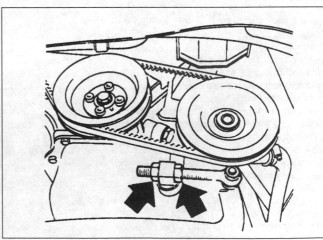

1.13b Rotate the tensioner screw locknuts (arrowed) to adjust drivebelt tension

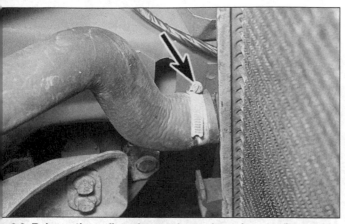

2.3 Release the radiator bottom hose clamp (arrowed) to drain the cooling system

2.8 The thermostat elbow coolant bleed screw (arrowed)

2 Coolant -
draining and refilling

⚠️ *Warning: Take care to avoid scalding when removing the cooling system expansion tank cap. Place a thick cloth over the cap before turning it anti-clockwise.*
Caution: Never operate the vehicle with plain water in the cooling system, except in an emergency. Apart from the risk of freezing in winter weather, serious corrosion and rust and scale formation may occur.
Warning: Antifreeze is poisonous and must be handled with due care.

Draining

1 The system should only be drained when it is cool. If it must be drained hot, take great care to avoid scalding.
2 Remove the expansion tank cap. If the system is hot, place a thick cloth over the cap before turning it anti-clockwise.
3 Place a container underneath the radiator

bottom hose. Disconnect the hose from the radiator and allow the system to drain **(see illustration)**.
4 There is no cylinder block drain plug, making it impossible to drain the system completely.

Filling

5 Make sure that all hoses and clips are in good condition. Refit any disturbed hoses and see that their clips are tight.
6 Fill the system via the expansion tank cap. If new coolant is being put in, start by pouring in the required quantity of neat antifreeze and follow it up with the water.
7 Massage the large coolant hoses to help displace air pockets during filling.
8 Most vehicles will be fitted with a self-venting cooling system this can be recognised by the two small vent hoses which enter the top of the expansion tank. If the system is not self-venting, open the bleed screw on the thermostat elbow during filling and close it when coolant runs out at the bleed screw **(see illustration)**.
9 When the system appears full, refit the expansion tank cap. Run the engine up to operating temperature, keeping a look-out for coolant leaks, then stop it and allow it to cool. Recheck the coolant level and top-up if necessary.
10 Recheck the tightness of all hose clips

when the engine has cooled, and again after a few hundred miles.

3 Timing belt -
removal and refitting

Caution: A timing belt which is damaged, oil-soaked or fuel soaked must be renewed or it will fail, resulting in serious engine damage.

Removal

1 Remove the alternator drivebelt (Section 1).
2 Remove the timing belt covers. The large cover is secured by four screws - note the fuel pipe clip under one of them. The injection pump sprocket cover is secured by three screws **(see illustration)**.
3 Remove the crankshaft pulley - it is secured to the sprocket by four Allen screws.
4 Disconnect the battery earth lead.
5 Remove the clutch/flywheel access cover from the bottom of the gearbox bellhousing **(see illustration)**.
6 Turn the crankshaft in the normal direction of rotation, using a spanner on the sprocket bolt, until the timing mark on the injection pump sprocket aligns with the reference mark on the pump bracket. In this position No 1 piston is at TDC on the firing stroke **(see illustration)**.

8B

3.2 Timing belt cover screw location
A *Large cover - short screws*
B *Large cover - long screw*
C *Pump sprocket cover screws*

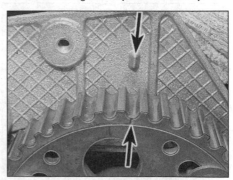

3.5 Removing the clutch/flywheel access cover

3.6 Injection pump sprocket timing mark aligned with mark on pump bracket

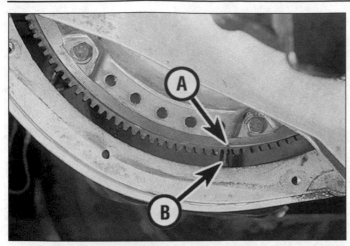

3.7 TDC mark on flywheel (A) and pointer on clutch housing (B)

3.10 Undoing a coolant pump bolt - other two arrowed (engine removed)

7 Check that the TDC mark on the flywheel and the pointer on the clutch housing are aligned **(see illustration)**.

8 If tool KM-537 or equivalent is available, remove the vacuum pump and lock the camshaft in position by fitting the tool. If the tool is not available or cannot be fitted, make alignment marks between the camshaft sprocket and its backplate for use when refitting.

9 Drain the coolant.

10 Slacken the three bolts which secure the coolant pump to the block **(see illustration)**. Using a large open-ended spanner on the flats of the pump, pivot it to release the tension on the belt.

11 Separate the right-hand front engine mounting by undoing the two bolts which are accessible from the top.

12 Mark the running direction of the belt if it is to be re-used. Also take care not to kink the belt, nor get oil, grease etc. on it.

13 Slip the belt off the sprockets and jockey wheel. Remove the belt by feeding it through the engine mounting.

14 If signs of oil contamination are found, trace the source of the oil leak and rectify it, then wash down the engine timing belt area and all related components to remove all traces of oil.

Refitting

15 Commence refitting by threading the belt through the engine mounting. Refit and tighten the engine mounting bolts.

16 Place the belt over the sprockets and the jockey wheel **(see illustration)**. Make sure that No 1 piston is still at TDC, the injection pump sprocket mark is aligned and the camshaft position is still correct.

17 Move the coolant pump so as to put some tension on the timing belt. Nip up the pump securing bolts, but do not tighten them fully yet.

18 Remove the camshaft locking tool, if used, and refit and secure the crankshaft pulley.

19 Belt tension can only be adjusted accurately using tension gauge KM-510-A or equivalent **(see illustration)**. A belt which is too tight will usually hum when running and a belt which is too slack will wear rapidly and may jump teeth.

20 Settle the belt by rotating the crankshaft through half a turn in the normal direction of rotation. Fit the tension gauge to the slack side of the belt (the alternator side) and read the tension. Desired values are given in the *Specifications*.

21 If adjustment is necessary, slacken the coolant pump bolts and pivot the pump to increase or decrease the tension. Nip up the coolant pump bolts.

22 Turn the crankshaft through one full turn then recheck the tension. Keep adjusting the belt tension until a stable value is obtained.

23 Tighten the coolant pump bolts to the specified torque. Refill the cooling system (Section 2).

24 Check the injection pump timing (Section 6).

25 Refit the belt covers, clutch/flywheel cover and other disturbed components.

26 Refit the roadwheel, lower the vehicle and tighten the wheel bolts.

4 Valve timing - checking and adjustment

1 Valve timing on these engines is more complicated than on the petrol equivalent because there are no timing marks as such on the camshaft or sprocket, neither is the sprocket keyed or pegged to the camshaft.

2 Note that the camshaft sprocket bolt should be renewed whenever it has been slackened.

3 If the valve timing has been lost completely be careful when turning the crankshaft or camshaft in case piston/valve contact occurs.

4 Two methods of checking the valve timing are described. For either method, begin by checking the timing belt tension.

5 Bring the engine to TDC, No 1 firing, by turning the crankshaft in the normal direction of rotation, using a spanner on the sprocket bolt, until the timing mark on the injection pump sprocket aligns with the reference mark on the pump bracket **(see illustration 3.6)**. Check that the TDC mark on the flywheel and the pointer on the clutch housing are aligned **(see illustration 3.7)**.

3.16 Timing belt correctly fitted

3.19 Timing belt tension gauge

4.6 Removing the camshaft cover

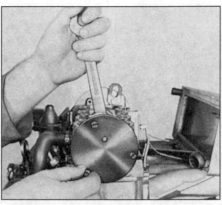

4.8a Fitting the camshaft alignment tool KM-537

4.8b Home-made tool for locking the camshaft in a set position

Remove the air cleaner. Disconnect the breather hose and remove the camshaft cover (see illustration). If necessary, also remove the vacuum pump.

Using tool KM-537 or equivalent

7 The maker's tool KM-537 consists of a plate which bolts onto the camshaft carrier in place of the vacuum pump. When the peg on the plate will enter the hole in the tail of the camshaft, the camshaft is correctly positioned for TDC, No 1 piston firing.

Making the tool

8 It is possible to make a substitute for tool KM-537 (see illustration), but the valve timing must be known to be correct first - thereafter the tool can be used to check the timing. As can be seen, the home-made tool is simply a metal bar with three holes drilled in it (see illustration). The accuracy of the tool depends on the precision with which the holes are drilled, and the snug fit of the screws or bolts in their holes. The crankshaft must be at TDC, No 1 firing, before marking up and constructing the tool.

9 Drill one of the end holes in the metal bar. Insert a short stud or dowel into the camshaft peg hole, marking the end with chalk or paint. The stud should be just long enough to touch the metal bar in its fitted position.

10 Secure the bar, using one of the vacuum pump screws, so that it is just free to move. Swing the bar past the stud or dowel so that an arc is marked on the bar. Remove the bar and drill a hole in the centre of the arc to

accept a bolt or screw which will fit snugly into the camshaft peg hole. Fit this bolt or screw and clamp it with a couple of nuts.

11 Mark around the other vacuum pump screw hole with paint or chalk. Offer the tool to the camshaft and carrier so that the peg hole bolt and first fixing screw are snug and the position of the second fixing screw hole is marked. Remove the tool and drill the second fixing screw hole.

12 Offer up the tool again and make sure that it fits without strain or slack; repeat the construction exercise if necessary.

Using the tool

13 With the crankshaft and injection pump timing marks correctly positioned, offer the tool to the camshaft carrier in place of the vacuum pump. If the tool can be located and secured so that the peg enters the hole in the camshaft, valve timing is correct. In fact, a tolerance of 1.0 mm in either direction at the flywheel TDC mark is allowed.

14 If the tool will not enter, remove it. Hold the camshaft using a spanner on the flats provided and slacken the camshaft sprocket bolt. Break the taper between the sprocket and camshaft if necessary by tapping the sprocket with a wooden or plastic mallet. Turn the camshaft until the alignment tool enters snugly. Remove the old camshaft sprocket bolt and insert a new bolt. Nip the bolt up until the sprocket taper bites, then remove the alignment tool. Hold the camshaft again and

tighten the sprocket bolt to the specified torque.

15 Back off the crankshaft a quarter turn, then regain TDC and check that the alignment tool still fits snugly.

Using a dial test indicator

16 Tool KM-537 cannot be used on later models (mid-1984 on) because the holes into which it screws have been deleted. The home-made tool which screws into the vacuum pump holes is not affected. Instead of tool KM-537, the makers specify the use of a dial test indicator (DTI or clock gauge) and suitable support. The support must allow the DTI to move across the camshaft carrier without changing height relative to the carrier top surface. The DTI foot (the part which will rest on the cam lobe) should have a flat bottom and be 7 to 10 mm in diameter.

17 To check the valve timing, position the timing marks as specified in paragraph 5, then place the DTI and support over the second cam from the sprocket end (No 1 cylinder inlet cam).

18 Zero the DTI on the base circle of the cam (see illustration).

19 Carefully move the DTI, and its support if applicable, exactly 10 mm towards the top of the cam. In this position the DTI should show a lift of 0.55 ± 0.05 mm. If so, the valve timing is correct (see illustration).

20 If adjustment is necessary, proceed as described in paragraph 14, but working towards a correct DTI reading instead of a correct fit of the tool.

All methods

21 Check the injection pump timing, then refit the belt covers, flywheel/clutch cover, cam cover and other disturbed components.

5	Coolant pump - removal and refitting

Removal

1 Drain the cooling system, saving the coolant if it is fit for re-use.

4.18 Dial test indicator zeroed on base circle of second cam . . .

4.19 . . . another reading is taken towards the top of the cam

8B

5.4a Fitting a new O-ring to the coolant pump

5.4b Fitting the coolant pump (engine removed)

2 Remove the timing belt, the timing belt idler pulley and backplate.

3 Remove the three bolts which retain the coolant pump. Lift out the pump - some coolant will be released. It may be necessary to remove the alternator to provide sufficient clearance to remove the pump completely.

Refitting

4 Use a new O-ring when refitting the pump. In order to prevent corrosion and the resultant

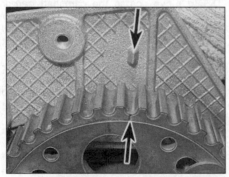

6.4 Injection pump sprocket timing mark aligned with mark on pump bracket

impossibility of moving the coolant pump to tension the timing belt, apply silicone grease to the pump O-ring and cylinder block mating surface. Insert but do not tighten the retaining bolts **(see illustrations)**.

5 Refit the timing belt backplate and the idler pulley.

6 Refit and tension the timing belt.

7 Refit the other disturbed components, then refill the cooling system.

6 Fuel injection pump timing - checking and adjustment

Checking

1 Timing of the injection pump should only be necessary in the following circumstances:

a) *When fitting a new or overhauled pump*
b) *If the timing is suspected of being wrong*
c) *If the timing belt has been re-tensioned or renewed*

A dial test indicator with a long probe and a suitable support will be needed.

2 The procedure as shown here was carrie out during engine rebuilding. With the engin in the vehicle, it will be necessary to remov the timing belt covers, the air cleaner snorke and the clutch/flywheel cover.

3 Check the valve timing (Section 4).

4 Bring the engine to TDC, No 1 firing. Th timing mark on the pump sprocket must b aligned with the pip on the pump bracket **(se illustration)**.

5 Turn the engine against the norma direction of rotation so that the flywheel TD mark is approximately 5.0 cm away from th TDC pointer.

6 Remove the central plug from the rear the injection pump **(see illustration)**.

7 Mount the dial test indicator with its prob entering the central plug hole. Zero th indicator **(see illustration)**.

8 Be prepared for fuel spillage durin subsequent operations. The manufacturer specify the use of a probe which screws int and presumably seals, the plug hole.

9 Bring the engine back to TDC, No 1 firing When the timing marks are aligned, the dial te indicator should show a lift corresponding t the desired timing setting - see *Specifications*

6.6 Removing the plug from the rear of the injection pump

6.7 Dial test indicator mounted with its probe in the plug hole

6.10a Slacken the injection pump sprocket clamping bolts . . .

Adjustment

10 If adjustment is necessary, slacken the three bolts which clamp together the two halves of the pump sprocket **(see illustration)**. Turn the inner part of the sprocket anti-clockwise (against the normal direction of rotation) as far as the slots will allow. The fit between the two parts of the sprocket is tight and a rod or soft metal drift

6.10b . . . and use a rod and mallet to move the inner part of the sprocket

may be needed to encourage the inner part to move **(see illustration)**.

11 With the sprocket positioned as just described and the engine still at TDC, No 1 firing, the dial test indicator should again read zero. Reset it if necessary.

12 Turn the inner part of the sprocket clockwise

until the dial test indicator shows the desired lift, then tighten the sprocket clamp bolts.

13 Repeat the checking procedure from paragraph 5.

14 When the injection timing is correct, remove the test gear and refit the plug to the rear of the pump.

15 Refit the timing belt covers and other disturbed components.

7 Vacuum pump -
removal and refitting

Removal

1 Disconnect the servo vacuum pipe from the pump. Do this by counterholding the large union nut and unscrewing the small one **(see illustration)**.

2 Remove the two pump securing screws and withdraw the pump from the camshaft housing **(see illustrations)**. Be prepared for some oil spillage.

3 Recover the small central oil pipe and the driving dog.

4 Discard the two O-rings fitted to the central oil pipe and also the pump body to camshaft housing seal **(see illustration)**.

Refitting

5 Fit new sealing rings to the pump assembly.

6 Refit the central oil pipe and the driving dog to the pump **(see illustration)**.

7 Offer the pump to the camshaft housing, making sure that the teeth of the driving dog engage with the slot in the camshaft end. Fit the pump securing screws and tighten them to the specified torque.

8 Reconnect and secure the vacuum pipe connection(s).

7.1 Disconnecting the servo vacuum pipe from the vacuum pump

7.2a Remove the two pump securing screws . . .

7.2b . . . and withdraw the vacuum pump from the camshaft housing

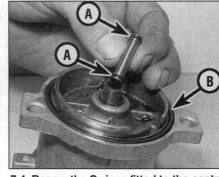

7.4 Renew the O-rings fitted to the central oil pipe (A) and the pump body to camshaft housing seal (B)

7.6 Refitting the central oil pipe with driving dog to the vacuum pump

8B

Notes

Chapter 9A
Vauxhall Cavalier &
Opel Vectra petrol 1988 to 1995

Contents

Specifications

Timing belt renewal interval . . . . Every 36 000 miles (60 000 km) or 4 years - whichever comes first

Manufacturer's engine codes

14 NV	1.4 litre (1389 cc) SOHC
16 SV	1.6 litre (1598 cc) SOHC
C16 NZ	1.6 litre (1598 cc) SOHC, catalyst
C16 NZ2	1.6 litre (1598 cc) SOHC, catalyst
X16 SZ	1.6 litre (1598 cc) SOHC, Ecotec engine
18 SV	1.8 litre (1796 cc) SOHC
C18 NZ	1.8 litre (1796 cc) SOHC, catalyst
20 NE	2.0 litre (1998 cc) SOHC
20 SEH	2.0 litre (1998 cc) SOHC, early SRi
20 XEJ	2.0 litre (1998 cc) DOHC
C20 NE	2.0 litre (1998 cc) SOHC, catalyst
C20 XE	2.0 litre (1998 cc) DOHC, catalyst
X20 XEV	2.0 litre (1998 cc) DOHC, catalyst, Ecotec engine

Timing belt (engines without automatic tension roller)

Tension, using Vauxhall gauge KM-510-A:

   1.4 and 1.6 litre:

New belt, cold	5.5
New belt, warm	8.0
Used belt, cold	4.0
Used belt, warm	7.0

   1.8 and 2.0 litre:

New belt, cold	4.5
New belt, warm	7.5
Used belt, cold	2.5
Used belt, warm	7.0

Torque wrench settings

	Nm	lbf ft
Alternator and inlet manifold to brackets:		
1.4 and 1.6 litre (except C16 NZ2)	20	15
C16 NZ2, 1.8 and 2.0 litre	18	13
Alternator to bracket:		
M8	30	22
M10	40	30
Alternator to shackle	25	18
Auxiliary drivebelt tensioner:		
To cylinder block	20	15
To support:		
1.4 and 1.6 litre (except C16 NZ2)	20	15
C16 NZ2, 1.8 and 2.0 litre	18	13
Camshaft housing cover	8	6
Camshaft sprocket:		
SOHC models	45	33
DOHC models:*		
Stage 1	50	37
Stage 2	Angle tighten by 60°	
Stage 3	Angle tighten by 15°	
Coolant pump to cylinder block:		
1.4 and 1.6 litre (except C 16 NZ2) (M6)	8	6
C16 NZ2, 1.8 and 2.0 litre (M8)	25	18
Crankshaft pulley:		
1.4 and 1.6 litre	See Crankshaft sprocket	
1.8 and 2.0 litre	20	15
Crankshaft sprocket:*		
1.4 and 1.6 litre (except C16 NZ2):		
Stage 1	55	41
Stage 2	Angle tighten by 45°	
Stage 3	Angle tighten by 15°	
C16 NZ2, 1.8 and 2.0 litre SOHC:		
Stage 1	130	96
Stage 2	Angle tighten by between 40° to 50°	
2.0 litre DOHC:		
Stage 1	250	185
Stage 2	Angle tighten by between 40° and 50°	
Engine bracket to cylinder block	60	44
Engine bracket to transmission	60	44
Engine mounting bracket to engine bracket	60	44
Engine mounting to engine mounting bracket	65	48
Engine mounting to front axle housing	40	30
Engine mounting to power steering pump support	60	44
Engine mounting to side member	65	48
Engine right mounting to subframe	65	48
Fluid pipe to power steering gear unions	42	31
Fluid pipe to power steering pump union	28	21
Fluid pipe to pipe and pipe to hose unions	28	21
Power steering pump mounting:		
1.6 litre models (up to 1992)	30	22
1.8 and 2.0 litre models (up to 1992):		
Bolts A and C (refer to text)	25	18
Bolts B (refer to text)	40	30
SOHC models (from 1993)	20	15
DOHC models (from 1993):		
Bolts 1 and 2 (refer to text)	25	18
Bolts 3 and 4 (refer to text)	18	13
Power steering pump pulley (1.6 litre models)	25	18
Roadwheel	110	81
Spark plugs	25	18
Timing belt covers:		
SOHC:		
Front cover to rear cover	4	3
To oil pump/camshaft housing:		
1.4 and 1.6 litre (except C16 NZ2)	12	9
C16 NZ2, 1.8 and 2.0 litre	6	4
DOHC	8	6

Torque wrench settings (continued)

	Nm	lbf ft
Timing belt tensioner pulley (DOHC):		
Bracket to block	25	18
To cylinder block:		
Engines up to 1993:*		
Stage 1	25	18
Stage 2	Angle tighten by 45°	
Stage 3	Angle tighten by 15°	
1993-on engines	25	18
To bracket	25	18
Timing belt tensioner to oil pump:		
1.4 and 1.6 litre (except C16 NZ2)	55	41

Use new bolts (or nuts)

1   Auxiliary drivebelt - removal, refitting and adjusting

Alternator

V-belt type (not-ribbed)

1 Disconnect the air inlet trunking from the air cleaner, and the air box or throttle body, as applicable, and remove it for improved access.

2 On some models with power steering, the alternator drivebelt also drives the power steering pump.

3 If necessary, first remove the power steering pump drivebelt, as described below.

4 Loosen the two alternator mounting nuts and bolts sufficiently to allow the alternator to be pivoted in towards the engine.

5 Slide the belt from the pulleys.

6 Fit the belt around the pulleys. Take up the slack in the belt by swinging the alternator away from the engine and lightly tightening the mounting nuts and bolts.

7 Although special tools are available for measuring the belt tension, a good approximation can be achieved if the belt is tensioned so that there is approximately 13.0 mm (0.5 in) of free movement under firm thumb pressure at the mid-point of the longest run between pulleys.

8 With the mounting bolts just holding the unit, lever the alternator away from the engine using a wooden lever at the mounting bracket end until the correct tension is achieved. Then tighten the mounting nuts and bolts. On no account lever at the free end of the alternator, as serious internal damage could be caused.

9 Where applicable, refit and tension the power steering pump drivebelt, as described below.

10 Refit the air inlet trunking.

Ribbed V-belt type

11 Later models equipped with power steering are fitted with a ribbed V-belt type drivebelt in conjunction with an automatic tensioning roller. Once the belt is installed, no further adjustment is necessary as the correct tension is maintained by the automatic tensioning roller.

12 For improved access, remove the air cleaner assembly and air inlet trunking.

13 If the original drivebelt is to be refitted, mark the rotational direction on the belt with chalk.

14 Using a spanner or socket on the automatic tensioning roller hexagon, turn the tensioning roller clockwise (as viewed from the right-hand side of the car) and hold it in this position. With the drivebelt tension released, slip the drivebelt off the pulleys, then allow the tensioner to return to its original position.

15 Support the engine under the sump with a jack and interposed block of wood.

16 From under the car, unbolt the right-hand engine mounting block from the body (see Section 9).

17 Lower the engine support jack just sufficiently to allow the drivebelt to be withdrawn from between the mounting block and the body.

18 Slip the drivebelt between the mounting block and body then raise the engine, by means of the jack, to its original position.

19 Clean the threads of the mounting block retaining bolts, apply locking fluid, and refit the bolts. Tighten the bolts to the specified torque.

20 Rotate the automatic tensioner roller anti-clockwise and route the drivebelt around the pulleys as shown (**see illustration**). With the belt correctly positioned, release the tensioner that will automatically apply the correct tension to the belt.

21 On completion, refit the air cleaner assembly and the air inlet trunking.

Power steering pump

22 Slacken the adjuster and mounting bolts.

23 Slacken the adjuster nuts, and adjust the length of the threaded rod to remove or tension the belt as desired (**see illustration**).

9A

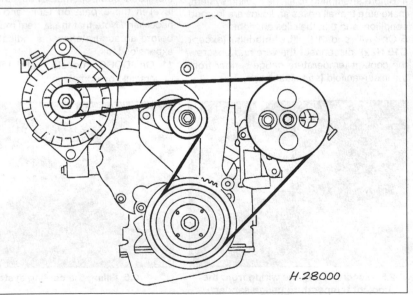

1.20 Correct routing of the ribbed V-belt

1.23 Adjusting the length of the power steering pump threaded rod

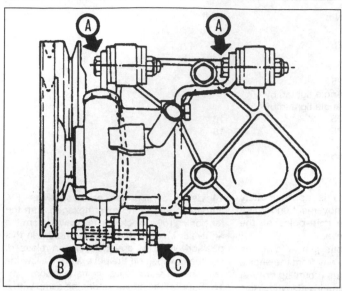

1.25a Mounting and adjuster bolts (arrowed) must be loosened to adjust drivebelt tension - 1.8 and 2.0 litre models, up to 1992

For A, B and C see Torque wrench settings in Specifications

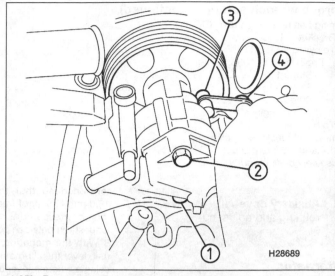

1.25b Power steering pump mounting (tightening torques shown in Specifications) - DOHC models

| 1 Pump to support | 3 Shackle to pump |
| 2 Pump to support | 4 Shackle to engine |

24 The correct belt tension can be approximated by adjusting the length of the threaded rod. This should give a belt deflection of approximately 10.0 mm (0.4 in) under moderate thumb pressure at the midpoint of the belt run between the pulleys. If in doubt, err on the slack side, as an excessively tight belt may cause pump damage.

25 Tighten the adjuster nuts, and tighten the adjuster and mounting bolts to the specified torque **(see illustrations)**.

2 Cooling system - draining and refilling

Draining

1 With the vehicle parked on level ground, remove the expansion tank filler cap **(see illustration)**. If the engine is warm, cover the filler cap with a thick cloth, and unscrew the cap slowly, to gradually relieve the system pressure. Take care to avoid scalding by steam or coolant escaping from the pressurised system.

2 On DOHC models, remove the engine undershield, with reference to Section 13.

3 Position a container beneath the radiator bottom hose connection, then slacken the hose clip and ease the hose from the radiator stub. If the hose joint has not been disturbed for some time, it will be necessary to manipulate the hose to break the joint. Allow the coolant to drain into the container.

Refilling

4 Before attempting to fill the cooling system, make sure that all hoses and clips are in good condition, and that the clips are tight.

5 On 1.4 and 1.6 litre models (except C16 NZ2), disconnect the wire and unscrew the coolant temperature gauge sender from the inlet manifold **(see illustration)**.

6 Remove the expansion tank cap, and fill the system by slowly pouring the coolant into the expansion tank to prevent air locks from forming **(see illustration)**.

7 On 1.4 and 1.6 litre models (except C16 NZ2), refit the coolant temperature gauge sender when coolant free of air bubbles emerges from the orifice in the inlet manifold.

8 Top-up the coolant level to the COLD (or KALT) mark on the expansion tank, then refit the expansion tank cap.

9 Start the engine and run it until it reaches normal operating temperature, then stop the engine and allow it to cool.

10 Check for leaks, particularly around disturbed components. Check the coolant level in the expansion tank, and top-up if necessary. Note that the system must be cold before an accurate level is indicated in the expansion tank.

11 On DOHC models, refit the engine undershield on completion.

2.1 Coolant expansion tank

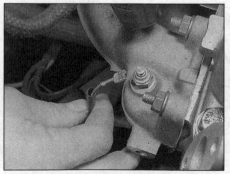

2.5 Disconnecting the wiring from the coolant temperature gauge sender - 1.6 litre model

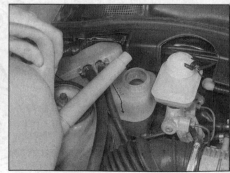

2.6 Filling the cooling system

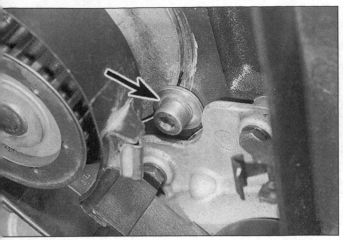

3.4 Coolant pump securing bolt (arrowed) - 2.0 litre SOHC model

3.5a Withdraw the coolant pump . . .

3 Coolant pump - removal and refitting

SOHC models

Removal

1 If the engine is in the vehicle, drain the cooling system, as described in Section 2.
2 On 1.4 and 1.6 litre models (except C16 NZ2), remove the rear timing belt cover. On C16 NZ2, 1.8 and 2.0 litre models, remove the timing belt.
3 Remove the timing belt tension roller from the oil pump, where applicable.
4 Unscrew and remove the coolant pump securing bolts (see illustration).
5 Withdraw the coolant pump from the cylinder block, and recover the O-ring (see illustrations). It may be necessary to tap the pump lightly with a plastic-faced hammer to free it from the cylinder block.
6 If desired, the rear timing belt cover can be

removed from the pump by rotating the cover to release it from the flange on the pump.
7 No overhaul of the coolant pump is possible, and if faulty, the unit must be renewed.

Refitting

8 Refitting is a reversal of removal, bearing in mind the following points.
9 Use a new O-ring when refitting the pump. Before refitting the pump, smear the pump mounting face in the cylinder block and the O-ring with a silicone grease or petroleum jelly.
10 Do not fully tighten the pump securing bolts until the timing belt has been fitted and tensioned.
11 Refit and tension the timing belt.
12 If the engine is in the vehicle, refill the cooling system, as described in Section 2.

DOHC models

Removal

13 Remove the engine undershield (Section 13).
14 If the engine is in the vehicle, drain the cooling system, as described in Section 2.

15 Remove the timing belt, camshaft sprockets, crankshaft sprocket, timing belt tensioner and idler rollers, and the timing belt rear cover.
16 Proceed as described in paragraphs 4 and 5.
17 No overhaul of the coolant pump is possible, and if faulty, the unit must be renewed.

Refitting

18 Refitting is a reversal of removal, bearing in mind the following points.
19 Always use a new O-ring. Before fitting the pump, smear the pump mating face in the cylinder block and the O-ring with a silicone grease or petroleum jelly.
20 Refit the pump, and ensure that the lugs on the pump and the cylinder block are aligned before tightening the pump securing bolts (see illustration).
21 Refit the remaining components, and tension the timing belt.
22 If the engine is in the vehicle, refill the cooling system, as described in Section 2. Replace the undershield.

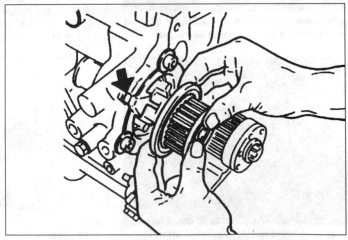

3.5b . . . and recover the O-ring - 2.0 litre SOHC model

3.20 Lugs (arrowed) on coolant pump and cylinder block must be aligned - DOHC models

4.5a Remove the main outer timing belt cover . . .

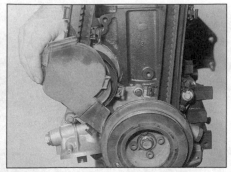

4.5b . . . and the smaller cover from the coolant pump - 2.0 litre engine

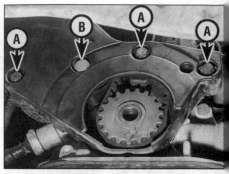

4.5c Timing belt lower (small) outer cover screws (A), tensioner screw (B)

4 Timing belt and sprockets (SOHC models) - removal, refitting and adjustment

Note: *A two-legged puller may be required to remove the crankshaft sprocket.*

Removal

Note: *Some of the later engines are fitted with spring-loaded automatic timing belt tensioners (see Sections 5 and 6).*

1 Disconnect the battery negative lead.
2 On models with power steering, remove the pump drivebelt, see Section 1.
3 Remove the alternator drivebelt, as described in Section 1.

4.7a Camshaft sprocket TDC mark aligned with notch in rear timing belt cover . . .

4 On C 16 NZ2, 1.8 and 2.0 litre models, disconnect the wiring from the coolant temperature gauge sender.
5 Release the securing clips (or hexagon-headed screws, if fitted), and remove the main outer timing belt cover, then unclip the smaller outer timing belt cover from the coolant pump. Where applicable, three screws retain the lower (small) outer cover to the rear cover, the fourth secures the tensioner **(see illustrations)**.
6 On 1.6 litre models with power steering, remove the power steering pump, as described in Section 11.
7 Turn the crankshaft using a socket or spanner on the crankshaft sprocket bolt, until the timing mark on the camshaft sprocket is aligned with the notch in the rear timing belt cover, and the notch in the crankshaft pulley is aligned with the pointer on the rear timing belt cover **(see illustrations)**. Note that on 1.4 litre engine there are two notches in the crankshaft pulley, representing 5° and 10° BTDC; the 10° BTDC notch should be aligned with the pointer **(see illustration)**.
8 Loosen the three coolant pump securing bolts **(see illustration)**, and turn the pump to relieve the tension in the timing belt, then slide the belt from the camshaft sprocket.
9 The crankshaft pulley must now be removed. On 1.4 and 1.6 litre engines (except C 16 NZ2), the pulley is secured by a single bolt, which also secures the crankshaft sprocket. On manual transmission models the

crankshaft can be prevented from turning by having an assistant engage first gear and depress the brake pedal.
10 With the crankshaft pulley removed, the timing belt can be withdrawn.
11 If desired, the sprockets and the rear timing belt cover can be removed as follows, otherwise go on to paragraph 23.
12 To remove the camshaft sprocket, first disconnect the breather hose(s) from the camshaft cover, then unscrew the securing bolts, noting the locations of the HT lead brackets and any other wiring brackets, and remove the camshaft cover.
13 Recover the gasket. Prevent the camshaft from turning by holding it with a spanner on the flats provided between Nos 3 and 4 camshaft lobes, and unscrew the camshaft sprocket bolt.
14 Withdraw the sprocket from the end of the camshaft.
15 To remove the crankshaft sprocket on 1.4 and 1.6 litre engines (except C 16 NZ2), if necessary, remove the lower securing bolts from the main rear timing belt cover and use two large screwdrivers behind the cover to lever off the sprocket. Remove the Woodruff key if it is loose.
16 To remove the crankshaft sprocket on C 16 NZ2, 1.8 and 2.0 litre engines, it will be necessary to prevent the crankshaft from turning, as described in paragraph 9. Take care when unscrewing the sprocket bolt, as it

4.7b . . . and notch in crankshaft pulley aligned with pointer on rear timing belt cover - 2.0 litre engine

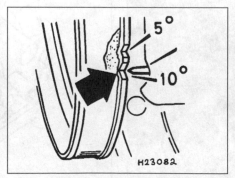

4.7c Crankshaft pulley 10° BTDC notch aligned with pointer on rear timing belt cover - 1.4 litre engine

4.8 Loosening a coolant pump securing bolt - 2.0 litre engine

4.17a Loosening the main rear timing belt cover lower securing bolt - 2.0 litre engine

4.17b Main rear timing belt cover lower securing bolts (arrowed) - 1.6 SV engine

4.18 Unscrewing the coolant pump rear belt cover securing bolt - 2.0 litre engine

is very tight. If necessary, use a two-legged puller to remove the sprocket. Recover the Woodruff key and the thrustwasher from the end of the crankshaft.

17 To remove the main rear timing belt cover on C 16 NZ2, 1.8 and 2.0 litre models, disconnect the TDC sensor wiring plug and unclip the wiring from the belt cover. Unscrew the two upper securing bolts and the lower securing bolt(s) (one in the case of C 16 NZ2, 1.8 and 2.0 litre engines, two on other SOHC engines). Withdraw the cover, manipulating it from the smaller rear belt cover on the coolant pump **(see illustrations)**.

18 If desired, the smaller rear belt cover can be removed from the coolant pump, after unscrewing the securing bolt **(see illustration)**, by rotating it to disengage it from the retaining flange on the pump.

Refitting

19 Refit the rear timing belt cover(s) using a reversal of the removal procedure, and ensuring that the main cover engages correctly with the smaller cover on the coolant pump.

20 On C 16 NZ2, 1.8 and 2.0 litre engines, refit the thrustwasher and the Woodruff key to the end of the crankshaft. Then refit the crankshaft sprocket, and tighten the securing bolt to the specified torque in the two stages given in the Specifications. Ensure that the washer is in place under the bolt head, and prevent the crankshaft from turning as during removal **(see illustrations)**.

21 On 1.4 and 1.6 litre engines (except C 16 NZ2), refit the Woodruff key to the end of the crankshaft where applicable. Then refit the

crankshaft sprocket with the flange and locating lug for the crankshaft pulley outermost **(see illustration)**.

22 Refit the camshaft sprocket, ensuring that

4.20a Refit the thrustwasher . . .

4.20b . . . the Woodruff key . . .

4.20c . . . the crankshaft sprocket . . .

4.20d . . . and the washer and bolt

4.20e Tighten the bolt to the specified torque . . .

4.20f . . . then through the specified angle - 2.0 litre engine

4.21 Crankshaft sprocket fits with flange and pulley locating lug outermost - 1.6 litre engine

9A

4.22a Refit the camshaft sprocket . . .

4.22b . . . and tighten the securing bolt to the specified torque - 2.0 litre engine

4.22c Fit the camshaft cover gasket . . .

4.22d . . . fit the cover and tighten the bolts. Note position of HT lead brackets

the locating pin on the end of the camshaft engages with the hole in the sprocket, and tighten the securing bolt to the specified torque. Prevent the camshaft from turning as during removal. Check the condition of the camshaft cover gasket and renew if necessary, then refit the camshaft cover, ensuring that the HT lead brackets and any other wiring bracket are correctly located, and reconnect the breather hose(s) **(see illustrations)**.

23 Temporarily refit the crankshaft pulley and ensure that the crankshaft pulley and camshaft sprocket timing marks are still aligned as described in paragraph 7, then refit the timing belt around the sprockets **(see illustration)**, starting at the crankshaft sprocket.

24 Refit the crankshaft pulley, and tighten the securing bolt(s) to the specified torque **(see illustrations)**. If necessary, prevent the crankshaft from turning as during removal.

25 Adjust the timing belt tension, as described below.

4.23 Refitting the timing belt - 2.0 litre engine

4.24a Refitting the crankshaft pulley - 1.6 litre engine

4.24b Tightening a crankshaft pulley securing bolt - 2.0 litre engine

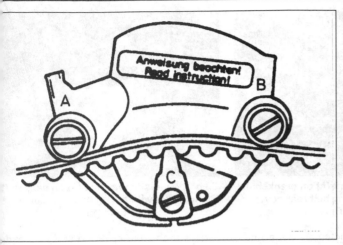

4.33 Tension blade KM-510-A correctly positioned on timing belt. Belt must pass through points A, B and C - SOHC engines

4.34 Note the reading on the scale of the tension gauge - 1.6 litre engine

26 On 1.6 litre models with power steering, refit the power steering pump, as described in Section 11.

27 Refit the outer timing belt covers, and on C 16 NZ2, 1.8 and 2.0 litre models, reconnect the coolant temperature gauge sender wiring.

28 Refit the alternator drivebelt and adjust the drivebelt tension, as described in Section 1.

29 On C 16 NZ2, 1.8 and 2.0 litre models with power steering, refit the power steering pump drivebelt and adjust the drivebelt tension, as described in Section 1.

30 Reconnect the battery negative lead.

Adjustment

Note: The manufacturers specify the use of a special gauge Vauxhall tool No KM-510-A for checking the timing belt tension.

Note: Later models have spring-loaded tensioners; refer to Sections 5 and 6 for timing belt adjustment.

31 The tension of a used timing belt should be checked with the engine at normal operating temperature. The tension of a new timing belt should be checked with the engine cold.

32 Turn the crankshaft through at least a quarter of a turn clockwise using a socket or spanner on the crankshaft sprocket bolt.

33 Place the locked gauge at the centre of the belt run between the coolant pump and the camshaft sprocket. The gauge should locate on the timing belt **(see illustration)**.

34 Slowly release the operating lever on the gauge, then lightly tap the gauge two or three times, and note the reading on the scale **(see illustration)**.

35 If the reading is not as specified, loosen the three coolant pump securing bolts, and rotate the pump in the required direction to achieve the desired reading on the gauge.

36 Rotate the pump clockwise to increase the belt tension, or anti-clockwise to decrease the tension.

37 Lightly tighten the coolant pump securing bolts.

38 Remove the tensioning gauge, and turn the crankshaft through one full turn clockwise.

39 Re-check the belt tension as described in paragraphs 33 and 34.

40 If the tension is not as specified, repeat paragraphs 35 to 39 inclusive until the desired, consistent, reading is obtained.

41 On completion of adjustment, remove the checking gauge, tighten the coolant pump bolts to the specified torque, and refit the outer timing belt covers.

5 Timing belt and tensioner (SOHC engines) - models from June 1990

Note: This tensioner was fitted to 14 NV, 16 SV and C16 NZ engines from June 1990. These can be identified by the squared-off top surfaces of the timing belt cover.

Removal

1 Removal of the timing belt is basically as described in Section 4, except the

5.2 Using a close-fitting drift to lock the tensioner. Note baseplate lug engaged in oil pump housing (arrowed)

tensioner has to be locked in its slackest position.

2 To lock the tensioner in its slackest position for removal and refitting, move the tensioner indicator arm clockwise until the holes align in the baseplate and the arm. Then insert a close-fitting pin, such as a drift, to retain them **(see illustration)**. The tensioner can then be unbolted, or the belt can be removed.

3 Check that the tensioner roller rotates smoothly and easily, with no noises or signs of free play, roughness or notchy movement. Check also that there is no sign of physical wear or damage. If the tensioner is faulty in any way, or if there is any reason to doubt the continued efficiency of its spring, the complete assembly must be renewed.

Refitting

4 Fit the timing belt, as described in Section 4, and ensure that the tensioner baseplate lug engages with the hole in the oil pump housing, then tighten the tensioner bolt securely and remove the locking pin; the tensioner should be quite free to move.

5 Set the belt tension as described below.

Adjustment

6 Whenever the timing belt is disturbed, whether during belt renewal or any other engine overhaul work, its tension must be set on assembly - note that this procedure must **only** be carried out on a **cold** engine.

7 It is assumed that the belt has been removed and refitted, i.e. that the crankshaft pulley and timing belt outer covers are removed, that the tensioner is unlocked (see above) and that No 1 cylinder is in its firing position (just before TDC on the compression stroke). Temporarily refit the crankshaft pulley bolt and remove the spark plugs so that the crankshaft can be rotated easily.

8 Note also that turning the coolant pump with the precision required is a great deal

9A

5.8 Using a special spanner to adjust the timing belt by moving the coolant pump

5.9a Align punch mark (A) on crankshaft sprocket with timing belt rear cover notch (B) . . .

5.9b . . . and stamped line (A) on camshaft sprocket with timing belt rear cover notch (B)

easier if a special spanner is used **(see illustration)**.

9 With the belt refitted and correctly routed, ensure that the punch mark on the crankshaft sprocket and the stamped line on the camshaft sprocket are aligned with their respective timing belt rear cover notches **(see illustrations)**.

10 Tighten the belt by slackening the coolant pump's three securing bolts, and turning it clockwise until the holes align in the tensioner indicator arm and baseplate (the tensioner indicator arm will then have moved fully clockwise to its stop). Lightly tighten the pump securing bolts, just sufficiently to prevent the pump from moving.

11 Using a spanner applied to the crankshaft pulley bolt, turn the crankshaft smoothly (without jerking it or the belt may jump a tooth), through 2 complete revolutions (720°) clockwise, until the camshaft and crankshaft sprocket timing marks are once again aligned as described in paragraph 9. The position of the coolant pump must not alter.

12 Slacken the timing belt by turning the coolant pump anti-clockwise until the tensioner's indicator pointer is in the centre of its baseplate notch; the timing belt tension is then correct **(see illustration)**. Tighten the coolant pump bolts to the specified torque wrench setting, then turn the crankshaft through two further turns clockwise and recheck the setting.

13 If the pointer and notch are not aligned, the operation must be repeated from paragraph 7. On completion, refit all components removed, with reference to Section 4.

6 Timing belt and tensioner (SOHC engines) - models from 1993

Note: *This tensioner was fitted to C16 NZ2, 18 SV, C18 NZ, 20 NE and C20 NE engines from model year 1993.*

Removal

1 Removal of the timing belt is basically as described in Section 4, except for the following details.

2 The timing belt main outer cover may be secured either by clips or by hexagon-headed

screws to the rear cover; in some cases, a combination of clips and screws may be used.

3 To release the belt tension before removal, unscrew the timing belt tensioner securing bolt slightly then, with a tool inserted in the slot on the tensioner arm, turn the tensioner arm until the timing belt is slack **(see illustration)**. If necessary, remove completely and examine the tensioner as described in Section 5, paragraph 3.

Refitting

4 Refit the tensioner into position and tighten the securing bolt slightly.

5 Ensure that the coolant pump is correctly positioned by checking that the lug on the coolant pump flange is aligned with the corresponding lug on the cylinder block. If this is not the case, slacken the coolant pump mounting bolts slightly and move the pump

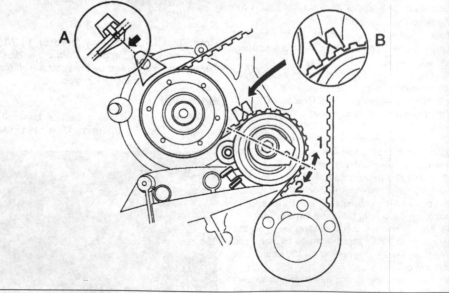

6.3 Timing belt automatic tensioner details (alternative type)

A   *Alignment lugs on coolant pump and cylinder block*
B   *Tensioner pointer aligned with notch in tensioner bracket*

1   *Move the tensioner arm anti-clockwise to release the belt tension*
2   *Move the tensioner arm clockwise to tension the belt*

5.12 Timing belt tension is correct when the tensioner indicator pointer aligns with the centre of the baseplate notch

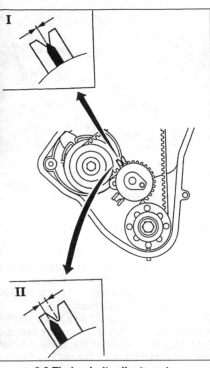

7.6a Camshaft sprocket TDC mark aligned with notch in camshaft cover

7.6b ... and notch in crankshaft pulley aligned with pointer on rear timing belt cover (circled)

6.8 Timing belt adjustment

Alignment for new belts
Alignment for run-in belts (gap is approximately 4 mm to the left of centre)

accordingly Tighten the bolts to the specified torque on completion.

Refit the timing belt then tension it as follows.

Adjustment

Slacken the automatic tensioner securing bolt and move the tensioner arm anti-clockwise, until the tensioner pointer lies at its stop. Tighten the tensioner securing bolt to hold the tensioner in this position.

Turn the crankshaft through two complete revolutions in the normal direction of rotation, and check that, with the crankshaft pulley TDC mark aligned with the pointer on the rear timing belt cover, the TDC mark on the camshaft sprocket is still aligned with the notch in the timing belt rear cover. Slacken the automatic tensioner securing bolt again

and move the tensioner arm clockwise, until the tensioner pointer is aligned with the notch in the tensioner bracket. In the first few hours of operation a new belt will be subjected to settling-in. If you are refitting a used belt (one that has been run-in), align the pointer to approximately 4 mm to the left of the notch **(see illustration)**.

9 Tighten the tensioner securing bolt securely. Turn the crankshaft through one complete revolution, in the normal direction of rotation, and check that the crankshaft and camshaft timing marks still align. Then refit the remainder of the components as described in Section 4.

7 Timing belt, sprockets and tensioner (DOHC engines) - removal, refitting and adjustment

Note: *A two-legged puller may be required to remove the crankshaft sprocket.*

Removal

Note: *Some of the later engines are fitted with a spring-loaded automatic timing belt tensioner (see Sections 8).*

1 Disconnect the battery negative lead.
2 Disconnect the air cleaner trunking from the airflow meter, then remove the cover and the air cleaner element from the air cleaner. If desired, for improved access, the complete air cleaner assembly can be removed, as described in Section 10.

3 Remove the power steering pump drivebelt, as described in Section 1.
4 Remove the alternator drivebelt, as described in Section 1.
5 Remove the three securing screws, and withdraw the outer timing belt cover. Recover the rubber grommets from the screw holes in the cover if they are loose.
6 Turn the crankshaft using a Torx socket on the crankshaft sprocket bolt, until the timing marks on the camshaft sprockets are aligned with the notches in the camshaft cover. The notch in the crankshaft pulley should also be aligned with the pointer on the rear timing belt cover **(see illustrations)**.
7 Extract the six securing bolts using a splined bit, and withdraw the crankshaft pulley **(see illustration)**. If necessary, counterhold the crankshaft using a socket on the crankshaft sprocket bolt. The crankshaft can be prevented from turning by having an assistant engage first gear and depress the brake pedal. Before removing the pulley, check that the timing marks are still aligned.
8 Loosen the securing bolt and release the timing belt tensioner pulley, then slide the belt from the sprockets and pulleys **(see illustration)**.
9 If desired, the sprockets, tensioner and idler pulleys, and the rear timing belt cover can be removed as follows, otherwise go on to paragraph 27.
10 To remove the camshaft sprockets, first disconnect the breather hoses from the camshaft cover **(see illustration)**.

9A

7.7 Crankshaft pulley and securing bolts viewed through right-hand wheel arch

7.8 Timing belt tensioner pulley securing bolt (arrowed)

7.10 Disconnecting a breather hose from the rear of the camshaft cover

7.11 Removing the spark plug cover

7.12 Unscrewing a camshaft cover securing bolt

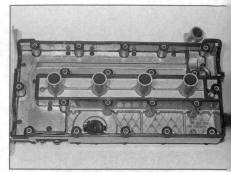

7.13 Camshaft cover removed to show one-piece rubber gasket

7.14 Spanner positioned to counterhold exhaust camshaft

11 Extract the two securing bolts and remove the spark plug cover **(see illustration)**, then disconnect the HT leads from the spark plugs, and unclip them from the end of the camshaft cover. If necessary, mark the HT leads for position, to avoid confusion when refitting.

12 Unscrew the twenty securing bolts and withdraw the camshaft cover **(see illustration)**.

13 Recover the one-piece rubber gasket **(see illustration)**.

14 Prevent the relevant camshaft from turning by holding it with a spanner on the

7.17 Timing belt pulley components

1 *Tensioner pulley securing bolt*
2 *Tensioner pulley mounting plate*
3 *Idler pulley securing bolt*

flats provided in front of No 1 cam lobe, and unscrew the camshaft sprocket bolt **(see illustration)**.

15 Withdraw the sprocket from the end of the camshaft, then repeat the procedure for the remaining camshaft sprocket.

16 Remove the crankshaft sprocket. It will be necessary to prevent the crankshaft from turning by bolting a metal bar to the sprocket using two of the crankshaft pulley bolts, or by

engaging first gear and applying the brakes. A Torx socket will be required to unscrew the sprocket bolt - take care, as the bolt is very tight. If necessary, use a two-legged puller to remove the sprocket. Recover the thrustwashers from the end of the crankshaft and from under the bolt head.

17 To remove the belt tensioner pulley, simply unscrew the securing bolt from the centre of the pulley, then withdraw the pulley complete with mounting plate **(see illustration)**. Recover the spacer sleeve from the pulley bolt.

18 To remove the belt idler pulley, unscrew the securing bolt from the centre of the pulley, then withdraw the pulley and recover the spacer sleeve from the pulley bolt.

19 The rear timing belt cover can now be removed after unscrewing the upper and middle studs for the timing belt outer cover screws. Note that the upper stud simply unscrews from the cylinder head, but the middle stud is secured by a bolt. Unscrew the two upper and single lower right-hand rear belt cover securing bolts, and withdraw the rear belt cover **(see illustrations)**.

Refitting

20 Refit the rear timing belt cover using a reversal of the removal procedure.

7.19a Timing belt outer cover screw upper stud (1) and rear belt cover upper securing bolts (2)

7.19b Rear timing belt cover lower right-hand securing bolt

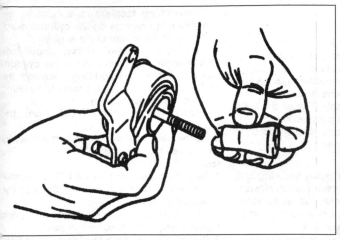

7.21 Belt tensioner pulley and spacer sleeve. Note that smaller diameter of spacer sleeve fits against pulley

7.24 Tightening a camshaft cover securing bolt

21 Refit the belt idler and tensioner pulleys, noting that the spacer sleeves should be fitted with their smaller diameters against the pulleys **(see illustration)**. Do not fully tighten the tensioner pulley bolt at this stage.

22 Refit the thrustwasher to the end of the crankshaft, then refit the crankshaft sprocket. Apply a little grease to the threads of the securing bolt, and tighten it to the specified torque in the two stages given in the Specifications. Ensure that the thrustwasher is in place under the bolt head, and prevent the crankshaft from turning as during removal.

23 Refit the camshaft sprockets. Ensure that the locating pins on the ends of the camshafts engage with the holes in the sprockets and with the sprocket timing marks facing forwards. Then tighten the securing bolts to the specified torque in the three stages given in the Specifications. Prevent the camshafts from turning as during removal.

24 Check the condition of the camshaft cover rubber gasket and renew if necessary, then refit the camshaft cover and tighten the securing bolts **(see illustration)**.

25 Refit the HT leads to the spark plugs (ensuring that they are refitted to their correct cylinders), then clip the leads to the end of the camshaft cover. Refit the spark plug cover and tighten the securing bolts.

26 Reconnect the breather hose to the camshaft cover.

27 Temporarily refit the crankshaft pulley, and ensure that the crankshaft pulley and camshaft sprocket timing marks are still aligned as described in paragraph 6. Then fit a new timing belt around the sprockets and pulleys, starting at the crankshaft sprocket.

28 Refit the crankshaft pulley, and tighten the securing bolts to the specified torque. If necessary, prevent the crankshaft from turning as during removal.

29 Adjust the timing belt tension, as described from paragraph 35 onwards.

30 Refit the outer timing belt cover, ensuring that the rubber grommets are in place in the screw holes, and tighten the securing screws.

31 Refit the alternator drivebelt and adjust the drivebelt tension, as described in Section 1.

32 Refit the power steering pump drivebelt and adjust the drivebelt tension, as described in Section 1.

33 Refit the air cleaner components as applicable, referring to Section 10, if necessary.

34 Reconnect the battery negative lead.

Adjustment

Note: *The manufacturers specify the use of special adjustment wrench Vauxhall tool No KM-666 for adjusting the timing belt tension.*

35 No checking of timing belt adjustment is specified, and the following adjustment procedure applies to a newly fitted belt. The adjustment must be carried out with the engine cold.

36 With the timing belt cover removed and the tensioner pulley bolt slackened, ensure that the TDC marks on the camshaft sprockets and the crankshaft pulley are aligned as described in paragraph 6. If necessary, turn the crankshaft to achieve alignment.

37 Fit the special tool KM-666 to the belt tensioner pulley mounting plate, in accordance with the tool manufacturer's instructions.

38 Working anti-clockwise from the TDC mark on the exhaust camshaft sprocket, mark the seventh tooth on the sprocket **(see illustration)**.

39 Turn the crankshaft clockwise until this tooth is aligned with the TDC notch in the camshaft cover. The crankshaft must be turned evenly and without jerking, to prevent the timing belt from jumping off the sprockets and pulleys.

9A

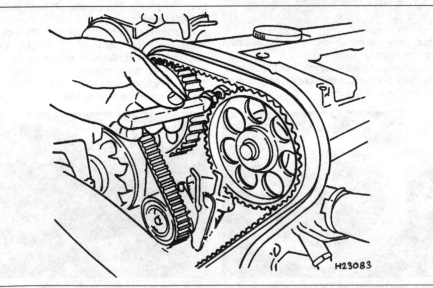

7.38 Working anti-clockwise from the TDC mark on the exhaust camshaft sprocket, mark the seventh tooth on the sprocket

40 Tighten the tensioner pulley bolt to the specified torque in the three stages given in the Specifications.

41 Remove the special tool.

42 Turn the crankshaft clockwise until the TDC marks on the camshaft sprockets are aligned with the notches in the camshaft cover, and check that the crankshaft pulley TDC mark is aligned with the pointer on the rear timing belt cover.

8 Timing belt and tensioner (DOHC engines) - models from 1993

Note: *This tensioner was fitted to C20 XE and X20 XEV engines from model year 1993.*

Removal

1 The operations are essentially the same as described in Section 7, except that the tensioner pulley incorporates an automatic adjuster that simplifies the procedure as follows.

2 To release the belt tension before removal, unscrew the timing belt tensioner pulley securing bolt slightly then, with a large screwdriver (or similar tool) inserted in the slot on the tensioner arm, turn the tensioner arm until the timing belt is slack. Tighten the securing bolt slightly to hold the tensioner in this position.

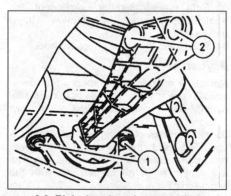

9.3 Right-hand engine mounting

1 Mounting block-to-body bolts
2 Mounting bracket-to-cylinder block bolts

Refitting

3 To refit the timing belt, first ensure that the coolant pump is correctly positioned by checking that the lug on the coolant pump flange is aligned with the corresponding lug on the cylinder block. If this is not the case, slacken the coolant pump mounting bolts slightly and move the pump accordingly. Tighten the bolts to the specified torque on completion.

4 Refit the timing belt as described in Section 7, then tension it as follows.

Adjustment

5 Slacken the tensioner pulley securing bolt and move the tensioner arm anti-clockwise, until the tensioner pointer lies at its stop. Tighten the tensioner pulley securing bolt to hold the tensioner in this position.

6 Turn the crankshaft through two complete revolutions in the normal direction of rotation and check that with the crankshaft pulley TDC mark aligned with the pointer on the rear timing belt cover, the TDC marks on the camshaft sprockets are still aligned with the notches in the camshaft cover.

7 Slacken the tensioner pulley securing bolt once again and move the tensioner arm clockwise, until the tensioner pointer is aligned with the notch in the tensioner. In the first few hours of operation a new belt will be subjected to settling-in. If you are refitting a used belt (one that has been run-in), align the pointer to approximately 4 mm to the left of the notch, refer to Section 6. Tighten the tensioner pulley securing bolt securely. Turn the crankshaft through one complete revolution in the normal direction of rotation and check that the crankshaft and camshaft timing marks still align, then refit the remainder of the components as described in Section 7.

9 Engine right-hand mounting - removal and refitting

Note: *New mounting-to-body bolts must be used on refitting*

1 If not already done, apply the handbrake, then raise the front of the vehicle, and support securely on axle stands.

2 Attach lifting tackle and a hoist to the engine lifting brackets on the cylinder head, and support the weight of the engine.

3 Working under the vehicle, unbolt the engine mounting bracket from the cylinder block, and unbolt the mounting block from the body, then withdraw the bracket/mounting assembly **(see illustration)**.

4 Unbolt the mounting block from the bracket.

5 Fit the new mounting block to the bracket, and tighten the securing bolts to the specified torque.

6 Refit the mounting bracket to the cylinder block, and tighten the securing bolts to the specified torque.

7 Fit new mounting block-to-body bolts, and tighten them to the specified torque.

8 Disconnect the lifting tackle and hoist from the engine.

9 Lower the vehicle to the ground.

10 Air cleaner - removal and refitting

Round type
Removal

1 Release the spring clips from the perimeter of the air cleaner cover.

2 Unscrew and remove the small cross-head screw securing the cover extension to the main body near the inlet duct.

3 Unscrew and remove the three central cross-head cap nuts securing the air cleaner to the carburettor, taking care not to drop the washers and seals **(see illustration)**.

4 Separate the cover from the main body, then lift out the element **(see illustration)**.

5 Release the crankcase ventilation hose from the plastic clip on the left-hand side of the air cleaner body.

6 Disconnect the inlet duct from the hot air hose on the exhaust manifold **(see illustration)**, and lift the air cleaner body from the carburettor/fuel injection.

7 With the body tilted to the rear, disconnect the crankcase ventilation hose from the stub

10.3 Air cleaner-to-carburettor mounting cap nuts

10.4 Removing the air cleaner element - note clip for crankcase ventilation hose (arrowed)

10.6 The air cleaner body locates over the hot air hose

10.7 Disconnecting the crankcase ventilation hose (arrowed)

10.16 Loosening the air trunking clamp screw at the airflow meter

10.25a Remove the securing screw . . .

10.25b . . . and withdraw the resonance box

10.26 Removing the resonance box connector tube

on the underside of the body **(see illustration)**. Where applicable, disconnect the vacuum hose from the air temperature control flap thermostat.

8 Remove the seal from under the air cleaner body.

Refitting

9 Check the hot air hose for condition, and renew it if necessary.

10 Fit a new air cleaner body-to-carburettor/fuel injection seal.

11 Connect the crankcase ventilation hose to the stub on the underside of the body, and connect the vacuum hose for the air temperature control flap.

12 Locate the body on the carburettor/fuel injection, and at the same time locate the inlet duct on the hot air hose on the exhaust manifold.

13 Engage the crankshaft ventilation hose in the plastic clip.

14 Locate the new element in the air cleaner body, and refit the cover using a reversal of the removal procedure.

Square type with air box

Removal

15 Unclip the coolant expansion tank hose from the air cleaner cover, and move it to one side out of the way.

16 Loosen the clamp screw and disconnect the air trunking from the airflow meter **(see illustration)**.

17 Disconnect the battery negative lead, then disconnect the wiring plug from the airflow meter.

18 Release the two securing clips from the left-hand side of the air cleaner cover, and unscrew the two captive securing screws from the right-hand side, then lift off the cover.

19 Lift out the filter element.

20 Loosen the preheat hoses, fastening nuts.

21 Undo the nuts securing the 2 rubber block studs which are secured through the lower half of the air cleaner housing.

22 Some models are fitted with an inlet air resonance box, to reduce induction noise. This box is located under the wheelarch, and connects to a pipe on the air inlet tube.

23 The resonance box must be removed before the air inlet tube can be removed. To

do this, first apply the handbrake, then jack up the front of the vehicle, and support securely on axle stands placed under the body side members.

24 Remove the securing screws, and withdraw the lower splash shield from the wing to expose the resonance box.

25 Unscrew the single securing screw, and pull the resonance box from the connector tube **(see illustrations)**.

26 If desired, the air inlet tube can be removed after pulling off the connector tube from under the wing **(see illustration)**.

27 Manipulate the air inlet tube to release the securing lugs from the front body panel. This is a tricky operation, and patience will be required. For improved access, the headlamp can be removed.

Refitting

28 Refitting of all components is a reversal of removal, noting that the air cleaner element fits with the rubber locating flange uppermost.

11 Power steering pump - removal and refitting

Note: *A new fluid pipe union O-ring must be used on refitting*

1.6 litre models (up to 1992)

Removal

1 Remove the air cleaner casing from the

right-hand front wing, as described in Section 10.

2 Remove the alternator/power steering pump drivebelt, with reference to Section 1.

3 Unscrew the three securing bolts, and remove the power steering pump pulley.

4 Unclip and remove the outer timing belt cover.

5 Disconnect the fluid pipe union and the hose from the pump. Be prepared for fluid spillage, and plug the open ends of the pump and the pipes, to prevent dirt ingress and further fluid spillage.

6 Unscrew the two pump securing bolts, and withdraw the pump from the cylinder block towards the alternator **(see illustration)**.

9A

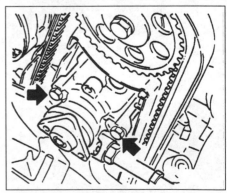

11.6 Power steering pump mounting bolts (arrowed) - 1.6 litre models, up to 1992

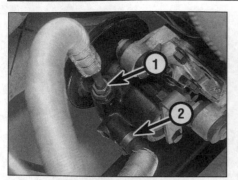

11.11 Power steering pump connections - 2.0 litre models

1 Fluid pipe union
2 Flexible hose connection

7 No overhaul of the pump is possible, and if faulty, a new unit must be fitted.

Refitting

8 Refitting is a reversal of removal, but renew the O-ring when reconnecting the fluid pipe union, and tension the alternator/power steering pump drivebelt (Section 1).
9 On completion, top-up the fluid level, and bleed the fluid circuit as described in Section 12.

1.6 (from 1993), 1.8 and 2.0 litre models

Removal

10 Remove the power steering pump drivebelt, as described in Section 1.
11 Disconnect the fluid pipe union and the flexible fluid hose from the pump **(see illustration)**. Be prepared for fluid spillage, and plug the open ends of the pump, pipe and hose, to prevent dirt ingress and further fluid loss.
12 Unscrew and remove the four mounting bolts. Recover the nuts, and take care not to lose the rubber insulators that fit into the mounting bracket.
13 Withdraw the pump from the vehicle.

12.1 Power steering fluid dipstick

14 No overhaul of the pump is possible, and if faulty, a new unit must be fitted.

Refitting

15 Refitting is a reversal of removal, but renew the O-ring when reconnecting the fluid pipe union. Tension the drivebelt, as described in Section 1.
16 On completion, top-up the fluid level, and bleed the fluid circuit (Section 12).

12 Power steering fluid circuit - bleeding and level check

1 With the engine stopped, initially fill the reservoir to the level of MAX mark on the dipstick attached to the reservoir filler cap **(see illustration)**.
2 Start the engine, and immediately top-up the fluid level to the MIN mark on the dipstick **(see illustration)**. Do not allow the reservoir to run dry at any time. The help of an assistant will ease this operation.
3 With the engine running at idle speed, turn the steering wheel slowly two or three times approximately 45° left and right of the centre, then turn the wheel twice from lock to lock.

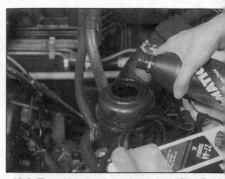

12.2 Topping-up the power steering fluid level

Do not hold the wheel on either lock, as this imposes strain on the hydraulic system.
4 Stop the engine, and check the fluid level. With the fluid at operating temperature (80°/176°F) the level should be on the MAX mark, and with the fluid cold (20°C/68°F), the level should be on the MIN mark. Top-up if necessary.

13 Engine undershield (DOHC models) - removal and refitting

Removal

1 Apply the handbrake, then jack up the front of the vehicle, and support on axle stands.
2 Extract the two securing screws, and remove the oil filter access panel.
3 Working around the edges of the splash shield, remove the self tapping screws that secure the shield to the body, noting that some of the screws also secure the wheelarch liners.
4 With the help of an assistant, pull the shield from the vehicle, and place it to one side to avoid damage.

Refitting

5 Refitting is a reversal of removal.

Chapter 9B
Vauxhall Cavalier &
Opel Vectra diesel 1988 to 1995

Contents

Specifications

Timing belt renewal interval .... Every 36 000 miles (60 000 km) or 4 years - whichever comes first

Note: Although the interval for timing belt renewal is increased for later models, it is strongly recommended that this shorter interval is applied to vehicles which are subjected to intensive use, ie, mainly short journeys or a lot of stop-start driving. The actual belt renewal interval is therefore very much up to the individual owner. That being said, it is highly recommended to err on the side of safety, and renew the belt at this earlier interval, bearing in mind the drastic consequences resulting from belt failure.

Auxiliary drivebelts

17D, 17DR and 17DTL engines

Tension (using gauge KM-128-A):

Alternator:

New .... 450 N

Used .... 250 to 400 N

Power steering pump:

New .... 450 N

Used .... 250 to 300 N

17DT engine

Tension (using gauge KM-128-A):

Alternator:

New .... 440 to 540 N

Used .... 320 to 390 N

Power steering pump:

New .... 450 N

Used .... 250 to 300 N

9B

Timing belt tension

17D engine (using tension gauge KM-510-A):
New belt, warm 7.5
New belt, cold 9.5
Run-in belt, warm 5.0
Run-in belt, cold 9.0
17DR,17DTL and 17DT engines . . . . Automatic tensioner

Injection pump timing setting

17D, 17DR and 17DTL engines:
Bosch . . . . 0.80 + 0.05 mm
Lucas/CAV . . . . x – 0.15 mm (where x = manufacturer's calibration marked on pump)
17DT engine . . . . 0.50 to 0.60 mm

Torque wrench settings

	Nm	lbf ft
17D, 17DR and 17DTL engines		
Alternator:		
Adjuster strap nuts and bolts	25	18
Pivot bolt	25	18
Coolant pump bolts	25	18
Camshaft sprocket bolt:*		
Stage 1	75	55
Stage 2	Angle tighten a further 60°	
Stage 3	Angle tighten a further 5°	
Crankcase pulley to sprocket	20	15
Engine mountings:		
Left-hand:		
Mounting bracket to transmission	60	44
Flexible mounting to bracket	60	44
Flexible mounting to sidemember	65	48
Right-hand:		
Mounting bracket to cylinder block	60	44
Flexible mounting to bracket	35	26
Flexible mounting to sidemember	65	48
Rear:		
Mounting bracket to transmission	60	44
Flexible mounting to bracket	45	33
Flexible mounting to sidemember	40	30
Fuel injection pump:		
Fuel lines to pump	25	18
Hub to pump	25	18
Pump to bracket(s)	25	18
Pump to support - M6 bolts	12	9
Sprocket to hub	25	18
Vent bolt to pump	25	18
Power steering pump:		
Drivebelt tensioner to pump	40	30
Timing belt:		
Guide roller to cylinder block	40	30
Tension roller to cylinder block	25	18
Vacuum pump to camshaft housing	28	21
Wheel bolts	90	66
17DT engine		
Alternator to mounting bracket:		
M8 bolt	24	18
M10 bolt	48	35
Camshaft sprocket bolts	10	7
Crankshaft:		
Pulley-to-sprocket bolts	20	15
Sprocket centre bolt	196	145
Fuel injection pump:		
Central vent bolt	20	15
Fuel lines to pump	25	18
Pump to bracket	40	30
Pump to cylinder block/flange	23	17
Sprocket to pump	70	52

Torque wrench settings

17DT engine (continued)

	Nm	lbf ft
Mountings:		
Left-hand damping block to bracket	60	44
Left and right-hand damping blocks to sidemember	65	48
Rear damping block:		
To bracket	45	33
To crossmember	40	30
Right-hand damping block to bracket	35	26
Right-hand mounting bracket:		
To cylinder block	40	30
To mounting	45	33
Power steering pump:		
Drivebelt tensioner to bracket	25	18
Drivebelt tensioner to pump	18	13
Pressure line to pump connections	28	21
Pump mounting bracket to cylinder block	60	44
Pump support to mounting bracket	25	18
Pump to support	25	18
Timing belt:		
Cover to cylinder block	8	6
Guide roller to cylinder block	76	56
Tension roller to cylinder block	19	14
Wheel bolts	110	81

* Bolts must be renewed every time

1 Auxiliary drivebelts - removal, refitting and adjustment

Alternator

17D, 17DR and 17DTL engines

1 Gain full access to the drivebelt by raising the car, supporting it on axle stands and removing the right-hand front roadwheel. Remove the air cleaner housing assembly.

2 To remove the drivebelt, first slacken the alternator pivot and adjuster strap nuts and bolts **(see illustration)**.

3 Where fitted, remove the power steering pump drivebelt.

4 Move the alternator towards the engine and slip the drivebelt off its pulleys.

5 Fit the new drivebelt in position over the pulleys and adjust it as follows:

6 Tighten the alternator fastening slightly, so that the alternator can just be moved by hand.

7 Move the alternator away from the engine until the belt tension is correct.

8 Vauxhall recommend the use of a special tool (KM-128-A) for tensioning the belt to the specified amount **(see illustration)**. In the absence of this tool, aim for a tension such that the belt can be deflected about 12 mm by firm finger pressure in the middle of its run. The belt tension must, however, be checked

with the special tool as soon as possible. If using a lever to move the alternator, only use a wooden or plastic one and only lever at the pulley end.

9 Tighten the alternator fastenings to the specified torque setting once the belt tension is correct.

10 Where applicable, refit and tension the steering pump drivebelt.

11 Refit the air cleaner housing assembly.

17DT engine

12 Gain full access to the alternator by jacking up the front right-hand side of the vehicle and supporting it on axle stands.

13 To remove the drivebelt, first slacken the alternator pivot and adjuster bolts.

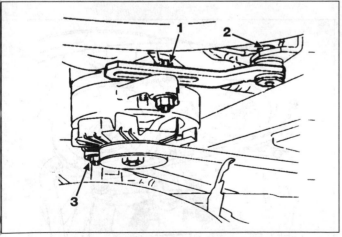

1.2 Alternator drivebelt adjustment points

1 Alternator to adjuster strap bolt
2 Adjuster strap pivot bolt
3 Alternator pivot bolt

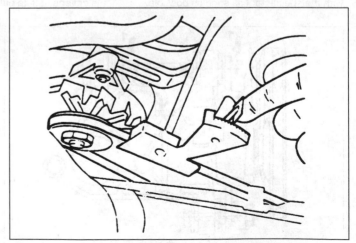

1.8 Using special tool KM-128-A to tension the alternator drivebelt

9B

1.18 Tensioning the alternator drivebelt

A   Socket drive in end of adjuster arm
B   Adjuster strap bolt
C   Pivot bolt

1.19 Using special tool KM-128-A to tension the alternator drivebelt

14 Where fitted, remove the power steering pump drivebelt.

15 Move the alternator towards the engine and slip the drivebelt off its pulleys.

16 Fit the new drivebelt in position over the pulleys and adjust it as follows:

17 Tighten the alternator fastenings slightly, so that the alternator can just be moved by hand.

18 Insert a socket drive in the end of the adjuster arm and use it as a lever to move the alternator away from the engine until the belt tension is correct. Nip the adjuster bolt tight whilst checking the belt tension **(see illustration)**.

19 Vauxhall recommend the use of a special tool (KM-128-A) for tensioning the belt to the specified amount **(see illustration)**. In the absence of this tool, aim for a tension such that the belt can be deflected about 12 mm by firm finger pressure in the middle of its run. The belt tension must, however, be checked with the special tool as soon as possible.

20 Tighten the alternator fastenings to the specified torque setting once the belt tension is correct.

21 Where applicable, refit and tension the steering pump drivebelt.

22 Lower the front of the vehicle, removing the axle stands and jack.

23 The tension of a new drivebelt should be rechecked after a few hundred miles.

Power steering pump

17D, 17DR and 17DTL engines

24 Gain full access to the drivebelt by jacking up the front right-hand side of the vehicle and supporting it on axle stands.

25 To remove the drivebelt, first loosen the pump mounting and tensioner bolts shown **(see illustration)**. Release the tensioner screw locknuts and rotate them to allow the drivebelt to slacken **(see illustration)**. Slip the drivebelt off its pulleys.

26 Fit the new drivebelt in position over th pulleys and adjust it as follows:

27 Rotate the tensioner screw locknuts un the belt tension is correct.

28 Vauxhall recommend the use of a specia tool (KM-128-A) for tensioning the belt to th specified amount. In the absence of this too aim for a tension such that the belt can b deflected approximately 12 mm by firm finge pressure in the middle of its run. The bel tension must, however, be checked with th special tool as soon as possible.

29 Once belt tension is correct, tighten th tensioner screw locknuts and lower th vehicle.

17DT engine

30 Gain access to the drivebelt by removing the air cleaner housing assembly.

31 To remove the drivebelt, first loosen th pump pivot and adjuster bolts.

32 Move the pump towards the engine and slip the drivebelt off its pulleys.

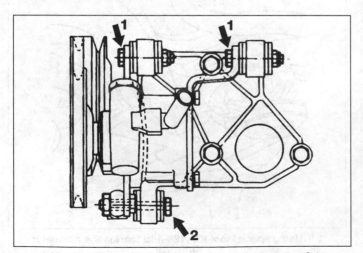

1.25a Power steering pump drivebelt adjustment points

1 Pump mounting bolts   *2 Tensioner bolt*

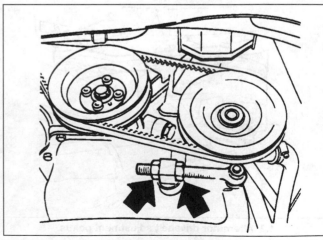

1.25b Rotate the tensioner screw locknuts (arrowed) to adjust drivebelt tension

3 Fit the new drivebelt in position over the pulleys and adjust it as follows:

4 Tighten the pump fastenings slightly, so that the pump can just be moved by hand.

5 Insert a socket drive in the end of the adjuster arm and use it as a lever to move the pump away from the engine until the belt tension is correct. Nip the adjuster bolt tight whilst checking the belt tension **(see illustration)**.

6 Vauxhall recommend the use of a special tool (KM-128-A) for tensioning the belt to the specified amount. In the absence of this tool, aim for a tension such that the belt can be deflected approximately 12 mm by firm finger pressure in the middle of its run. The belt tension must, however, be checked with the special tool as soon as possible.

7 Once belt tension is correct, tighten the pump fastenings to the specified torque setting.

8 Refit the air cleaner housing assembly.

9 The tension of a new drivebelt should be rechecked after a few hundred miles.

2 Coolant - draining and refilling

 Warning: Take care to avoid scalding when removing the cooling system expansion tank cap. Place a thick cloth over the cap before turning it anti-clockwise.
Caution: Never operate the vehicle with plain water in the cooling system, except in an emergency. Apart from the risk of freezing in winter weather, serious corrosion and rust and scale formation may occur.
Warning: Antifreeze is poisonous and must be handled with due care.

Draining

1 The system should only be drained when it is cool. If it must be drained hot, take great care to avoid scalding.

2 Remove the expansion tank cap. If the system is hot, place a thick cloth over the cap before turning it anti-clockwise.

3 Place a container underneath the radiator

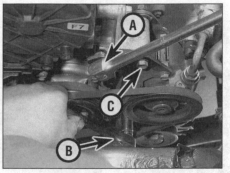
1.35 Tensioning the power steering pump drivebelt

A *Socket drive in end of adjuster arm*
B *Adjuster strap bolt*
C *Pivot bolt*

bottom hose. Disconnect the hose from the radiator and allow the system to drain.

4 A cylinder block drain plug is only provided on 17DT engines, making it possible to drain the cooling system completely if necessary **(see illustration)**.

Filling

5 Make sure that all hoses and clips are in good condition. Refit any disturbed hoses and see that their clips are tight. Before refitting the cylinder block drain plug (if applicable), coat its threads with sealing compound (to GM spec. 15 03 166).

6 Fill the system via the expansion tank cap. If new coolant is being put in, start by pouring in the required quantity of neat antifreeze and follow it up with the water.

7 Massage the large coolant hoses to help displace air pockets during filling.

8 Most vehicles will be fitted with a self-venting cooling system this can be recognised by the two small vent hoses which enter the top of the expansion tank. If the system is not self-venting, open the bleed screw on the thermostat elbow during filling and close it when coolant runs out at the bleed screw.

9 When the system appears full, refit the expansion tank cap. Run the engine up to operating temperature, keeping a look-out for coolant leaks, then stop it and allow it to cool. Recheck the coolant level and top-up if necessary.

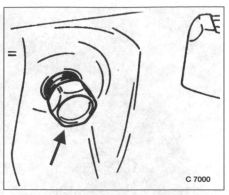
2.4 The cylinder block coolant drain plug (arrowed) - 17DT engine

10 Recheck the tightness of all hose clips when the engine has cooled, and again after a few hundred miles.

3 Timing belt - removal and refitting

Caution: A timing belt which is damaged, oil-soaked or fuel soaked must be renewed or it will fail, resulting in serious engine damage.

17D engine

Removal

1 Remove the alternator drivebelt (Section 1).

2 Remove the air filter housing. Remove the timing belt covers. Two versions of the moulded plastic timing belt covers have been used since the introduction of this engine, the later version being identified by the squared-off top surface of the outer belt cover. On the earlier version, a screwdriver blade can be used to release the outer cover retaining clips and the cover sections can then be removed to gain access to the timing belt. On the later version, the method of retention is by bolts instead of clips. This arrangement is, in fact, the same as used on the 17DR engine **(see illustrations)**.

3 Remove the crankshaft pulley - it is secured to the sprocket by four Allen screws **(see illustration)**.

9B

3.2a Removing the timing belt upper cover

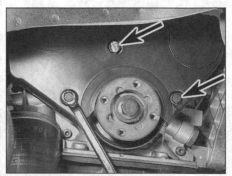
3.2b Removing the timing belt lower cover retaining bolts

3.3 The crankshaft pulley viewed through the front wheel arch

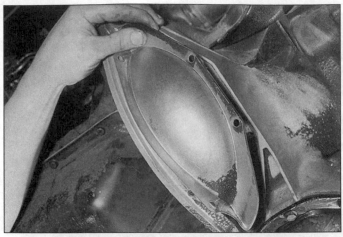

3.5 Removing the clutch/flywheel access cover

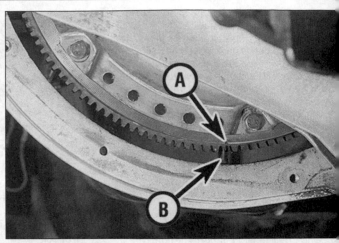

3.7 TDC mark on flywheel (A) and pointer on clutch housing (B)

3.10 Undoing a coolant pump bolt - other two arrowed (engine removed)

3.11 Right-hand front engine mounting-to-side chassis member securing bolts (arrowed)

4 Disconnect the battery earth lead.

5 Remove the clutch/flywheel access cover from the bottom of the gearbox bellhousing **(see illustration)**.

6 Turn the crankshaft in the normal direction of rotation, using a spanner on the sprocket bolt, until the timing mark on the injection pump sprocket aligns with the reference mark on the pump bracket. In this position No 1 piston is at TDC on the firing stroke.

7 Check that the TDC mark on the flywheel

and the pointer on the clutch housing are aligned **(see illustration)**.

8 If a suitable tool is available, remove the vacuum pump and lock the camshaft in position by fitting the tool. If a tool is not available or cannot be fitted, make alignment marks between the camshaft sprocket and its backplate for use when refitting.

9 Drain the coolant.

10 Slacken the three bolts which secure the coolant pump to the block **(see illustration)**. Using a large open-ended spanner on the flats

of the pump, pivot it to release the tension of the belt.

11 Separate the right-hand front engine mounting by undoing the two bolts which are accessible from the top **(see illustration)**.

12 Mark the running direction of the belt if it is to be re-used. Also take care not to kink the belt, nor get oil, grease etc. on it.

13 Slip the belt off the sprockets and jockey wheel. Remove the belt by feeding it through the engine mounting.

14 If signs of oil contamination are found, trace the source of the oil leak and rectify, then wash down the engine timing belt area and all related components to remove all traces of oil.

Refitting

15 Commence refitting by threading the belt through the engine mounting. Refit and tighten the engine mounting bolts.

16 Place the belt over the sprockets and the jockey wheel **(see illustration)**. Make sure that No 1 piston is still at TDC, the injection pump sprocket mark is aligned and the camshaft position is still correct.

17 Move the coolant pump so as to put some tension on the timing belt. Nip up the pump securing bolts, but do not tighten them fully yet.

18 Remove the camshaft locking tool, if used, and refit and secure the crankshaft pulley.

19 Belt tension can only be adjusted accurately using tension gauge KM-510-A or equivalent **(see illustration)**. A belt which is too tight will usually hum when running and a belt which is too slack will wear rapidly and may jump teeth.

20 Settle the belt by rotating the crankshaft through half a turn in the normal direction of rotation. Fit the tension gauge to the slack side of the belt (the alternator side) and read the tension. Desired values are given in the *Specifications*.

21 If adjustment is necessary, slacken the

3.16 Timing belt correctly fitted

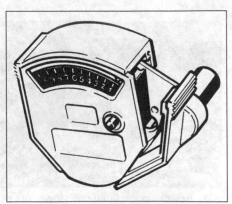

3.19 Timing belt tension gauge

3.28 Release the drivebelt tensioner securing bolt, then turn the tensioner arm with an Allen key until the belt is slack

coolant pump bolts and pivot the pump to increase or decrease the tension. Nip up the coolant pump bolts.

2 Turn the crankshaft through one full turn, then recheck the tension. Keep adjusting the belt tension until a stable value is obtained.

3 Tighten the coolant pump bolts to the specified torque. Refill the cooling system (Section 2).

4 Check the injection pump timing (Section 6).

5 Refit the belt covers, clutch/flywheel cover and other disturbed components.

6 Refit the roadwheel, lower the vehicle and tighten the wheel bolts.

17DR and 17DTL engines

Removal, refitting and tensioning

27 The procedure for these engines with an automatic timing belt tensioner is essentially the same as described for the 17D engine, except that it is not necessary to drain the coolant, remove the engine mounting, nor to slacken the coolant pump mounting bolts and move the pump to adjust the belt tension. Instead, belt adjustment is catered for by means of the automatic tensioner, as follows.

28 To release the belt tension prior to removal, unscrew the timing belt tensioner securing bolt slightly then, with a suitable Allen key inserted in the slot on the tensioner arm, turn the tensioner arm until the timing belt is slack (see illustration). Tighten the securing bolt slightly to hold the tensioner in this position. The timing belt can now be removed.

29 Prior to fitting the timing belt, first ensure that the coolant pump is correctly positioned by checking that the lug on the pump flange is aligned with the corresponding lug on the cylinder block. If this is not the case, slacken the pump mounting bolts slightly and move the pump accordingly. Tighten the bolts to the specified torque on completion.

30 Initially refit the timing belt as described above, ensuring that No 1 piston is still at TDC, that the injection pump sprocket mark is

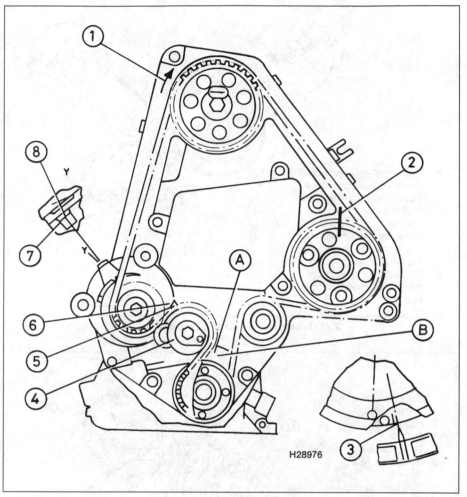

3.30a Timing belt routing

A To tension drivebelt	4 Tensioning roller
B To loosen drivebelt	5 Tensioning roller pointer
1 Direction of rotation	6 Alignment mark - tensioning roller
2 Fuel injection pump marking - No.1 cylinder TDC	7 Alignment mark - coolant pump
3 Flywheel marking - No.1 cylinder TDC	8 Alignment mark - cylinder block

still aligned and the camshaft position is still correct (see illustration). On 17DTL engines, flywheel position for TDC must be determined by the use of a setting tool (Adjuster KM-851) fitted next to the flywheel as shown (see illustration).

31 Tension the timing belt by first slackening the automatic tensioner securing bolt and moving the tensioner arm anti-clockwise until the tensioner pointer is at its stop. Tighten the tensioner securing bolt to hold the tensioner in this position.

32 Turn the crankshaft through two complete revolutions in the normal direction of rotation until No 1 piston is once again at the TDC position. Check that the injection pump sprocket and camshaft sprocket positions are still correct.

33 Slacken the automatic tensioner securing bolt once again and move the tensioner arm until the tensioner pointer and

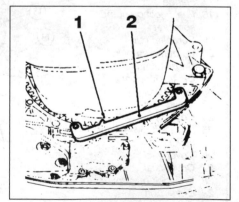

3.30b On 17DTL engines, flywheel position for TDC must be determined by the use of a setting tool (Adjuster KM-851)

1 Flywheel marking - No.1 cylinder TDC
2 Setting tool

9B

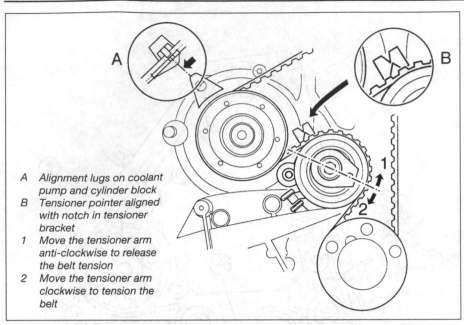

A Alignment lugs on coolant pump and cylinder block
B Tensioner pointer aligned with notch in tensioner bracket
1 Move the tensioner arm anti-clockwise to release the belt tension
2 Move the tensioner arm clockwise to tension the belt

3.33 Timing belt automatic tensioner details

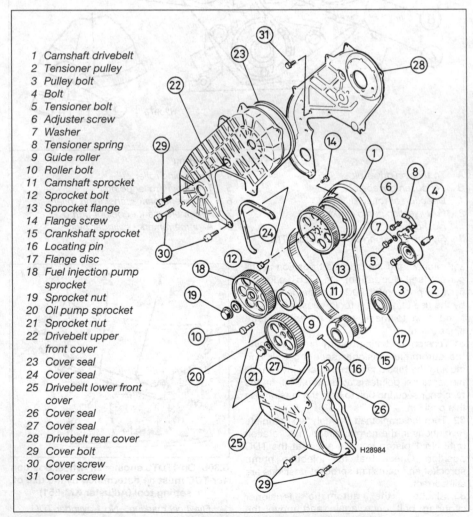

1 Camshaft drivebelt
2 Tensioner pulley
3 Pulley bolt
4 Bolt
5 Tensioner bolt
6 Adjuster screw
7 Washer
8 Tensioner spring
9 Guide roller
10 Roller bolt
11 Camshaft sprocket
12 Sprocket bolt
13 Sprocket flange
14 Flange screw
15 Crankshaft sprocket
16 Locating pin
17 Flange disc
18 Fuel injection pump sprocket
19 Sprocket nut
20 Oil pump sprocket
21 Sprocket nut
22 Drivebelt upper front cover
23 Cover seal
24 Cover seal
25 Drivebelt lower front cover
26 Cover seal
27 Cover seal
28 Drivebelt rear cover
29 Cover bolt
30 Cover screw
31 Cover screw

3.36 Camshaft drivebelt and associated components

tensioner bracket notch coincide **(se illustration)**. Tighten the tensioner securir bolt securely.
34 Check the valve timing and injectic pump timing.
35 Refitting the remainder of the componen is the reversal of removal.

17DT engine

36 The timing belt also drives the c pump and fuel injection pump **(se illustration)**.

Removal

37 Disconnect the battery earth lead.
38 Gain access to the timing belt cover b first removing the air inlet collector box fro its mounting on
the right-hand side of the engine bay.
39 Remove the box lid retaining screws an clips and the outlet tube retaining clamp at th engine air filter box. With the lid remove remove the box retaining nuts and release th box inlet tube to allow the box to be lifte from position, unclipping the alternator cabl ties if necessary. Note that the inlet tube ma be a very tight fit on the box stub, ensure tha the retaining tangs are fully depressed befor attempting to release the tube **(se illustrations)**.
40 Release the brake servo vacuum lir

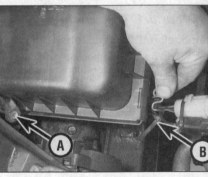

3.39a Release the air intake collector bo lid retaining clips, screws (A) and alternator cable ties (B) . . .

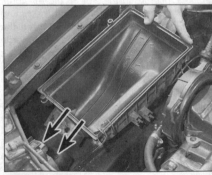

3.39b . . . and depress the retaining tang (arrowed) before releasing the collector box

3.40a Release the brake servo vacuum line retaining clamp (arrowed) . . .

3.40b . . . and pull the line from the servo unit

retaining clamp and pull the line from the servo unit **(see illustrations)**.

1 Remove the upper part of the timing belt cover by undoing its nine securing bolts (noting their respective lengths) and lifting it from position.

2 Turn the steering wheel so that access to the side of the engine can be gained through the right-hand wheelarch, in front of the roadwheel.

3 Support the engine by positioning a jack beneath its sump and raising it slightly. Protect the sump by placing a piece of thick wood between it and the jack.

4 Remove the engine right-hand mounting by first removing its two centre bolts. Remove the two mounting-to-vehicle body retaining bolts and then the three mounting-to-engine bolts to allow the complete mounting assembly to be withdrawn.

5 Slacken the power steering pump upper and lower retaining bolts to allow the pump to be moved towards the engine, see Section 1. With the V-belt slackened, detach it from the crankshaft, coolant pump and power steering pump pulleys.

46 Slacken the alternator pivot and retaining bolts and move it towards the engine. With the V-belt slackened, detach it from the crankshaft, coolant pump and alternator pulleys.

47 Turn the crankshaft in the normal direction of rotation until the timing mark on its pulley aligns with the reference pointer on the engine block **(see illustration)**. In this position No 1 piston is at TDC on the firing stroke.

48 Now check that the locking bolt holes in the camshaft and fuel injection pump sprockets are aligned with their respective threaded holes in the engine casing before inserting the locking bolts (bolt sizes M6 x 1.00 for camshaft and M8 x 1.25 for injection pump) **(see illustrations)**.

49 Mark the fitted position of the crankshaft pulley. Remove the four pulley retaining bolts and detach the pulley, gently tapping its rim to free it if necessary.

50 Undo the three bolts and remove the lower part of the timing belt cover from the engine.

51 Release the timing belt tensioner by

3.47 Align the timing mark on the crankshaft pulley with the reference pointer on the engine block to bring No 1 piston to TDC on the firing stroke

loosening the pulley centre bolt, the upper spring bracket securing bolt and the lower pivot securing nut. Push the tensioner spring towards the front of the engine to release belt tension and then nip tight the bracket securing bolt.

3.48a Insert the locking bolt (arrowed) through the camshaft sprocket . . .

3.48b . . . and insert the locking bolt through the injection pump sprocket

9B

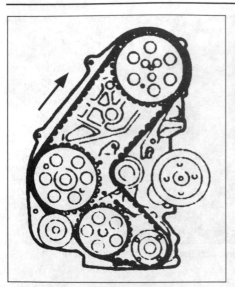

3.55 Ensure the camshaft drivebelt is correctly routed

Arrow denotes direction of belt travel

52 Mark the running direction of the timing belt if it is to be re-used. Also take care not to kink the belt, nor get oil, grease etc. on it.
53 Slip the belt off the injection pump sprocket first and then the remaining sprockets to remove it from the engine.

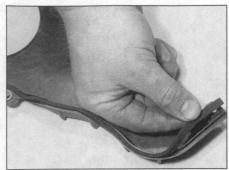

3.58 Checking the sealing strip in the lower front section of camshaft drivebelt cover

54 If signs of oil contamination are found, trace the source of the oil leak and rectify it, then wash down the engine timing belt area and all related components to remove all traces of oil.

Refitting and tensioning

55 Commence refitting by first placing the timing belt over the camshaft sprocket and then the injection pump sprocket etc. until it is correctly routed **(see illustration)**. The crankshaft must not be disturbed and the camshaft and fuel injection pump sprockets should still be locked in alignment.

56 Remove the camshaft and fuel injection pump sprocket alignment bolts.
57 Release the tensioner spring bracket securing bolt to allow the tensioner to act upon the timing belt. Turn the crankshaft against the normal direction of rotation by approximately 60 degrees to automatically tension the timing belt and then tighten the tensioner pulley centre bolt, the upper spring bracket securing bolt and the lower pivot securing nut to the specified torque settings (where given).
58 Refit the lower part of the timing belt cover to the engine, renewing any damaged sealing strips and tightening the retaining bolts to the specified torque setting **(see illustration)**.
59 Refit the crankshaft pulley in its previously noted position, tightening the retaining bolts to the specified torque setting.
60 Check the injection pump timing (Section 6).
61 Refit and tension both auxiliary drivebelts referring to Section 1.
62 Refit the engine right-hand mounting in the reverse sequence to removal, tightening all retaining bolts to the specified torque settings, see Section 4.
63 Refit the upper part of the timing belt cover, renewing any damaged sealing strips and tightening the retaining bolts to the specified torque setting.
64 Refit all other removed components.
65 Remove the jack from beneath the engine and reconnect the battery earth lead.

4 Engine/transmission mountings (17DT engine) - removal and refitting

Note: *Only remove and refit one engine mounting at a time*

1 The flexible mountings can be renewed if they have deteriorated. To facilitate removal take the weight of the engine/transmission on a hoist, or use a jack with a protective wooden block from below. Only remove and refit one mounting at a time.
2 Unbolt the mounting brackets from the engine/transmission and from the bodyframe **(see illustrations)**. Separate the flexible component from the brackets.

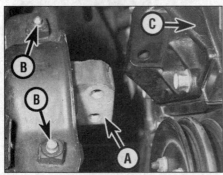

4.2a Engine/transmission right-hand mounting assembly

A *Flexible mounting to engine bracket bolt location*
B *Flexible mounting to vehicle body bolts*
C *Engine bracket*

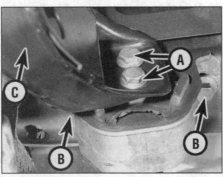

4.2b Engine/transmission left-hand mounting assembly

A *Flexible mounting to engine bracket bolts*
B *Flexible mounting to vehicle body bolts*
C *Engine bracket*

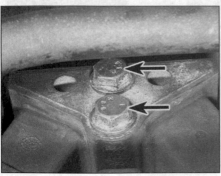

4.2c Engine/transmission rear flexible mounting to engine bracket bolts

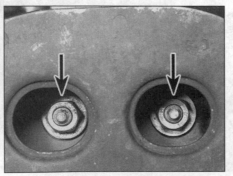

4.2d Engine/transmission rear flexible mounting to vehicle body nuts

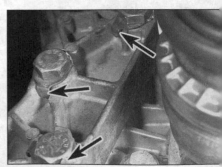

4.2e Engine/transmission rear mounting engine bracket bolts. Note locking washer tabs (arrowed)

Fit the new flexible component and refit the mounting. Only nip up the retaining bolts at first, then tighten them to the specified torque.

4 Lower the hoist or jack and check that the mounting is not under strain. Slacken and retighten the bolts as necessary.

5 Valve timing - checking and adjustment

17D, 17DR and 17DTL engines

1 Valve timing on these engines is more complicated than on the petrol equivalents because there are no timing marks as such on the camshaft or sprocket, neither is the sprocket keyed or pegged to the camshaft.

2 Note that the camshaft sprocket bolt should be renewed whenever it has been slackened.

3 If the valve timing has been lost completely, be careful when turning the crankshaft or camshaft in case piston/valve contact occurs.

4 The valve timing on this engine is checked using a dial test indicator. Before starting work, it is necessary to make sure that the drivebelt tension is set correctly.

5 Bring the engine to TDC, No 1 firing, by turning the crankshaft in the normal direction of rotation, using a spanner on the sprocket bolt, until the timing mark on the injection pump sprocket aligns with the reference mark on the belt cover (see illustration 6.4). Check that the TDC mark on the flywheel and the pointer on the clutch housing are aligned (see illustration 3.7).

6 Remove the air cleaner. Disconnect the breather hose and remove the camshaft cover (see illustration). If necessary, also remove the vacuum pump.

7 You will need a dial test indicator (DTI) with a 10 mm diameter measuring foot. Special tool KM-661-1 should ideally be available. This is a support bar which rests on the top face of the camshaft carrier and positions the DTI above the camshaft (see illustration). A home-made support can be used if tool KM-661-1 is not available.

8 An additional tool (KM-661-2) is prescribed by the manufacturer. This comprises a slotted steel plate with a stop screw which is secured by bolts to the camshaft carrier, immediately above the flats on the camshaft. The second part of the tool is effectively an open-jawed spanner which fits over the flats on the camshaft and passes up through the slotted plate. The stop screw bears on the spanner handle, allowing precise positioning of the camshaft (see illustrations). In the absence of the manufacturer's tool, it should not prove difficult to make up an equivalent device at home.

Checking

9 To check the valve timing, turn the crankshaft in the normal direction of rotation and stop when the crankshaft is approximately 90° BTDC, with No 1 cylinder on the compression stroke. Fit the DTI to the support bar and position the foot of the gauge over the base circle of the second cam from the sprocket end (No 1 cylinder inlet cam). Set the DTI to zero.

10 Carefully move the DTI and the support bar (without disturbing the position of the DTI in the support bar) exactly 10 mm to the left, as viewed from the camshaft sprocket end of the engine (ie. towards the peak of the cam lobe). Turn the crankshaft to the TDC position for No 1 cylinder (see Section 3). In this position, the DTI should show a lift of 0.55 ± 0.03 mm. If so, the valve timing is correct.

Adjustment

11 If adjustment is necessary, slacken the camshaft sprocket bolt, noting that since this must be renewed each time it is disturbed. It is as well to fit a new bolt loosely at this stage. Release the taper between the sprocket and the camshaft, if necessary by tapping the sprocket with a wooden or plastic mallet.

12 Using the flats on the camshaft, turn it until the DTI reads approximately 0.80 mm of lift. Check that the crankshaft is still set to TDC.

13 Assemble and fit the holding tool, KM-661-2 or equivalent. Using the stop screw, gradually set the cam lift to 0.60 to 0.64 mm. Tighten the camshaft sprocket bolt tight enough for the camshaft taper to lock the sprocket, then remove the holding tool.

14 Carefully lift away the DTI and its support bar, taking care not to disturb the DTI position in the bar. Turn the crankshaft through two complete revolutions, then position the DTI once more and check that a lift figure of 0.55 ± 0.03 mm is shown at TDC. If the correct figure is not shown, repeat the adjustment sequence. If the figure is correct, tighten the (new) camshaft sprocket bolt to the specified torque, check the valve timing once more, then remove the tools.

15 Remember that the injection pump timing must be checked after any change in the valve timing setting. Refit the various covers removed during the checking operation.

17DT engine

Checking

16 Disconnect the battery earth lead.

17 Gain access to the timing belt upper cover by first removing the air inlet collector box from its mounting on the right-hand side of the engine bay - see Section 3.

18 Release the brake servo vacuum line retaining clamp and pull the line from the servo unit.

19 Remove the upper part of the cover by undoing its nine securing bolts (noting their respective lengths) and lifting it from position.

20 Turn the crankshaft in the normal direction of rotation until the timing mark on its pulley aligns with the reference pointer on the engine block. In this position No 1 piston is at TDC on the firing stroke.

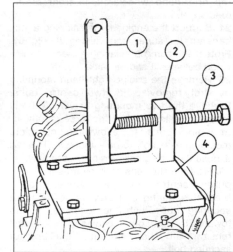

5.8 Service tool KM-661-2 in use

1   Open-jawed spanner
2   Stop screw bracket welded to baseplate
3   Stop screw
4   Baseplate located by camshaft cover bolts

5.6 Removing the camshaft cover

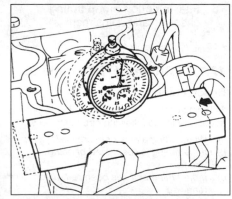

5.7 Dial test indicator (DTI) in position above camshaft
Note dotted lines indicating the two base positions during the test procedure

9B

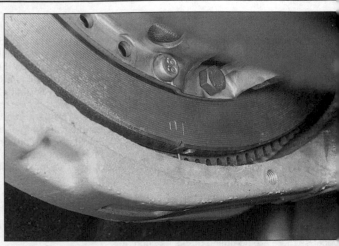

6.4 Fuel injection pump sprocket timing mark aligned with moulded mark on drivebelt inner cover

6.5 Flywheel timing marks are visible through clutch housing inspection cover - 17D and 17DR engines

21 Now check that the valve timing is correct by ensuring that the locking bolt holes in the camshaft and fuel injection pump sprockets are aligned with their respective threaded holes in the engine casing before inserting the locking bolts (bolt sizes M6 x 1.00 for camshaft and M8 x 1.25 for injection pump). The mark on the crankshaft pulley should align with the pointer on the engine block.

Adjustment

22 If the locking bolt holes in the camshaft and fuel injection pump sprockets are not in alignment with their respective threaded holes in the engine casing, then the valve timing must be adjusted as follows.
23 Turn the steering wheel so that access to the side of the engine can be gained through the right-hand wheelarch, in front of the roadwheel.
24 Support the engine by positioning a jack beneath its sump and raising it slightly. Protect the sump by placing a piece of thick wood between it and the jack.
25 Remove the engine right-hand mounting by first removing its two centre bolts. Remove the two mounting-to-vehicle body retaining bolts and then the three mounting-to-engine bolts to allow the complete mounting assembly to be withdrawn. This will expose the timing belt tensioner assembly.
26 Release the tensioner by loosening the pulley centre bolt, the upper spring bracket securing bolt and the lower pivot securing nut. Push the tensioner spring towards the front of the engine to release belt tension and then nip tight the bracket securing bolt.
27 Slip the belt off the camshaft and injection pump sprockets.
28 Rotate the camshaft and fuel injection pump sprockets by the least amount until the locking bolt holes are aligned with their respective threaded holes in the engine casing. Insert the locking bolts. The mark on

the crankshaft pulley should still align with the pointer on the engine block.
29 Place the timing belt over the camshaft sprocket and then the injection pump sprocket.
30 Remove the sprocket locking bolts.
31 Release the tensioner spring bracket securing bolt to allow the tensioner to act upon the drivebelt. Turn the crankshaft against the normal direction of rotation by approximately 60 degrees to automatically tension the belt and then tighten the tensioner pulley centre bolt, the upper spring bracket securing bolt and the lower pivot securing nut to the specified torque settings (where given).
32 Confirm valve timing by turning the crankshaft in the normal direction of rotation two full turns and rechecking that all timing marks are in correct alignment.
33 With valve timing correct, reassemble all disturbed components whilst noting the specified torque settings.

6 Fuel injection pump timing - checking and adjustment

17D, 17DR and 17DTL engines

Bosch pump

1 Timing of the injection pump should only be necessary in the following circumstances:
a) When fitting a new or overhauled pump
b) If the timing is suspected of being wrong
c) If the timing belt has been re-tensioned or renewed

A dial test indicator with a long probe and a suitable support will be needed.
2 The procedure as shown here was carried out during engine rebuilding. With the engine

in the vehicle, it will be necessary to remov the timing belt covers, the air cleaner snorke and the clutch/flywheel cover.
3 Check the valve timing (Section 5).
4 Bring the engine to TDC, No 1 firing. Th timing mark on the pump sprocket must b aligned with the moulded mark on the timin belt inner cover (see illustration).
5 On 17D and 17DR engines, remove th clutch housing cover plate. With No 1 pisto set to TDC on the firing stroke, the TDC mar on the flywheel and the pointer on the clutc housing will be aligned (see illustration).
6 On 17DTL engines, remove the flywhee cover plate. Flywheel position for TDC mus be determined by the use of a setting too (Adjuster KM-851) fitted next to the flywhee as shown (see illustration). With No 1 pisto set to TDC on the firing stroke, the TDC mar on the flywheel and the pointer on the settin tool will be aligned.
7 Turn the engine against the norma direction of rotation so that the flywheel TD mark is approximately 5.0 cm away from th TDC pointer.

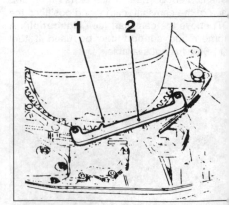

6.6 Determining flywheel position for TD by the use of a setting tool (Adjuster KM-851) - 17DTL engines
1 Flywheel TDC mark   2 Setting tool

6.8 Removing the plug from the rear of the injection pump

6.9 Dial test indicator mounted with its probe in the plug hole

Remove the central plug from the rear of the injection pump **(see illustration)**.

Mount the dial test indicator with its probe entering the central plug hole. Zero the indicator **(see illustration)**.

10 Be prepared for fuel spillage during subsequent operations. The manufacturers specify the use of a probe which screws into, and presumably seals, the plug hole.

11 Bring the engine back to TDC, No 1 firing. When the timing marks are aligned, the dial test indicator should show a lift corresponding to the desired timing setting - see Specifications.

12 If adjustment is necessary, slacken the three bolts which clamp together the two halves of the pump sprocket. Turn the inner part of the sprocket anti-clockwise (against the normal direction of rotation) as far as the slots will allow. The fit between the two parts of the sprocket is tight and a rod or soft metal drift may be needed to encourage the inner part to move.

13 With the sprocket positioned as just described and the engine still at TDC, No 1 firing, the dial test indicator should again read zero. Reset it if necessary.

14 Turn the inner part of the sprocket

clockwise until the dial test indicator shows the desired lift, then tighten the sprocket clamp bolts.

15 Repeat the checking procedure from paragraph 7.

16 When the injection timing is correct, remove the test gear and refit the plug to the rear of the pump.

17 Refit the timing belt covers and other disturbed components.

Lucas/CAV pump

18 There are some slight changes from the timing procedure above when dealing with the Lucas/CAV injection pump as detailed below.

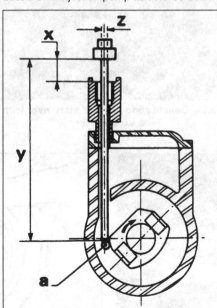

6.19b Special DTI probe shown in position during pump timing check - Lucas/CAV injection pump

a   Timing piece
x   Timing value (as shown on plate)
y   95.5 ± 0.01 mm
z   7.00 mm shank diameter

19 Note that the closing plug is located on the upper surface of the pump rather than at the end of the pump casing as on the Bosch pump. In the absence of the measuring tool KM-690-A and the dial test indicator KM-571-B, you will need a standard dial test indicator (DTI), together with some method of mounting it above the timing hole at the appropriate height. Also required is a headed probe made to the dimensions shown, this being placed in the timing hole before the DTI is mounted in position **(see illustrations)**.

20 Check the amount of lift indicated on the DTI when the crankshaft timing marks are brought into alignment. There is no standard specified lift figure for Lucas/CAV pumps. Each pump is calibrated during manufacture and the lift figure marked on a plate which is fitted to the pump lever **(see illustration)**. If the lift figure shown on the DTI does not correspond with that given on the plate, adjust the pump sprocket as described in above. Once adjustment is complete, remove the DTI with probe and refit the closing plug.

17DT engine

Note: *The following procedure was carried out with the engine removed from the vehicle. Should the engine be in the vehicle, then*

9B

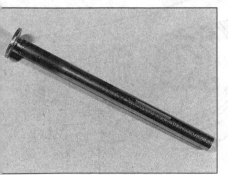

6.19a Home-made probe used for checking Lucas/CAV pump timing

6.20 Lucas/CAV pump showing DTI set up for timing check. Individual value for each pump is stamped on plate (arrowed)

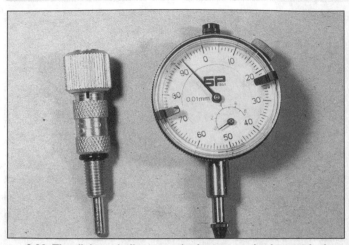

6.22 The dial test indicator and adapter required to set fuel injection pump timing

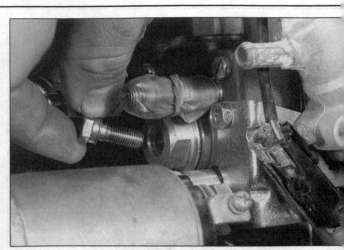

6.27 Removing the central plug from the injection pump

access to the injection pump will be restricted. Depending on vehicle type, remove the inlet manifold and/or the starter motor for access to the pump.

Note: *Ensure that valve timing is correct before checking fuel injection pump timing (see Section 6).*

21 Timing of the injection pump should only be necessary in the following circumstances:

a) *When fitting a new or overhauled pump*
b) *If the timing is suspected of being wrong*
c) *If the timing belt has been re-tensioned or renewed*

22 Obtain a dial test indicator (DTI) and adapter **(see illustration)**. The manufacturer specifies the use of an adapter which screws into, and seals, the plug hole.

23 Disconnect the battery earth lead.

24 Clean around the injection pipe unions t the pump and cylinder head.

25 Disconnect Nos 1 and 2 injection pipe from the injectors and the pump and remov them from the engine. Be prepared for fu spillage during subsequent operations.

26 Blank off all exposed pipe connections prevent the ingress of dirt and moisture.

27 Remove the central plug from the injectio pump **(see illustration)**.

28 Turn the crankshaft in the normal directio of rotation until the timing mark on its pulle aligns with the reference pointer on the engin block **(see illustration)**. In this position No piston is at TDC on the firing stroke.

29 Deactivate the cold start lever by using screwdriver as shown **(see illustration)**.

30 Fit the adapter and dial test indicator wit the indicator probe entering the central plu hole and contacting the pump piston **(se illustration)**.

31 Turn the crankshaft in the normal directio of rotation to approximately 60° before TD (No 1 firing) **(see illustration)**. At this poin

6.28 The timing mark on the crankshaft pulley aligned with the reference pointer on the engine block

6.29 Deactivating the cold start lever with a screwdriver

6.30 The adapter and dial test indicator fitted to the injection pump

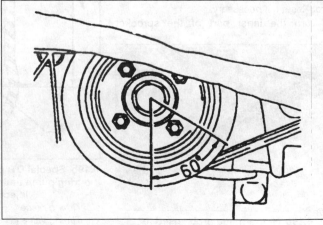

6.31 Turn the crankshaft in the normal direction of rotation to approximately 60° before TDC (No 1 firing)

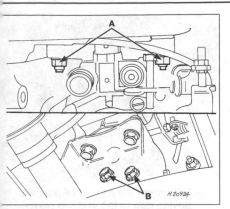

6.34 The fuel injection pump securing nuts (A) and pump bracket bolts (B)

the injection pump piston will be at bottom dead centre (BDC).

32 Zero the indicator, checking its adjustment by rotating the crankshaft slightly in either direction to ensure BDC.

33 Bring the engine back to TDC (No 1 firing).

When the timing mark on the pulley is aligned with the reference pointer, the dial test indicator should show a lift corresponding to the desired timing setting - see the *Specifications* at the start of this Chapter.

34 If adjustment is necessary, loosen the two nuts which secure the injection pump and the two bolts which secure the pump bracket **(see illustration)**.

35 Loosen Nos 3 and 4 injection pipes at the injectors and pump.

36 Rotate the pump until the dial test indicator shows the desired lift, then tighten the loosened nuts and bolts to the specified torque settings. Rotating the top of the pump towards the engine will lower the lift value, whereas rotating the pump in the opposite direction will raise the lift value.

37 Repeat the checking procedure.

38 With the pump timing correct, remove the DTI and adapter then refit the plug to the pump.

39 Remove any blanking materials and reconnect all injection pipe unions, working in

the reverse sequence to removal and tightening them to the specified torque settings.

40 Refit any other disturbed components, start the engine and check for fuel leaks.

7 Vacuum pump (17D, 17DR and 17DTL engines) - removal and refitting

Removal

1 Disconnect the servo vacuum pipe from the pump. Do this by counterholding the large union nut and unscrewing the small one **(see illustration)**.

2 On 17DR and 17DTL engines, disconnect the EGR system vacuum supply hose from the pump **(see illustration)**.

3 Remove the two pump securing screws and withdraw the pump from the camshaft housing **(see illustrations)**. Be prepared for some oil spillage.

7.1 Disconnecting the servo vacuum pipe from the vacuum pump

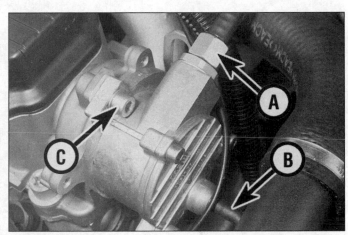

7.2 Vacuum pump connections - 17DR and 17DTL engines
A Servo vacuum pipe
B EGR system vacuum supply hose
C Pump securing screws (2 off)

7.3a Remove the two pump securing screws . . .

7.3b . . . and withdraw the vacuum pump from the camshaft housing

9B

4 Recover the small central oil pipe and the driving dog.

5 Discard the two O-rings fitted to the central oil pipe and also the pump body to camshaft housing seal **(see illustration)**.

Refitting

6 Fit new sealing rings to the pump assembly.

7 Refit the central oil pipe and the driving dog to the pump **(see illustration)**.

8 Offer the pump to the camshaft housing, making sure that the teeth of the driving dog engage with the slot in the camshaft end. Fit the pump securing screws and tighten them to the specified torque.

9 Reconnect and secure the vacuum pipe connection(s).

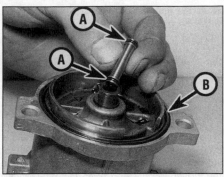

7.5 Renew the O-rings fitted to the central oil pipe (A) and the pump body to camshaft housing seal (B)

7.7 Refitting the central oil pipe with driving dog to the vacuum pump

Chapter 10A
Vauxhall/Opel Corsa petrol 1993 to 1997

Contents

Specifications

Timing belt renewal interval . . . . Every 36 000 miles (60 000 km) or 4 years - whichever comes first

Note: *Although the mileage interval for timing belt renewal is increased for later models, it is strongly recommended that the interval is reduced on vehicles which are subjected to intensive use, ie, mainly short journeys or a lot of stop-start driving. The actual belt renewal interval is therefore very much up to the individual owner. That being said, it is highly recommended to err on the side of safety, and renew the belt at this earlier interval, bearing in mind the drastic consequences resulting from belt failure.*

Torque wrench settings	Nm	lbf ft
Alternator adjuster bracket-to-cylinder head bolts (models with V-belt)	25	18
Alternator drivebelt tensioner roller-to-engine bolt (models with ribbed belt)	20	15
Alternator mounting bracket-to-engine bolts:		
SOHC engines (M10)	40	30
DOHC engine	35	26
Alternator-to-adjuster bracket bolts (models with V-belt)	25	18
Alternator-to-mounting bracket bolts:		
SOHC engines (M10)	40	30
SOHC engines (M8)	30	22
DOHC engine	35	26
Camshaft cover bolts	8	6
Camshaft cover plastic shield screws (DOHC engine)	4	3
Camshaft sprocket bolt:		
SOHC engines	45	33
DOHC engine	65	48
Coolant pump bolts	8	6
Crankshaft sprocket/pulley bolt:*		
Stage 1	95	70
Stage 2	Angle-tighten a further 30°	
Stage 3	Angle-tighten a further 15°	

10A

Torque wrench settings (continued)

	Nm	lbf ft
Left-hand engine/gearbox/transmission mounting block-to-body bolts**	65	48
Left-hand engine/gearbox/transmission mounting block-to-gearbox/transmission bracket bolts	60	44
Left-hand engine/gearbox/transmission mounting bracket-to-gearbox/transmission bolts	60	44
Rear engine/gearbox/transmission mounting block-to-body bolts	65	48
Rear engine/gearbox/transmission mounting block-to-gearbox/transmission bracket bolts	65	48
Rear engine/gearbox/transmission mounting bracket-to-gearbox/transmission bolts	70	52
Right-hand engine mounting block-to-body bolts:		
SOHC engine models without power steering	65	48
SOHC engine models with power steering	20	15
DOHC engine models	20	15
Right-hand engine mounting block-to-engine bracket bolt/nut	60	44
Right-hand engine mounting bracket-to-engine bolts:		
SOHC engine models without power steering	65	48
SOHC engine models with power steering	60	44
DOHC engine models	60	44
Spark plugs	25	18
Tie-bar bush bracket bolts:*		
Stage 1	50	37
Stage 2	Angle-tighten a further 90° to 105°	
Tie-bar front nut	90	66
Timing belt cover bolts:		
Outer	4	3
Rear:		
SOHC engines	12	9
DOHC engine	6	4
Timing belt tension indicator bolt (SOHC engines)	20	15
Timing belt tensioner bolt (DOHC engine)	20	15
Timing belt idler roller bolts (DOHC engine)	25	18
Roadwheel bolts	110	81

*Use new bolts
**Use thread locking compound

---

1 Auxiliary drivebelt - removal, refitting and adjustment

Models with V-belt

Removal and refitting

1 To remove the belt, simply loosen the mounting nuts and bolts, and the bolt securing the adjuster bracket, and slacken the belt sufficiently to slip it from the pulleys (see illustrations).

2 Refit the belt, and tension it as described below.

Adjustment

3 Although special tools are available for measuring the belt tension, a good approximation can be achieved if the belt is tensioned so that there is approximately 13.0 mm of free movement under firm thumb pressure at the mid-point of the longest run between pulleys. If in doubt, err on the slack side, as an excessively-tight belt may cause damage to the alternator or other components.

1.1a Loosening the alternator upper mounting nut and bolt

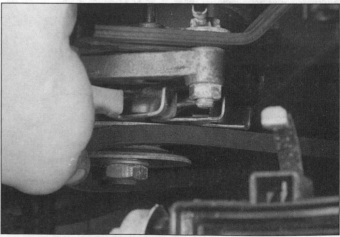

1.1b Removing the auxiliary drivebelt (V-belt type)

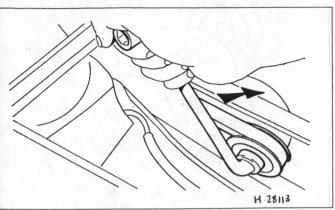

1.7a Lever the tensioner roller against the spring pressure . . .

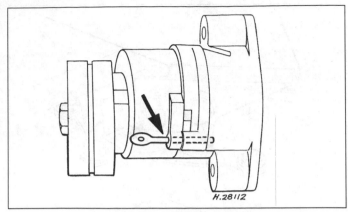

1.7b . . . until the roller can be locked in position using a suitable tool (arrowed)

If adjustment is required, loosen the alternator upper mounting nut and bolt - use two spanners, one to counterhold the bolt (see illustration 1.1a). Lever the alternator away from the engine using a wooden lever at the mounting bracket until the correct tension is achieved, then tighten the bolt securing the adjuster bracket, and the alternator mounting nuts and bolts. On no account lever at the free end of the alternator, as serious internal damage could be caused to the alternator.

Models with ribbed belt - models without power steering and air conditioning

Removal and refitting

5 To remove the drivebelt, remove the air cleaner assembly for improved access, as described in Section 10.

6 Mark the running direction of the belt if it is to be refitted.

7 Using a suitable spanner or socket and wrench engaged with the tensioner roller bolt, lever the tensioner roller against the spring pressure. The roller can then be locked in position, using a suitable pin punch or similar tool inserted through the lug on the roller assembly, to engage with the corresponding hole in the tensioner backplate (see illustrations).

8 With the tensioner locked in position, slip the drivebelt from the pulleys.

9 Refit the drivebelt by slipping the belt over the pulleys. If the original belt is being refitted, ensure that the running direction marks made on the belt are positioned as noted before removal.

10 Using the method described previously, lever the tensioner roller until the locking tool can be removed from the backplate. Use the spanner or wrench to gradually release the tensioner in order to tension the belt. Do not allow the tensioner to spring back unrestrained.

11 Check that the belt is correctly located on all the pulleys.

12 Refit the air cleaner assembly.

Adjustment

13 An automatic drivebelt tensioner is fitted, and there is no requirement to check the drivebelt tension.

Models with ribbed belt - models with power steering and air conditioning

Removal and refitting

14 Proceed as described in paragraphs 5 and 6.

15 Obtain a wire rod of approximately 4 mm (0.16 in) diameter x 280 mm (11 in). Make up a suitable tool as shown to lock the tensioner in position as the belt is removed (see illustration).

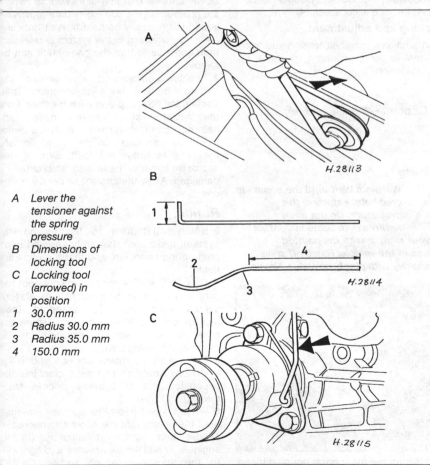

A Lever the tensioner against the spring pressure
B Dimensions of locking tool
C Locking tool (arrowed) in position
1 30.0 mm
2 Radius 30.0 mm
3 Radius 35.0 mm
4 150.0 mm

1.15 Tools used to lock tensioner in position - models with power steering and air conditioning

10A

1.18 Remove the nut and bolt (arrowed) securing the right-hand engine mounting bracket to the mounting block

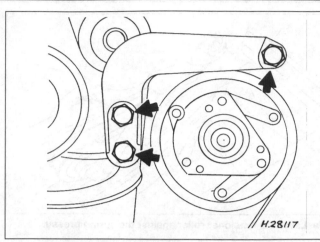

1.21 Unbolt the engine bracket (bolts arrowed) and withdraw it downwards

16 Using a suitable spanner or socket and wrench engaged with the tensioner roller bolt, lever the tensioner roller against the spring pressure. The roller can then be locked in position, using the tool inserted through the lug on the roller assembly, to engage with the corresponding hole in the tensioner backplate.

17 Attach a suitable hoist and lifting tackle to the engine lifting brackets on the cylinder head, and support the weight of the engine.

18 Working under the vehicle, remove the nut and bolt securing the right-hand engine mounting bracket to the mounting block on the body **(see illustration)**.

19 Remove the right-hand front suspension tie-bar.

20 Using the lifting tackle, lower the engine approximately 50.0 mm.

21 Unbolt the engine bracket from the power steering pump bracket **(see illustration)**, and withdraw it downwards from the engine compartment.

22 Withdraw the auxiliary drivebelt from the pulleys.

23 Proceed as described in paragraphs 9 to 11 inclusive.

24 Refit the engine bracket, and tighten the securing bolts.

25 Raise the engine, using the lifting tackle, and refit the right-hand front suspension tie-bar.

26 Refit the nut and bolt securing the right-hand engine mounting to the mounting block on the body, and tighten the nut and bolt to the specified torque.

27 Disconnect the hoist and lifting tackle.

28 Refit the air cleaner assembly.

Checking and adjustment

29 An automatic drivebelt tensioner is fitted, and there is no requirement to check the drivebelt tension.

---

2 Coolant - draining and refilling

Draining

⚠️ **Warning: Wait until the engine is cold before starting this procedure. Do not allow antifreeze to come in contact with your skin, or with the painted surfaces of the vehicle. Rinse off spills immediately with plenty of water. Never**

leave antifreeze lying around in an open container, or in a puddle on the driveway or garage floor. Children and pets are attracted by its sweet smell, but antifreeze is fatal if ingested.

1 To drain the cooling system, first cover the expansion tank cap with a wad of rag, and slowly turn the cap anti-clockwise to relieve the pressure in the cooling system (a hissing sound will normally be heard). Wait until any pressure remaining in the system is released then continue to turn the cap until it can be removed.

2 Position a suitable container beneath the radiator bottom hose connection, then slacken the hose clip and ease the hose from the radiator stub. If the hose joint has not been disturbed for some time it will be necessary to gently manipulate the hose to break the joint. Do not use excessive force, or the radiator stub could be damaged. Allow the coolant to drain into the container.

Refilling

3 Before attempting to fill the cooling system, make sure that all hoses and clips are in good condition, and that the clips are tight.

4 On SOHC engine models, disconnect the wire and unscrew the coolant temperature sender from the inlet manifold **(see illustration)**. On DOHC models, unscrew the bleed screw which is situated in the thermostat housing cover.

5 Remove the expansion tank cap, and fill the system by slowly pouring the coolant into the expansion tank to prevent airlocks from forming.

6 When coolant free of air bubbles emerges from the orifice, refit the coolant temperature sender and tighten it securely (SOHC engines), or refit the bleed screw and tighten it to the specified torque setting (DOHC engines) **(see illustration)**.

7 Top-up the coolant level to the KALT (or

2.4 On SOHC engine models, remove the coolant temperature sender (arrowed) before filling the cooling system

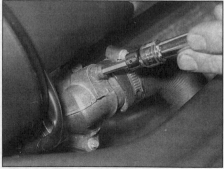

2.6 Refitting the thermostat housing bleed screw - DOHC engine

3.6a Camshaft sprocket timing mark aligned with notch in rear timing belt cover (No 1 piston at TDC) - SOHC engines

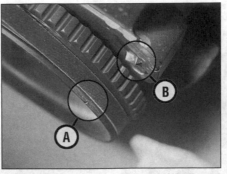

3.6b Notch in crankshaft pulley (A) aligned with timing pointer (B) on timing belt cover (No 1 piston at TDC) - SOHC engines

3.6c Crankshaft sprocket timing mark aligned with mark on rear timing belt cover and oil pump lower flange (No 1 piston at TDC) - SOHC engines

COLD) mark on the expansion tank, then refit the expansion tank cap.

8 Start the engine and run it until it reaches normal operating temperature, then stop the engine and allow it to cool.

9 Check for leaks, particularly around disturbed components. Check the coolant level in the expansion tank, and top-up if necessary. Note that the system must be cold before an accurate level is indicated in the expansion tank.

3 Top dead centre (TDC) for No 1 piston - locating

1 Top dead centre (TDC) is the highest point in the cylinder that a piston reaches as the crankshaft turns. Each piston reaches TDC at the end of the compression stroke, and again at the end of the exhaust stroke. For the purpose of timing the engine, TDC refers to the position of No 1 piston at the end of its compression stroke. On all engines in this manual, No 1 piston and cylinder are at the timing belt end of the engine.

2 All engine overhaul procedures use the factory timing marks, which vary according to engine type.

3 Disconnect both battery leads.

4 Remove the upper outer timing belt cover as described in Section 6.

5 Using a suitable spanner or socket on the crankshaft pulley bolt (note that on manual gearbox models, the crankshaft can be turned by engaging top gear, and pushing the vehicle backwards or forwards as necessary), rotate the crankshaft to bring No 1 piston to TDC as follows, according to engine type. Whatever method is used, turning the engine will be made much easier if the spark plugs are removed first.

SOHC engines

6 The timing marks must be aligned as follows (see illustrations).
a)   The timing mark on the camshaft sprocket

must be aligned with the notch in the rear timing belt cover.

b)   The notch in the crankshaft pulley, or the timing mark on the TDC sensor wheel (as applicable) must be aligned with the pointer (raised line) on the timing belt cover. Note that if the crankshaft pulley and lower outer timing belt cover have been removed, the timing mark on the

crankshaft sprocket can be used instead of the mark on the pulley. The mark on the crankshaft sprocket must align with the corresponding mark on the rear timing belt cover, and the oil pump lower flange.

DOHC engines

7 The timing marks must be aligned as follows (see illustrations).

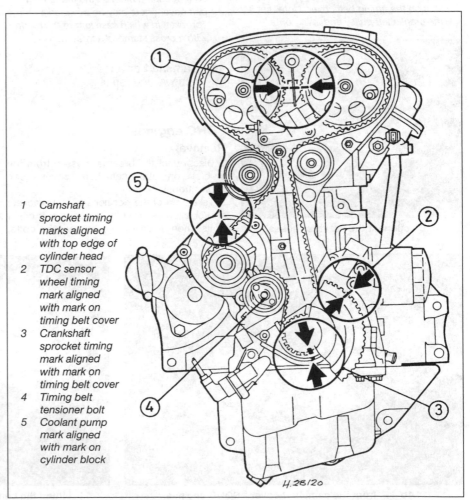

1   Camshaft sprocket timing marks aligned with top edge of cylinder head
2   TDC sensor wheel timing mark aligned with mark on timing belt cover
3   Crankshaft sprocket timing mark aligned with mark on timing belt cover
4   Timing belt tensioner bolt
5   Coolant pump mark aligned with mark on cylinder block

3.7a Timing mark positions with No 1 piston at TDC - DOHC engine

3.7b Camshaft sprocket timing marks (A) aligned with top edge of cylinder head (B) - DOHC engine

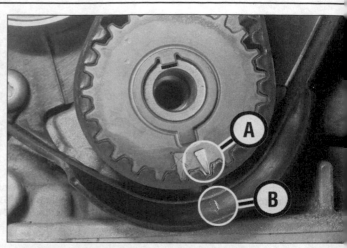

3.7c Crankshaft sprocket timing mark (A) aligned with mark (B) on timing belt cover - DOHC engine

a) The timing marks on the camshaft sprockets must be directly opposite each other, and aligned with the top edge of the cylinder head.

b) The timing mark on the TDC sensor wheel must be aligned with the pointer (raised line) on the timing belt cover. Note that if the crankshaft pulley and lower outer timing belt cover have been removed, the timing mark on the crankshaft sprocket can be used instead of the mark on the pulley. The mark on the crankshaft sprocket must align with the corresponding mark on the rear timing belt cover (there may be two marks on the sprocket, in which case ignore the mark with a cross stamped across it).

4 Camshaft cover - removal and refitting

SOHC engines

Removal

1 Disconnect the breather hose(s) from the stub(s) on the camshaft cover **(see illustrations)**.

2 Take note of the positions of any brackets and/or clips secured by the camshaft cover bolts, then unscrew and remove the bolts, along with the clips and/or brackets, as applicable.

3 Lift the camshaft cover from the camshaft housing **(see illustration)**. If the cover is stuck, do not lever between the cover and camshaft housing mating surfaces - if necessary, gently tap the cover sideways to free it. Recover the cork gasket or rubber seal, as applicable.

Refitting

4 Before refitting, examine the inside of the cover for a build-up of oil sludge or any other contamination, and if necessary clean the cover with paraffin, or a water-soluble solvent. Where applicable, examine the condition of the crankcase ventilation filter inside the camshaft cover, and clean as described for the inside of the cover if clogging is evident (if desired, the filter can be removed from the cover, after removing the securing bolts). Dry the cover thoroughly before refitting.

5 Where applicable, examine the condition of the rubber seal, and if necessary renew it.

4.1a Disconnect the breather hoses . . .

4.1b . . . from the camshaft cover - SOHC engines

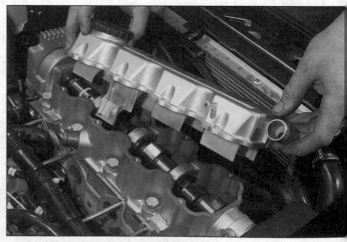

4.3 Lifting the camshaft cover from the camshaft housing - SOHC engines

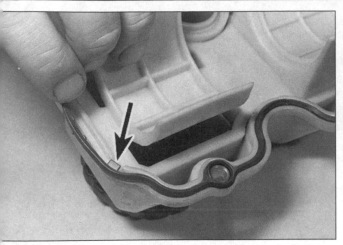

4.5 Tag on seal (arrowed) engages with notch in camshaft cover - SOHC engines

4.8 Ensure that the brackets (arrowed) are in place on the camshaft cover bolts - SOHC engines

Note that on certain models, the seal rests in a groove in the cover, and a tag on the seal engages with the notch in the cover when the seal is correctly positioned (see illustration). If a cork gasket was fitted, it should always be renewed on refitting.

6 Thoroughly clean the mating faces of the camshaft housing and the cover.

7 Position the cover on the camshaft housing, noting that the breather pipe stub(s) should be nearest the timing belt end of the engine.

8 Refit the securing bolts, ensuring that any clips and/or brackets are in place under their heads as noted before removal, and tighten the bolts to the specified torque in a diagonal sequence (see illustration).

9 Reconnect the breather hose(s) to the stub(s) on the cover.

DOHC engines

Removal

10 Remove the upper section of the inlet manifold as described in Section 11.

11 Disconnect the breather hoses from the flywheel end of the camshaft cover (see illustration).

12 Using the tool provided (attached to one of the spark plug HT lead connectors), pull the HT leads from the spark plugs, and lay them to one side, clear of the camshaft cover.

13 Progressively loosen the camshaft cover securing bolts (preferably working from the ends of the cover towards the centre, in a spiral pattern), then withdraw the bolts (see illustration).

14 Lift the camshaft cover from the cylinder head (see illustration), and recover the rubber gaskets and O-rings.

Refitting

15 Commence refitting by examining the condition of the rubber gaskets and O-rings. If necessary, renew the gaskets and O-rings.

16 Ensure that the gaskets and O-rings are correctly located on the camshaft cover (see illustrations).

17 Fit the cover to the cylinder head, then refit the securing bolts. Tighten the bolts to the specified torque, working from the centre to the ends of the cover, in a spiral pattern.

18 Reconnect the HT leads to the spark plugs.

19 Reconnect the breather hose to the camshaft cover.

20 Refit the upper section of the inlet manifold as described in Section 11.

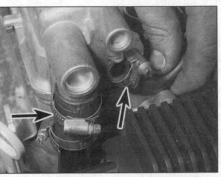

4.11 Disconnect the breather hoses (arrowed) from the camshaft cover

4.13 Unscrew the bolts . . .

4.14 . . . and lift the camshaft cover from the cylinder head

4.16a Ensure that the gaskets are correctly located

4.16b Hold the O-rings in position using a little grease

10A

5.4 Removing the crankshaft pulley - note notch in pulley and locating lug on sprocket (arrowed)

5.7 Using an angle gauge to tighten the crankshaft pulley bolt to the final stage

5 Crankshaft pulley - removal and refitting

Note: *Due to the high specified torque for the sprocket/pulley securing bolt, it is suggested that consideration is given to renewing the bolt on refitting, although this is not specified by the manufacturers.*

Removal

1 Access is most easily obtained from under the wheelarch, after jacking up the vehicle and removing the right-hand front wheel. If necessary for subsequent operations, rotate the crankshaft to position No 1 piston to TDC as described in Section 3.

2 Remove the auxiliary drivebelt as described in Section 1.

3 To prevent the crankshaft from turning as the bolt is unscrewed, select top gear and have an assistant apply the brakes hard (manual gearbox models only). Alternatively, remove the starter motor, and lock the flywheel ring gear teeth using a suitable tool.

4 Unscrew the bolt and recover the washer fitted behind it, then remove the pulley **(see illustration)**. Note that on DOHC engines, an

E18 Torx socket will be required to unscrew the pulley bolt.

Refitting

5 On refitting, ensure that the notch in the pulley fits over the locating lug on the crankshaft sprocket.

6 Prevent the crankshaft from turning as during removal, then fit the securing bolt, ensuring that the washer is in place under the bolt head.

7 Tighten the bolt to the specified torque, in the stages given in the Specifications **(see illustration)**.

8 Refit and tension the auxiliary drivebelt, as described in Section 1.

6 Timing belt covers - removal and refitting

SOHC engines

Upper outer cover - removal

1 For improved access, remove the air cleaner assembly, and the air inlet trunking, as described in Section 10.

2 Remove the auxiliary drivebelt, as described in Section 1.

3 Unscrew the three securing bolts, and unclip the lower edge of the upper cover from the lower cover. Withdraw the upper cover **(see illustration)**.

Upper outer cover - refitting

4 Refitting is a reversal of removal, but refit and tension the auxiliary drivebelt as described in Section 1.

Lower outer cover - removal

5 For improved access, raise the front right-hand side of the vehicle, and support securely on axle stands. Remove the roadwheel.

6 If desired, to further improve access, remove the underwing shield (see Section 13).

7 Remove the crankshaft pulley as described in Section 5.

8 Where applicable, unclip the TDC sensor wiring from the lower timing belt cover.

9 Unscrew the securing bolts, and remove the lower timing belt cover **(see illustrations)**.

Lower outer cover - refitting

10 Refitting is a reversal of removal. Refit the crankshaft pulley as described in Section 5.

6.3 Upper timing belt cover securing bolts (arrowed) - SOHC engines

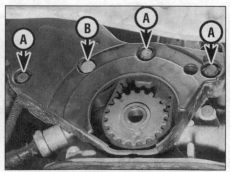

6.9a Unscrew the securing bolts (A) . . .
B Timing belt tensioner securing bolt

6.9b . . . and remove the lower timing belt cover - SOHC engines

6.14 Unscrewing a rear timing belt cover upper securing screw - SOHC engines

6.15 Crankshaft speed/position sensor wiring clipped to rear of rear timing belt cover - SOHC engines

Rear cover - removal

11 Remove the outer covers as described previously in this Section.

12 Remove the timing belt and sprockets as described in Sections 7 and 8.

13 Unscrew the securing bolt, and remove the timing belt tension indicator assembly from the cylinder block.

14 Unscrew the two upper and two lower screws securing the rear timing belt cover **(see illustration)**.

15 Withdraw the rear cover, and where applicable, unclip the crankshaft speed/position sensor wiring from the rear of the cover **(see illustration)**.

Rear cover - refitting

16 Refitting is a reversal of removal, bearing in mind the following points.

a) *Refit the timing belt sprockets as described in Section 8.*

b) *Refit and tension the timing belt as described in Section 7.*

c) *Refit the outer timing belt covers as described previously in this Section.*

DOHC engines

Upper outer cover - removal

17 For improved access, remove the air cleaner assembly (where applicable, complete with the air mass meter), as described in Section 10.

18 Unclip the camshaft position sensor wiring from the timing belt cover, noting its routing.

19 Unscrew the three securing bolts, and remove the cover **(see illustration)**.

Upper outer cover - refitting

20 Refitting is a reversal of removal, ensuring that the camshaft position sensor wiring is routed as noted before removal.

Lower outer cover - removal

21 For improved access, raise the front right-hand side of the vehicle, and support securely on axle stands. Remove the roadwheel.

22 If desired, to further improve access, remove the underwing shield (see Section 13).

23 Remove the upper outer timing belt cover, as described previously in this Section.

24 Remove the crankshaft pulley, as described in Section 5.

25 Remove the two securing bolts, then release the four clips, and withdraw the lower outer cover **(see illustrations)**.

6.19 Removing the upper outer timing belt cover - DOHC engine

6.25a Lower outer timing belt cover upper securing bolt (arrowed) . . .

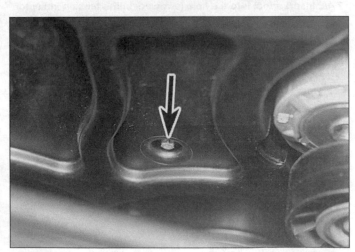

6.25b . . . and lower (arrowed) securing bolt - DOHC engine

10A

6.30 Rear timing belt cover securing bolts - arrowed (seen with timing belt and sprockets still fitted)

Lower outer cover - refitting

26 Refitting is a reversal of removal, but refit the crankshaft pulley with reference to Section 5.

Rear cover - removal

27 Remove the outer covers as described previously in this Section.

28 Remove the timing belt, sprockets and inlet-side idler roller, as described in Sections 7 and 8.

29 Unscrew the securing bolt and remove the timing belt tensioner.

30 Unscrew the two upper and two lower securing screws, and withdraw the rear cover from the engine **(see illustration)**.

Rear cover - refitting

31 Refitting is a reversal of removal, bearing in mind the following points:

a) *Refit the timing belt sprockets as described in Section 8.*

b) *Refit and tension the timing belt as described in Section 7.*

c) *Refit the outer timing belt covers as described previously in this Section.*

7 Timing belt - removal and refitting

SOHC engines

Removal

Note: *The engine must be cold when removing the timing belt.*

1 Disconnect the battery negative lead.

2 Remove the outer timing belt covers as described in Section 6.

3 If not already done, turn the crankshaft to bring No 1 piston to top dead centre, as described in Section 3.

4 Insert a suitable tool (such as a pin punch) into the hole in the timing belt tension indicator arm, then lever the arm clockwise to its stop, and lock in position by inserting the tool into the corresponding hole in the tension indicator backplate **(see illustrations)**. Leave the tool in position to lock the tension indicator until the belt is refitted.

5 Loosen the three coolant pump securing bolts, using a suitable Allen key or hexagon bit, then turn the pump to relieve the tension in the timing belt **(see illustration)**.

6 Slide the timing belt from the sprockets, and withdraw it from the engine **(see illustration)**. Take note of any arrows marked on the belt to indicate the direction of rotation (if necessary, mark the belt to aid correct refitting).

Refitting

7 Ensure that No 1 piston is still positioned at top dead centre, as described in Section 3.

7.4a Insert a tool into the hole (arrowed) in the tension indicator arm . . .

7.4b . . . then lever the arm clockwise and lock in position - SOHC engines

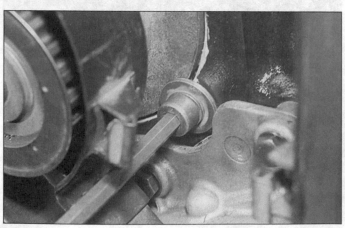

7.5 Loosening a coolant pump securing bolt

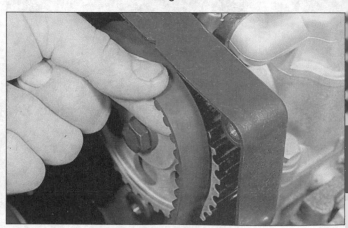

7.6 Sliding the timing belt from the camshaft sprocket - SOHC engines

7.10 Using special tool KM-421-A to turn the coolant pump - SOHC engines

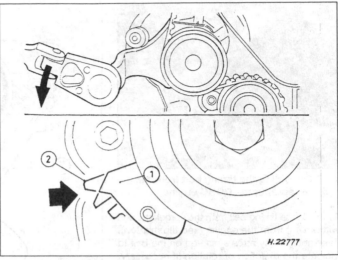

7.13 Turn the coolant pump (special tool shown) anti-clockwise until the tension indicator pointer (1) is positioned in the centre of the V (2) - SOHC engines

Refit the timing belt around the sprockets, starting at the crankshaft sprocket.

Remove the tool holding the belt tensioner retracted.

0 Turn the coolant pump clockwise to increase the belt tension until the tensioner indicator arm moves fully clockwise to its stop (ie the holes in the indicator arm and the tensioner backplate are aligned). Note that a special tool is available to turn the coolant pump (Vauxhall/Opel tool KM-421-A or equivalent) **(see illustration).**

1 Tighten the coolant pump securing bolts sufficiently to prevent the pump from moving during the following operation.

2 Using a suitable socket or spanner on the crankshaft pulley bolt, turn the crankshaft clockwise through two complete revolutions, until No 1 piston is again positioned at top dead centre. Turn the crankshaft smoothly without jerking, to avoid the belt jumping on the pulleys. Check that the timing marks are correctly aligned as described in Section 3.

13 Carefully turn the coolant pump anti-clockwise to slacken the belt, until the tension indicator pointer is positioned in the centre of the V on the tensioner backplate **(see illustration)**, then tighten the coolant pump securing bolts to the specified torque.

14 Turn the crankshaft clockwise through two complete revolutions, as described previously, and check that the tension indicator pointer is still positioned as described in paragraph 13 - if not, the procedure must be repeated until the pointer aligns correctly.

15 On completion, refit the spark plugs (where applicable), and refit the outer timing belt covers as described in Section 6. Reconnect the battery negative lead.

DOHC engines
Removal
Note: *The engine must be cold when removing the timing belt.*

16 Disconnect the battery negative lead.

17 Remove the outer timing belt covers as described in Section 6.

18 If not already done, turn the crankshaft to bring No 1 piston to top dead centre, as described in Section 3.

19 Unscrew the two bolts securing the camshaft position sensor mounting bracket to the cylinder head, and move the sensor/bracket assembly to one side **(see illustration)**.

20 Loosen the belt tensioner securing bolt sufficiently to completely relieve the tension in the belt. If necessary, turn the tensioner clockwise to relieve the tension, using a suitable hexagon bit or Allen key engaged with the hole provided in the tensioner front plate **(see illustration)**.

7.19 Withdraw the camshaft position sensor - DOHC engine

7.20 Timing belt tensioner securing bolt (1) and hexagon hole (2) in front plate - DOHC engine

10A

7.21 Sliding the timing belt from the sprockets - DOHC engine

21 Slide the timing belt from the sprockets, and withdraw it from the engine **(see illustration)**. Take note of any arrows marked on the belt to indicate the direction of rotation (if necessary, mark the belt to aid correct refitting).

Refitting

22 Ensure that No 1 piston is still positioned at top dead centre, as described in Section 3.
23 If the coolant pump has been disturbed, check the position of the pump. The mark on the edge of the pump must be aligned with the corresponding mark on the cylinder block. If necessary, loosen the securing bolts, and turn the pump as required to align the marks, then tighten the bolts to the specified torque.
24 Refit the timing belt around the sprockets, starting at the crankshaft sprocket, and working in the order shown **(see illustration)**. **Note:** *When fitting the belt over the inlet camshaft sprocket, ensure that the belt does not jump a tooth on the sprocket, and make sure that the timing marks on both camshaft sprockets stay positioned directly opposite each other, and aligned with the top edge of the cylinder head.*
25 With the tensioner securing bolt loosened, engage a suitable hexagon bit or Allen key with the hole provided in the tensioner front plate, and turn the tensioner anti-clockwise until maximum tension is attained. The tension indicator pointer should be positioned to the

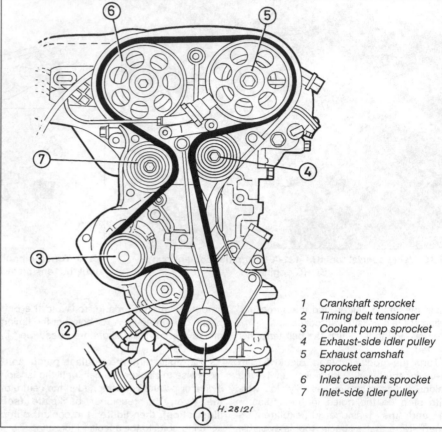

1 Crankshaft sprocket
2 Timing belt tensioner
3 Coolant pump sprocket
4 Exhaust-side idler pulley
5 Exhaust camshaft sprocket
6 Inlet camshaft sprocket
7 Inlet-side idler pulley

7.24 Fit the timing belt around the sprockets in the order shown - DOHC engine

right of the V on the tensioner backplate **(see illustration)**. Note that there is no stop on the tensioner front plate, so it is possible to turn the plate beyond the maximum tension position.
26 Tighten the tensioner securing bolt in this position.
27 Using a suitable socket or spanner on the crankshaft pulley bolt, turn the crankshaft clockwise through two complete revolutions, until No 1 piston is again positioned at top dead centre. Turn the crankshaft smoothly

without jerking, to avoid the belt jumping on the pulleys. Check that the timing marks are correctly aligned as described in Section 3.
28 Engage the hexagon bit or Allen key with the hole in the tensioner front plate, then slacken the tensioner securing bolt, and carefully turn the front plate clockwise to slacken the belt. If a new timing belt has been fitted, the tension indicator pointer should be positioned in the centre of the V on the tensioner backplate **(see illustration)**. If a run-

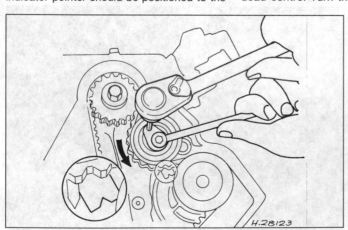

7.25 Turn the tensioner anti-clockwise until maximum tension is attained, with the pointer positioned to the right of the V (inset) - DOHC engine

7.28 To set the belt tension on a new belt, turn the tensioner clockwise until the pointer is positioned in the centre of the V - DOHC engine

8.2 Improvised tool being used to hold the camshaft sprocket stationary - SOHC engines

8.5 Lug (1) on camshaft engages with hole (2) in sprocket - SOHC engines

8.6 Tightening the camshaft sprocket securing bolt while holding the camshaft using a spanner on the camshaft flats - SOHC engines

belt has been fitted (one that has been used for more than a few hours), the tension indicator pointer should be positioned approximately 4 mm to the left of the centre of the V. Tighten the tensioner securing bolt to the specified torque.

29 Turn the crankshaft clockwise through two complete revolutions, as described previously, and check that the tension indicator pointer is still positioned as described in paragraph 28 - if not, the procedure must be repeated until the pointer aligns correctly.

30 On completion, refit the spark plugs (where applicable), and refit the outer timing belt covers as described in Section 6. Reconnect the battery negative lead.

8 Timing belt sprockets and idler rollers - removal and refitting

Camshaft sprocket - SOHC engines

Removal

1 Remove the timing belt as described in

Section 7. Note that if only the camshaft sprocket is to be removed, the timing belt can be left engaged with the remaining sprockets, and slipped from the camshaft sprocket once the tension has been relieved.

2 The camshaft must be prevented from turning as the sprocket bolt is unscrewed, and this can be achieved in one of two ways as follows.

a) *Make up a tool similar to that shown (see illustration), and use it to hold the sprocket stationary by means of the holes in the sprocket face.*

b) *With the camshaft cover removed as described in Section 4, prevent the camshaft from turning by holding it with a suitable spanner on the flats provided between Nos 3 and 4 camshaft lobes.*

3 Unscrew the camshaft sprocket bolt and withdraw it, noting the washer under the bolt head.

4 Withdraw the sprocket from the end of the camshaft, where applicable manipulating the timing belt from the sprocket as it is withdrawn.

Refitting

5 Commence refitting by offering the camshaft sprocket to the camshaft, making

sure that the lug on the end of the camshaft engages with the corresponding hole in the camshaft sprocket **(see illustration)**.

6 Refit the sprocket securing bolt, ensuring that the washer is in place, and tighten the bolt to the specified torque, preventing the camshaft from turning as during removal **(see illustration)**.

7 Where applicable, refit the camshaft cover as described in Section 4.

8 Refit and tension the timing belt as described in Section 7.

Camshaft sprockets - DOHC engines

Removal

9 Remove the timing belt as described in Section 7.

10 The camshaft sprocket bolt must be prevented from turning as the sprocket bolt is unscrewed, and this can be achieved in one of two ways as follows **(see illustrations)**.

a) *Pass a suitable Torx bit and extension bar through one of the holes in the camshaft sprocket, to engage with the rear timing belt cover bolt. Use the Torx bit and extension bar to counterhold the sprocket as the bolt is loosened.*

8.10a Using a Torx bit engaged with the rear timing belt cover bolt hole to counterhold the inlet camshaft sprocket - DOHC engine

8.10b Counterholding the inlet camshaft using a spanner on the flats in front of No 1 cam lobe - DOHC engine

10A

8.11 Removing the inlet camshaft sprocket - DOHC engine

8.16 Refit the crankshaft sprocket with the locating flange and locating lug for pulley outermost - SOHC engines

b) *With the camshaft cover removed as described in Section 4, prevent the camshaft from turning by holding it with a suitable spanner on the flats provided in front of No 1 cam lobe.*

11 Unscrew the camshaft sprocket bolt and withdraw it, noting the washer under the bolt head **(see illustration)**.

12 Withdraw the sprocket from the end of the camshaft.

Refitting

13 Proceed as described in paragraphs 5 to 8 inclusive, noting the following points:
a) *Ensure that the sprocket is fitted so that the timing mark is visible on the outer face.*
b) *If both camshaft sprockets have been removed, ensure that they are refitted to their correct camshafts - the exhaust camshaft sprocket is fitted with lugs which activate the camshaft position sensor.*

Crankshaft sprocket

Note: *It is recommended that a new securing bolt is used when refitting the crankshaft pulley - see Section 5.*

Removal

14 Remove the timing belt as described in Section 7.

15 Remove the sprocket from the end of the crankshaft.

Refitting

16 Refit the crankshaft sprocket with the locating flange and locating lug for the crankshaft pulley outermost **(see illustration)**.

17 Refit and tension the timing belt as described in Section 7.

Idler rollers - DOHC engines

Removal

18 Remove the timing belt as described in Section 7.

19 Unscrew the securing bolt, and remove the relevant idler roller.

Refitting

20 If both idler rollers have been removed, note that the larger-diameter roller fits on the inlet side of the engine **(see illustration)**.

21 Refit the relevant idler roller, and tighten the securing bolt to the specified torque.

22 Refit the timing belt as described in Section 7.

9 Timing belt tension indicator (SOHC) and tensioner (DOHC) - removal and refitting

Removal

1 On SOHC engines, the tension indicator simply provides a way of ensuring that the timing belt tension is correct - the belt is tensioned by adjusting the position of the coolant pump. On the DOHC engine, the tensioner is used to tension the timing belt and it incorporates a tension indicator, similar to that used on the SOHC engines.

2 Remove the timing belt as described in Section 7.

3 Unscrew the central securing bolt, and withdraw the tension indicator/tensioner **(see illustration)**.

Refitting

4 Refit the tension indicator, ensuring that the lug on the indicator/tensioner backplate

8.20 Timing belt idler rollers (arrowed) - DOHC engine

9.3 Withdrawing the timing belt tension indicator - SOHC engines

9.4 Lug (1) on tension indicator backplate must engage with hole (2) in oil pump - SOHC engines (shown with engine removed from vehicle)

10.4 Disconnect the wiring plug from the air mass meter - C 16 XE DOHC engine models

10.6 Disconnecting the intake air temperature control vacuum pipe from the air cleaner

engages with the corresponding hole in the oil pump (see illustration).

Refit the indicator/tensioner securing bolt, and on SOHC engines, tighten it to the specified torque. On DOHC engines, do not tighten the bolt until the timing belt has been tensioned.

Refit and tension the timing belt, as described in Section 7.

10 Air cleaner assembly - removal and refitting

Removal

Disconnect the battery negative lead.

Where applicable, disconnect the wiring plug from the intake air temperature sensor, located in the air inlet trunking.

Disconnect the air inlet trunking from the airbox on the fuel injection unit (single-point fuel injection models), or the throttle body (multi-point fuel injection models), as applicable.

Release the securing clips, then lift off the air cleaner cover, and remove it from the vehicle. On C 16 XE DOHC engine models, disconnect the wiring plug from the air mass meter (see illustration).

Lift out the air cleaner element.

Where applicable, disconnect the intake air temperature control vacuum pipe from the air cleaner casing (see illustration).

Where applicable, disconnect the hot-air trunking from the exhaust manifold hot-air shroud (see illustration).

8 Remove the clip securing the air intake trunking to the engine compartment front crossmember, then disconnect the trunking from the front of the air cleaner casing, and withdraw the trunking (see illustrations).

9 Pull the air cleaner front locating grommet to release it from the hole in the air cleaner casing, then pull the casing upwards over the grommet (see illustration).

10 Pull the assembly forwards to release the rear locating rubbers, and withdraw it from the engine compartment (see illustrations).

Refitting

11 Refitting is a reversal of removal.

10.7 Disconnecting the hot-air trunking from the exhaust manifold hot-air shroud

10.8a Remove the air intake trunking securing clip from the crossmember . . .

10.8b . . . and disconnect the trunking from the air cleaner casing

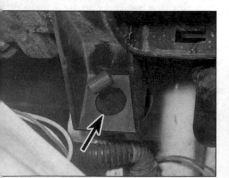

10.9 Pull the front locating grommet (arrowed) upwards . . .

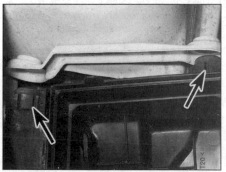

10.10a . . . then pull the air cleaner assembly forwards to release the rear locating rubbers (arrowed) . . .

10.10b . . . and withdraw the assembly

10A

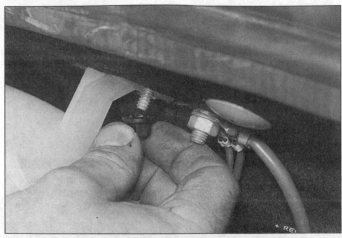

11.3a Removing an expansion tank securing nut

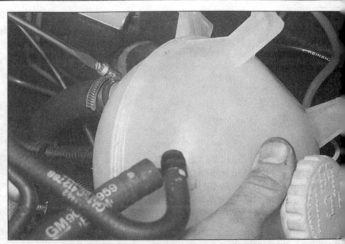

11.3b Access to the lower hose is easier once the tank has been removed

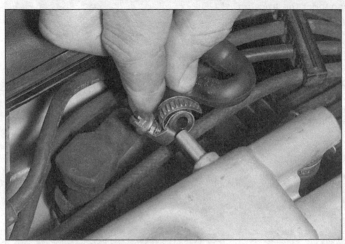

11.5a Disconnect the breather hose from the camshaft cover . . .

11.5b . . . and the brake servo vacuum hose from the upper section of the inlet manifold

11 Inlet manifold upper section (DOHC) - removal and refitting

Note: *A new throttle body-to-mounting bracket gasket must be used on refitting. A new O-ring and gasket may be required when refitting the upper section of the inlet manifold to the throttle body mounting bracket and the lower section of the inlet manifold.*

Removal

1 Disconnect the battery negative lead.
2 Partially drain the cooling system as described in Section 1 (drain sufficient coolant to empty the coolant expansion tank).
3 Disconnect the hoses from the coolant expansion tank, then unscrew the securing nuts, and withdraw the expansion tank. Note that the lower hose is more easily disconnected once the tank has been removed **(see illustrations)**.
4 Remove the oil filler cap, then remove the two securing screws, and lift off the plastic shield which fits over the top of the camshaft cover.
5 Disconnect the breather hose from the camshaft cover, and the brake servo vacuum hose from the upper section of the inlet manifold **(see illustrations)**.
6 Disconnect the manifold vacuum hoses from the fuel pressure regulator and the evaporative emission control solenoid valve, located at the flywheel end of the upper section of the inlet manifold. Alternatively, disconnect these hoses from the manifold itself.
7 Disconnect the breather hose (which runs across the top of the fuel tank vent valve) from the camshaft cover.
8 Release the fuel tank vent valve retaining clip, where fitted, (using a screwdriver or similar tool), and withdraw the valve upwards from its mounting bracket. Leave the remaining hose(s) connected, and place the valve to one side, clear of the working area **(see illustration)**.

9 Loosen the clamp screw, and disconnec the air trunking from the lower end of th throttle body.
10 On C 16 XE engines, remove the starte motor as described in Section 12. Move th air trunking away from the throttle body, t gain access to the throttle body securing bolt (if desired, the bolt securing the air trunking t

11.8 Move the fuel tank vent valve to one side

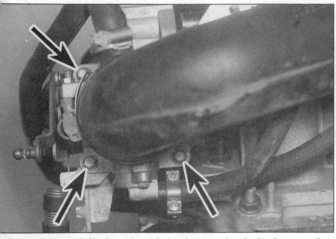

11.11a Three of the four throttle body securing bolts (arrowed) - viewed from underneath with engine removed

11.11b Throttle body securing bolt (arrowed)

he bracket on the inlet manifold can be emoved).

1 On C 16 XE engines, working underneath he vehicle, remove the four bolts which ecure the throttle body to its mounting racket and the upper section of the inlet anifold **(see illustrations)**.

2 On all engines, unscrew the securing olts, and withdraw the upper section of the inlet manifold. Note that on C 16 XE engines, he throttle body will now be loose - ensure hat none of the hoses or wiring connectors re strained. Recover the gasket between the upper and lower sections of the manifold if it s loose **(see illustrations)**.

3 On C 16 XE engines, recover the O-ring etween the throttle body mounting bracket nd the upper section of the inlet manifold, nd the gasket between the throttle body and he mounting bracket.

Refitting

4 Commence refitting by checking the ondition of the rubber gasket which fits etween the upper and lower sections of the

inlet manifold. Renew the gasket if necessary. Similarly, on C 16 XE engines, check the condition of the O-ring between the throttle body mounting bracket and the upper section of the inlet manifold, and renew if necessary **(see illustration)**.

15 Clean the gasket faces of the throttle body and its mounting bracket. Ensure that no dirt enters the throttle body.

11.12a Remove the securing bolts . . .

16 Refit the upper section of the inlet manifold, ensuring that the gasket between the upper and lower manifold sections locates correctly. Make sure that the O-ring between the throttle body mounting bracket and the upper section of the inlet manifold is in position (where applicable).

17 Where applicable, fit a new gasket between the throttle body and its mounting

11.12b . . . and withdraw the upper section of the inlet manifold

11.12c Recover the gasket

11.14 Check the condition of the O-ring

10A

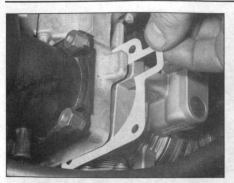

11.17 Fit a new gasket between the throttle body and its mounting bracket

12.3 Starter motor wiring securing nut (arrowed) - viewed from underneath vehicle

bracket **(see illustration)**. Refit and tighten the bolts securing the throttle body to its mounting bracket and the upper section of the inlet manifold.

18 Reconnect the air trunking to the lower end of the throttle body, and tighten the securing clamp.

19 If removed, refit the starter motor, with reference to Section 12 if necessary.

20 Refit the fuel tank vent valve to its bracket, and reconnect the vacuum hose.

21 Reconnect the breather hose to the camshaft cover.

22 Reconnect the fuel pressure regulator vacuum hose.

23 Reconnect the breather hose and the brake servo vacuum hose to the upper section of the inlet manifold.

24 Refit the plastic shield which fits over the top of the camshaft cover, and refit the oil filler cap.

25 Reconnect the hoses to the coolant expansion tank, then refit the expansion tank.

26 Reconnect the battery negative lead.

27 Top-up and bleed the cooling system as described in Section 2.

12 Starter motor - removal and refitting

Removal

1 Disconnect the battery negative lead.

2 Apply the handbrake, then jack up the front of the vehicle, and support securely on axle stands.

3 Note the wiring connections on the solenoid, then unscrew the securing nuts (where applicable) and disconnect them **(see illustration)**.

4 Where applicable, unscrew nut securing the earth cable to the upper starter motor mounting stud. Recover the washer, and disconnect the cable from the stud.

5 Unscrew the starter motor mounting stud

and bolt, or the two bolts, as applicable, and withdraw the motor from under the vehicle.

Refitting

6 Refitting is a reversal of removal, but where applicable, ensure that the earth cable is reconnected to the stud.

13 Body exterior fittings - removal and refitting

Wheelarch liners and body under-panels

1 The various plastic covers fitted to the underside of the vehicle are secured in position by a mixture of screws, nuts and retaining clips, and removal will be fairly obvious on inspection. Work methodically around the liner/panel, removing its retaining screws and releasing its retaining clips until is free to be removed from the underside of the vehicle. Most clips used on the vehicle, with the exception of the fasteners which are used to secure the wheelarch liners, are simply prised out of position. The wheelarch liner clips are released by tapping their centre pins through the clip, and then removing the outer section of the clip; new clips will be required on refitting if the centre pins are not recovered.

2 When refitting, renew any retaining clips that may have been broken on removal, and ensure that the panel is securely retained by all the relevant clips, nuts and screws. Vauxhall/Opel also recommend that plastic nuts (where used) are renewed, regardless of their apparent condition, whenever they are disturbed.

Chapter 10B
Vauxhall/Opel Corsa diesel 1993 to 1997

Contents

Specifications

Timing belt renewal interval . . . . Every 36 000 miles (60 000 km) or 4 years - whichever comes first

Note: Although the interval for timing belt renewal is increased for later models, it is strongly recommended that this shorter interval is applied to vehicles which are subjected to intensive use, ie, mainly short journeys or a lot of stop-start driving. The actual belt renewal interval is therefore very much up to the individual owner. That being said, it is highly recommended to err on the side of safety, and renew the belt at this earlier interval, bearing in mind the drastic consequences resulting from belt failure.

Auxiliary drivebelts
Tension (using gauge KM-128-A):
  Alternator:
    New . . . . 440 to 540 N
    Used . . . . 320 to 390 N
  Power steering pump:
    New . . . . 450 N
    Used . . . . 250 to 300 N

Injection pump
Timing setting . . . . 0.50 to 0.60 mm

Torque wrench settings

	Nm	lbf ft
15D and 15DT engines		
Alternator:		
Adjuster strap nuts and bolts	25	18
Mounting bracket to cylinder block	40	30
Pivot bolt	25	18
Camshaft sprocket bolts	10	7
Crankshaft:		
Pulley-to-sprocket bolts	20	15
Sprocket sentre bolt	133 to 161	98 to 119
Fuel injection pump:		
Central vent bolt	20	15
Fuel lines to pump	25	18
Pump to bracket	40	30
Pump to cylinder block/flange	23	17
Sprocket to pump	70	52
Right-hand mounting bracket:		
To cylinder block	45	33
To damping block	45	33
Engine rear suspension bracket:		
To damping block	65	48
To gearbox	90	66
To underbody	75	55
Power steering pump:		
Drivebelt tensioner to pump	40	30
Tension strut to crossmember	60	44
Timing belt cover to cylinder block	8	6
Timing belt guide roller to cylinder block	80	59
Timing belt tensioner roller bolt and nut	19	14
Wheel bolts	90	66

10B

Torque wrench settings (continued)

	Nm	lbf ft
17DT engine		
Alternator to mounting bracket:		
M8 bolt	24	18
M10 bolt	48	35
Camshaft sprocket bolts	10	7
Crankshaft:		
Pulley-to-sprocket bolts	20	15
Sprocket centre bolt	196	145
Fuel injection pump:		
Central vent bolt	20	15
Fuel lines to pump	25	18
Pump to bracket	40	30
Pump to cylinder block/flange	23	17
Sprocket to pump	70	52
Mountings:		
Left-hand damping block to bracket	60	44
Left and right-hand damping blocks to sidemember	65	48
Rear damping block:		
To bracket	45	33
To crossmember	40	30
Right-hand damping block to bracket	35	26
Right-hand mounting bracket:		
To cylinder block	40	30
To mounting	45	33
Power steering pump:		
Drivebelt tensioner to bracket	25	18
Drivebelt tensioner to pump	18	13
Pressure line to pump connections	28	21
Pump mounting bracket to cylinder block	60	44
Pump support to mounting bracket	25	18
Pump to support	25	18
Timing belt:		
Cover to cylinder block	8	6
Guide roller to cylinder block	76	56
Tensioner roller to cylinder block	19	14
Wheel bolts	110	81

1 Auxiliary drivebelts - removal, refitting and adjustment

Alternator

Removal and refitting

1 Gain full access to the alternator by jacking up the front right-hand side of the vehicle and supporting it on axle stands.
2 To remove the drivebelt, first slacken the alternator pivot and adjuster bolts.
3 Where fitted, remove the power steering pump drivebelt.
4 Move the alternator towards the engine and slip the drivebelt off its pulleys.
5 Fit the new drivebelt in position over the pulleys and adjust it as follows:

Adjustment

6 Tighten the alternator fastenings slightly, so that the alternator can just be moved by hand.
7 Insert a socket drive in the end of the adjuster arm and use it as a lever to move the alternator away from the engine until the belt tension is correct. Nip the adjuster bolt tight whilst checking the belt tension **(see illustration)**.

8 Vauxhall recommend the use of a special tool (KM-128-A) for tensioning the belt to the specified amount **(see illustration)**. In the absence of this tool, aim for a tension such that the belt can be deflected about 12 mm by firm finger pressure in the middle of its run. The belt tension must, however, be checked with the special tool as soon as possible.
9 Tighten the alternator fastenings to the specified torque setting once the belt tension is correct.

1.7 Tensioning the alternator drivebelt
A *Socket drive in end of adjuster arm*
B *Adjuster strap bolt*
C *Pivot bolt*

10 Where applicable, refit and tension the steering pump drivebelt.
11 Lower the front of the vehicle, removing the axle stands and jack.
12 The tension of a new drivebelt should be rechecked after a few hundred miles.

Power steering pump

Removal and refitting

13 Gain access to the drivebelt by removing the air cleaner housing assembly.

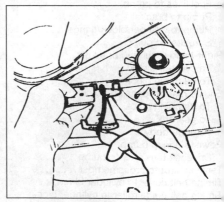

1.8 Using special tool KM-128-A to tension the alternator drivebelt

Vauxhall/Opel Corsa diesel 1993 to 1997 10B•3

4 To remove the drivebelt, first loosen the pump pivot and adjuster bolts.

5 Move the pump towards the engine and slip the drivebelt off its pulleys.

6 Fit the new drivebelt in position over the pulleys and adjust it as follows:

Adjustment

7 Tighten the pump fastenings slightly, so that the pump can just be moved by hand.

8 Insert a socket drive in the end of the adjuster arm and use it as a lever to move the pump away from the engine until the belt tension is correct. Nip the adjuster bolt tight whilst checking the belt tension (see illustration).

9 Vauxhall recommend the use of a special tool (KM-128-A) for tensioning the belt to the specified amount. In the absence of this tool, aim for a tension such that the belt can be deflected approximately 12 mm by firm finger pressure in the middle of its run. The belt tension must, however, be checked with the special tool as soon as possible.

20 Once belt tension is correct, tighten the pump fastenings to the specified torque setting.

21 Refit the air cleaner housing assembly.

22 The tension of a new drivebelt should be rechecked after a few hundred miles.

2 Coolant -
draining and refilling

> ⚠ **Warning: Take care to avoid scalding when removing the cooling system expansion tank cap. Place a thick cloth over the cap before turning it anti-clockwise.**
> **Caution: Never operate the vehicle with plain water in the cooling system, except in an emergency. Apart from the risk of freezing in winter weather, serious corrosion and rust and scale formation may occur.**
> **Warning: Antifreeze is poisonous and must be handled with due care.**

Draining

1 The system should only be drained when it is cool. If it must be drained hot, take great care to avoid scalding.

2 Remove the expansion tank cap. If the system is hot, place a thick cloth over the cap before turning it anti-clockwise.

3 Place a container underneath the radiator

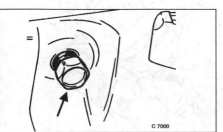

2.4 The cylinder block coolant drain plug (arrowed) - 17DT engine

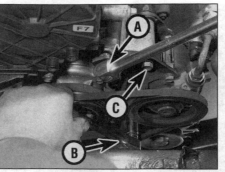

1.18 Tensioning the power steering pump drivebelt

A   Socket drive in end of adjuster arm
B   Adjuster strap bolt
C   Pivot bolt

bottom hose. Disconnect the hose from the radiator and allow the system to drain.

4 A cylinder block drain plug is provided, making it possible to drain the cooling system completely if necessary (see illustration).

Filling

5 Make sure that all hoses and clips are in good condition. Refit any disturbed hoses and see that their clips are tight. Before refitting the cylinder block drain plug, coat its threads with sealing compound (to GM spec. 15 03 166).

6 Fill the system via the expansion tank cap. If new coolant is being put in, start by pouring in the required quantity of neat antifreeze and follow it up with the water.

7 Massage the large coolant hoses to help displace air pockets during filling.

8 Most vehicles will be fitted with a self-venting cooling system this can be recognised by the two small vent hoses which enter the top of the expansion tank. If the system is not self-venting, open the bleed screw on the thermostat elbow during filling and close it when coolant runs out at the bleed screw.

9 When the system appears full, refit the expansion tank cap. Run the engine up to operating temperature, keeping a look-out for coolant leaks, then stop it and allow it to cool. Recheck the coolant level and top-up if necessary.

10 Recheck the tightness of all hose clips when the engine has cooled, and again after a few hundred miles.

3 Timing belt -
removal and refitting

> *Caution: A timing belt which is damaged, oil-soaked or fuel soaked must be renewed or it will fail, resulting in serious engine damage.*

15D and 15DT engines

1 The timing belt also drives the oil pump and fuel injection pump (see illustration).

1	Timing belt
2	Tensioner pulley
3	Bolt
4	Bolt
5	Washer
6	Tensioner spring
7	Guide roller
8	Bolt
9	Camshaft sprocket
10	Bolt
11	Sprocket flange
12	Screw
13	Crankshaft sprocket
14	Locating pin
15	Flange disc
16	Fuel injection pump sprocket
17	Nut
18	Oil pump sprocket
19	Nut
20	Drivebelt upper front cover
21	Cover seal
22	Cover seal
23	Drivebelt lower front cover
24	Cover seal
25	Cover seal
26	Drivebelt rear cover
27	Bolt
28	Screw
29	Screw
30	Screw

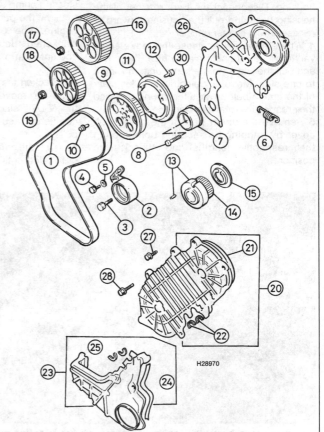

3.1 Timing belt and associated components

10B

3.11 Align the timing mark on the crankshaft pulley with the reference pointer on the engine block to bring No 1 piston to TDC on the firing stroke

3.12a Insert the locking bolt (arrowed) through the camshaft sprocket . . .

Removal

2 Disconnect the battery earth lead.

3 Gain access to the timing belt cover by first removing the air cleaner housing from its mounting on the right-hand side of the engine bay. Do this by first detaching the outlet tube retaining clamp at the engine manifold. Release the housing inlet scoop from the vehicle front crossmember and manoeuvre it clear of the housing. Disconnect the front retainer at the housing base and pull the housing forward to release it from its rear retainer.

4 Where necessary, release the brake servo vacuum line retaining clamp from the cover and pull the line from the servo unit, moving it to one side. Move any electrical cables clear of the timing belt cover after having released their respective retaining clamps.

5 Remove the upper part of the timing belt cover by undoing its securing bolts (noting their respective lengths) and lifting it from position.

6 Gain access to the side of the engine through the right-hand wheelarch.

7 Support the engine by positioning a jack beneath its sump and raising it slightly. Protect the sump by placing a piece of thick wood between it and the jack.

8 Remove the engine right-hand mounting assembly, see Section 4.

9 Where applicable, slacken the power steering pump upper and lower retaining bolts to allow the pump to be moved towards the engine, see Section 1. With the V-belt slackened, detach it from the crankshaft, coolant pump and power steering pump pulleys.

10 Slacken the alternator pivot and retaining bolts and move it towards the engine. With the V-belt slackened, detach it from the crankshaft, coolant pump and alternator pulleys.

11 Turn the crankshaft in the normal direction of rotation until the timing mark on its pulley

aligns with the reference pointer on the engine block (see illustration). In this position No 1 piston is at TDC on the firing stroke.

12 Now check that the locking bolt holes in the camshaft and fuel injection pump sprockets are aligned with their respective threaded holes in the engine casing before inserting the locking bolts (bolt sizes M6 x 1.00 for camshaft and M8 x 1.25 for injection pump) (see illustrations).

13 Mark the fitted position of the crankshaft pulley. Remove the pulley bolts and detach the pulley, tapping its rim to free it if necessary.

14 Remove the lower part of the timing belt cover to fully expose the belt.

15 Release the timing belt tensioner pulley and remove the spring (see illustration).

16 Mark the running direction of the timing belt if it is to be re-used. Also take care not to kink the belt, nor get oil, grease, etc. on it.

17 Unbolt the flange from the camshaft

3.12b . . . and insert the locking bolt through the injection pump sprocket

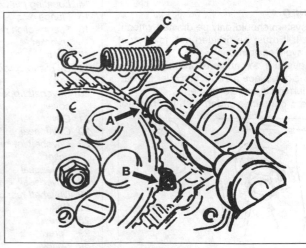

3.15 Release the timing belt tensioner pulley securing bolts (A and B) and remove the spring (C)

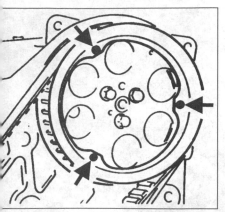

3.17 Remove the camshaft sprocket flange securing screws (arrowed)

procket **(see illustration)**. Slip the belt off the sprocket and then the remaining sprockets to remove it from the engine.

8 If signs of oil contamination are found, trace the source of the oil leak and rectify it, then wash down the engine timing belt area and all related components to remove all traces of oil.

Refitting

9 Commence refitting by first placing the

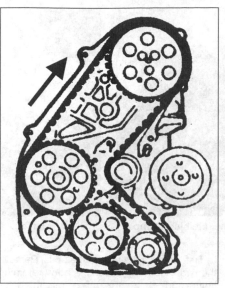

3.19 Ensure the timing belt is correctly routed

Arrow denotes direction of belt travel

timing belt over the camshaft sprocket and then the injection pump sprocket, etc. until it is correctly routed **(see illus-**

3.21 Refit the drivebelt tensioner spring and check that the tensioner assembly moves freely before tightening the tensioner securing bolts

tration). The crankshaft must not be disturbed and the camshaft and fuel injection pump sprockets should still be locked in alignment. Refit the flange to the camshaft sprocket.

20 Remove the camshaft and fuel injection pump sprocket alignment bolts.

21 Refit the timing belt tensioner spring and check that the tensioner assembly moves freely before tightening the tensioner securing bolts to the specified torque setting **(see illustration)**.

22 Refit the lower part of the timing belt cover to the engine, renewing any damaged sealing strips and tightening the retaining bolts to the specified torque setting.

23 Refit the crankshaft pulley in its previously noted position, tightening its retaining bolts to the specified torque setting.

24 Check the injection pump timing (Section 6).

25 Refit and tension each auxiliary drivebelt, referring to Section 1.

26 Refit the engine right-hand mounting in the reverse sequence to removal, tightening all retaining bolts to the specified torque settings.

27 Refit the upper part of the timing belt cover, renewing any damaged sealing strips and tightening the retaining bolts to the specified torque setting.

28 Refit all other removed components.

29 Remove the jack from beneath the engine and reconnect the battery earth lead.

17DT engine

30 The timing belt also drives the oil pump and fuel injection pump **(see illustration)**.

Removal

31 Disconnect the battery earth lead.

32 Gain access to the timing belt cover by first removing the air inlet collector box from its mounting on the right-hand side of the engine bay.

33 Release the brake servo vacuum line

1 Camshaft drivebelt
2 Tensioner pulley
3 Pulley bolt
4 Bolt
5 Tensioner bolt
6 Adjuster screw
7 Washer
8 Tensioner spring
9 Guide roller
10 Roller bolt
11 Camshaft sprocket
12 Sprocket bolt
13 Sprocket flange
14 Flange screw
15 Crankshaft sprocket
16 Locating pin
17 Flange disc
18 Fuel injection pump sprocket
19 Sprocket nut
20 Oil pump sprocket
21 Sprocket nut
22 Drivebelt upper front cover
23 Cover seal
24 Cover seal
25 Drivebelt lower front cover
26 Cover seal
27 Cover seal
28 Drivebelt rear cover
29 Cover bolt
30 Cover screw
31 Cover screw

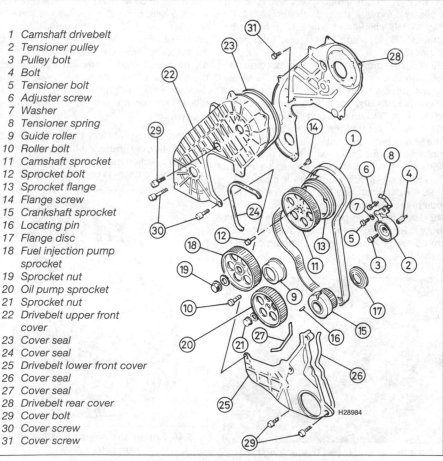

3.30 Camshaft drivebelt and associated components

3.33a Release the brake servo vacuum line retaining clamp (arrowed) . . .

3.33b . . . and pull the line from the servo unit

retaining clamp and pull the line from the servo unit (see illustrations).

34 Remove the upper part of the timing belt cover by undoing its nine securing bolts (noting their respective lengths) and lifting it from position.

35 Turn the steering wheel so that access to the side of the engine can be gained through the right-hand wheelarch, in front of the roadwheel.

36 Support the engine by positioning a jack beneath its sump and raising it slightly. Protect the sump by placing a piece of thick wood between it and the jack.

37 Remove the engine right-hand mounting

3.40 Align the timing mark on the crankshaft pulley with the reference pointer on the engine block to bring No 1 piston to TDC on the firing stroke

by first removing its two centre bolts. Remove the two mounting-to-vehicle body retaining bolts and then the three mounting-to-engine bolts to allow the complete mounting assembly to be withdrawn.

38 Slacken the power steering pump upper and lower retaining bolts to allow the pump to be moved towards the engine, see Section 1. With the V-belt slackened, detach it from the crankshaft, coolant pump and power steering pump pulleys.

39 Slacken the alternator pivot and retaining bolts and move it towards the engine. With the V-belt slackened, detach it from the crankshaft, coolant pump and alternator pulleys.

40 Turn the crankshaft in the normal direction of rotation until the timing mark on its pulley aligns with the reference pointer on the engine block (see illustration). In this position No 1 piston is at TDC on the firing stroke.

41 Now check that the locking bolt holes in the camshaft and fuel injection pump sprockets are aligned with their respective threaded holes in the engine casing before inserting the locking bolts (bolt sizes M6 x 1.00 for camshaft and M8 x 1.25 for injection pump) (see illustrations).

42 Mark the fitted position of the crankshaft pulley. Remove the four pulley retaining bolts and detach the pulley, gently tapping its rim to free it if necessary.

43 Undo the three bolts and remove th lower part of the timing belt cover from th engine.

44 Release the timing belt tensioner b loosening the pulley centre bolt, the uppe spring bracket securing bolt and the lowe pivot securing nut. Push the tensioner sprin towards the front of the engine to release bel tension and then nip tight the bracke securing bolt.

45 Mark the running direction of the timin belt if it is to be re-used. Also take care not t kink the belt, nor get oil, grease, etc. on it.

46 Slip the belt off the injection pum sprocket first and then the remainin sprockets to remove it from the engine.

47 If signs of oil contamination are found, trac the source of the oil leak and rectify it, the wash down the engine timing belt area and a related components to remove all traces of oil.

Refitting

48 Commence refitting by first placing th timing belt over the camshaft sprocket an then the injection pump sprocket etc. until it i correctly routed (see illustration). Th

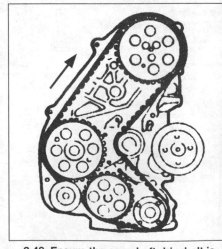

3.48 Ensure the camshaft drivebelt is correctly routed

Arrow denotes direction of belt travel

3.41a Insert the locking bolt (arrowed) through the camshaft sprocket . . .

3.41b . . . and insert the locking bolt through the injection pump sprocket

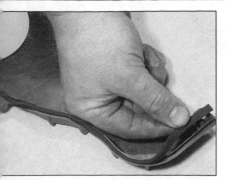

3.51 Checking the sealing strip in the lower front section of camshaft drivebelt cover

crankshaft must not be disturbed and the camshaft and fuel injection pump sprockets should still be locked in alignment.

9 Remove the camshaft and fuel injection pump sprocket alignment bolts.

0 Release the tensioner spring bracket securing bolt to allow the tensioner to act upon the timing belt. Turn the crankshaft against the normal direction of rotation by approximately 60 degrees to automatically tension the timing belt and then tighten the tensioner pulley centre bolt, the upper spring bracket securing bolt and the lower pivot securing nut to the specified torque settings (where given).

1 Refit the lower part of the timing belt cover to the engine, renewing any damaged sealing strips and tightening the retaining bolts to the specified torque setting **(see illustration)**.

2 Refit the crankshaft pulley in its previously noted position, tightening the retaining bolts to the specified torque setting.

3 Check the injection pump timing (Section 6).

4 Refit and tension both auxiliary drivebelts, referring to Section 1.

5 Refit the engine right-hand mounting in the reverse sequence to removal, tightening all retaining bolts to the specified torque settings, see Section 4.

6 Refit the upper part of the timing belt cover, renewing any damaged sealing strips and tightening the retaining bolts to the specified torque setting.

7 Refit all other removed components.

8 Remove the jack from beneath the engine and reconnect the battery earth lead.

4 Engine/transmission mountings - removal and refitting

Note: Only remove and refit one engine mounting at a time

5D and 15DT engines

The flexible mountings can be renewed if they have deteriorated. To facilitate removal, take the weight of the engine/transmission on

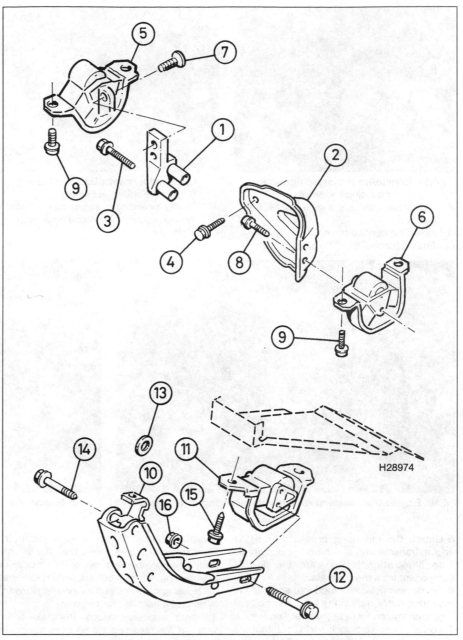

4.1 Engine/transmission mounting components

1 Right-hand mounting bracket	9 Screw
2 Left-hand mounting bracket	10 Rear mounting bracket
3 Screw	11 Flexible block - rear mounting
4 Screw	12 Screw
5 Flexible block - right-hand mounting	13 Washer
6 Flexible block - left-hand mounting	14 Screw
7 Screw	15 Screw
8 Screw	16 Nut

a hoist, or use a jack with a protective wooden block from below **(see illustration)**.

2 With the mounting refitted, only nip up the retaining bolts at first, then tighten them to the specified torque.

3 Lower the hoist or jack and check that the mounting is not under strain. Slacken and retighten the bolts as necessary.

17DT engine

4 The flexible mountings can be renewed if they have deteriorated. To facilitate removal, take the weight of the engine/transmission on a hoist, or use a jack with a protective wooden block from below. Only remove and refit one mounting at a time.

10B

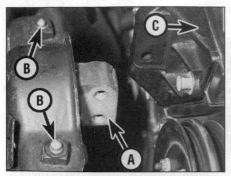

4.5a Engine/transmission right-hand mounting assembly

A Flexible mounting to engine bracket bolt location
B Flexible mounting to vehicle body bolts
C Engine bracket

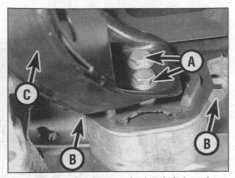

4.5b Engine/transmission left-hand mounting assembly

A Flexible mounting to engine bracket bolts
B Flexible mounting to vehicle body bolts
C Engine bracket

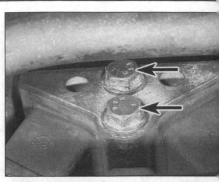

4.5c Engine/transmission rear flexible mounting to engine bracket bolts

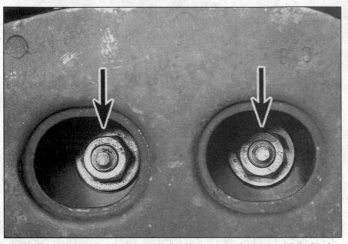

4.5d Engine/transmission rear flexible mounting to vehicle body nuts

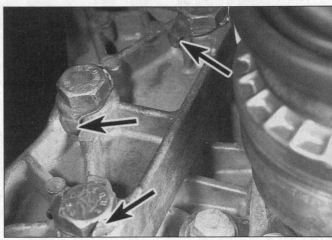

4.5e Engine/transmission rear mounting engine bracket bolts. Note locking washer tabs (arrowed)

5 Unbolt the mounting brackets from the engine/transmission and from the bodyframe **(see illustrations)**. Separate the flexible component from the brackets.
6 Fit the new flexible component and refit the mounting. Only nip up the retaining bolts at first, then tighten them to the specified torque.
7 Lower the hoist or jack and check that the mounting is not under strain. Slacken and retighten the bolts as necessary.

5 Valve timing - checking and adjustment

Note: When carrying out the following procedure, refer to the illustrations referred to in Section 3 on timing belt removal and refitting.

15D and 15DT engines
Checking
1 Disconnect the battery earth lead.
2 Gain access to the timing belt cover by first removing the air cleaner housing from its mounting on the right-hand side of the engine bay. Do this by first detaching the outlet tube

retaining clamp at the engine manifold. Release the box inlet scoop from the vehicle front crossmember and manoeuvre it clear of the housing. Disconnect the front retainer at the housing base and pull the housing forward to release it from its rear retainer.
3 Where necessary, release the brake servo vacuum line retaining clamp from the cover and pull the line from the servo unit, moving it to one side. Move any electrical cables clear of the drivebelt cover after having released their respective retaining clamps.
4 Remove the upper part of the belt cover by undoing its securing bolts (noting their respective lengths) and lifting it from position.
5 Turn the crankshaft in the normal direction of rotation until the timing mark on its pulley aligns with the reference pointer on the engine block. In this position No 1 piston is at TDC on the firing stroke.
6 Now check that the valve timing is correct by ensuring that the locking bolt holes in the camshaft and fuel injection pump sprockets are aligned with their respective threaded holes in the engine casing before inserting the locking bolts (bolt sizes M6 x 1.00 for

camshaft and M8 x 1.25 for injection pump. The mark on the crankshaft pulley shou[ld] align with the pointer on the engine block.

Adjustment
7 If the locking bolt holes in the camshaft a[nd] fuel injection pump sprockets are not [in] alignment with their respective threaded hol[es] in the engine casing, then the valve timi[ng] must be adjusted as follows.
8 Gain access to the side of the engi[ne] through the right-hand wheelarch.
9 Support the engine by positioning a ja[ck] beneath its sump and raising it slight[ly]. Protect the sump by placing a piece of thi[ck] wood between it and the jack.
10 Remove the engine right-hand mounti[ng] assembly to expose the belt tension[er] assembly.
11 Release the tensioner pulley and remo[ve] the spring.
12 Unbolt the flange from the camsha[ft] sprocket and slip the belt off the camsha[ft] and injection pump sprockets.
13 Rotate the camshaft and fuel injecti[on] pump sprockets by the least amount until t[he] locking bolt holes are aligned with th[e]

respective threaded holes in the engine casing. Insert the locking bolts. The mark on the crankshaft pulley should still align with the pointer on the engine block.

4 Place the timing belt over the injection pump and camshaft sprockets.

5 Remove the sprocket locking bolts.

6 Refit the tensioner spring and check that the tensioner assembly moves freely before first tightening the tensioner roller bolt and then the nut to the specified torque setting.

7 Confirm valve timing by turning the crankshaft in the normal direction of rotation two full turns and rechecking that all timing marks are in correct alignment.

8 With valve timing correct, reassemble all disturbed components whilst noting the specified torque settings.

7DT engine

Checking

9 Disconnect the battery earth lead.

10 Gain access to the timing belt upper cover by first removing the air inlet collector box from its mounting on the right-hand side of the engine bay - see Section 3.

11 Release the brake servo vacuum line retaining clamp and pull the line from the servo unit.

12 Remove the upper part of the cover by undoing its nine securing bolts (noting their respective lengths) and lifting it from position.

13 Turn the crankshaft in the normal direction of rotation until the timing mark on its pulley aligns with the reference pointer on the engine block. In this position No 1 piston is at TDC on the firing stroke.

14 Now check that the valve timing is correct by ensuring that the locking bolt holes in the camshaft and fuel injection pump sprockets are aligned with their respective threaded holes in the engine casing before inserting the locking bolts (bolt sizes M6 x 1.00 for camshaft and M8 x 1.25 for injection pump). The mark on the crankshaft pulley should align with the pointer on the engine block.

Adjustment

25 If the locking bolt holes in the camshaft and fuel injection pump sprockets are not in alignment with their respective threaded holes in the engine casing, then the valve timing must be adjusted as follows.

26 Turn the steering wheel so that access to the side of the engine can be gained through the right-hand wheelarch, in front of the roadwheel.

27 Support the engine by positioning a jack beneath its sump and raising it slightly. Protect the sump by placing a piece of thick wood between it and the jack.

28 Remove the engine right-hand mounting by first removing its two centre bolts. Remove the two mounting-to-vehicle body retaining bolts and then the three mounting-to-engine bolts to allow the complete mounting assembly to be withdrawn. This will expose the timing belt tensioner assembly.

29 Release the tensioner by loosening the pulley centre bolt, the upper spring bracket securing bolt and the lower pivot securing nut. Push the tensioner spring towards the front of the engine to release belt tension and then nip tight the bracket securing bolt.

30 Slip the belt off the camshaft and injection pump sprockets.

31 Rotate the camshaft and fuel injection pump sprockets by the least amount until the locking bolt holes are aligned with their respective threaded holes in the engine casing. Insert the locking bolts. The mark on the crankshaft pulley should still align with the pointer on the engine block.

32 Place the timing belt over the camshaft sprocket and then the injection pump sprocket.

33 Remove the sprocket locking bolts.

34 Release the tensioner spring bracket securing bolt to allow the tensioner to act upon the drivebelt. Turn the crankshaft against the normal direction of rotation by approximately 60 degrees to automatically tension the belt and then tighten the tensioner pulley centre bolt, the upper spring bracket securing bolt and the lower pivot securing nut

to the specified torque settings (where given).

35 Confirm valve timing by turning the crankshaft in the normal direction of rotation two full turns and rechecking that all timing marks are in correct alignment.

36 With valve timing correct, reassemble all disturbed components whilst noting the specified torque settings.

6 Fuel injection pump timing - checking and adjustment

Note: *The following procedure was carried out with the engine removed from the vehicle. Should the engine be in the vehicle, then access to the injection pump will be restricted. Depending on vehicle type, remove the inlet manifold and/or the starter motor for access to the pump.*

Note: *Ensure that valve timing is correct before checking fuel injection pump timing (see Section 5).*

Checking

1 Timing of the injection pump should only be necessary in the following circumstances:

a) *When fitting a new or overhauled pump*
b) *If the timing is suspected of being wrong*
c) *If the timing belt has been re-tensioned or renewed*

2 Obtain a dial test indicator (DTI) and adapter **(see illustration)**. The manufacturer specifies the use of an adapter which screws into, and seals, the plug hole.

3 Disconnect the battery earth lead.

4 Clean around the injection pipe unions to the pump and cylinder head.

5 Disconnect Nos 1 and 2 injection pipes from the injectors and the pump and remove them from the engine. Be prepared for fuel spillage during subsequent operations.

6 Blank off all exposed pipe connections to prevent the ingress of dirt and moisture.

7 Remove the central plug from the injection pump **(see illustration)**.

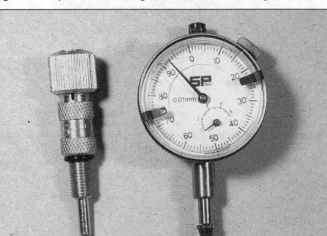

6.2 The dial test indicator and adaptor required to set fuel injection pump timing

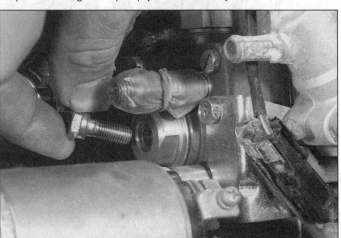

6.7 Removing the central plug from the injection pump

10B

6.8 The timing mark on the crankshaft pulley aligned with the reference pointer on the engine block

6.9 Deactivating the cold start lever with a screwdriver

6.10 The adaptor and dial test indicator fitted to the injection pump

8 Turn the crankshaft in the normal direction of rotation until the timing mark on its pulley aligns with the reference pointer on the engine block **(see illustration)**. In this position No 1 piston is at TDC on the firing stroke.

9 Deactivate the cold start lever by using a screwdriver as shown **(see illustration)**.

10 Fit the adapter and dial test indicator with the indicator probe entering the central plug hole and contacting the pump piston **(see illustration)**.

11 Turn the crankshaft in the normal direction of rotation to approximately 60° before TDC (No 1 firing) **(see illustration)**. At this point, the injection pump piston will be at bottom dead centre (BDC).

12 Zero the indicator, checking its adjustment by rotating the crankshaft slightly in either direction to ensure BDC.

13 Bring the engine back to TDC (No 1 firing). When the timing mark on the pulley is aligned with the reference pointer, the dial test indicator should show a lift corresponding to the desired timing setting - see the *Specifications* at the start of this Chapter.

Adjustment

14 If adjustment is necessary, loosen the two nuts which secure the injection pump and the two bolts which secure the pump bracket **(see illustration)**.

15 Loosen Nos 3 and 4 injection pipes at the injectors and pump.

16 Rotate the pump until the dial test indicator shows the desired lift, then tighten the loosened nuts and bolts to the specified torque settings. Rotating the top of the pump towards the engine will lower the lift value, whereas rotating the pump in the opposite direction will raise the lift value.

17 Repeat the checking procedure.

18 With the pump timing correct, remove the DTI and adapter then refit the plug to the pump.

19 Remove any blanking materials and reconnect all injection pipe unions, working the reverse sequence to removal and tightening them to the specified torque settings.

20 Refit any other disturbed components, start the engine and check for fuel leaks.

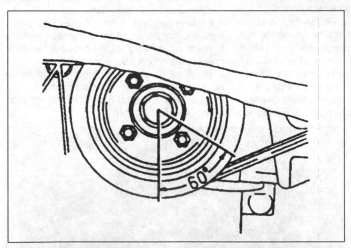

6.11 Turn the crankshaft in the normal direction of rotation to approximately 60° before TDC (No 1 firing)

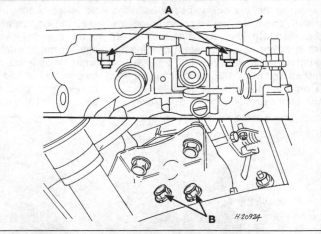

6.14 The fuel injection pump securing nuts(A) and pump bracket bolts (B)

Chapter 11A
Vauxhall/Opel Frontera petrol 1991 to 1998

Contents

Specifications

Timing belt renewal interval . . . . Every 36 000 miles (60 000 km) or 4 years - whichever comes first

Note: Although the interval for timing belt renewal is increased for later models, it is strongly recommended that this shorter interval is applied to vehicles which are subjected to intensive use, ie, mainly short journeys or a lot of stop-start driving. The actual belt renewal interval is therefore very much up to the individual owner. That being said, it is highly recommended to err on the side of safety, and renew the belt at this earlier interval, bearing in mind the drastic consequences resulting from belt failure.

Engine code (2.0 litre)*

Pre 1995 models	C20NE
1995 onwards models	X20SE

* The engine code forms the first five digits of the engine number

Timing belt tension (2.0 litre)

Using special (KM-510-A) tool - pre 1993 models

New belt:

Cold engine	0.5
Hot engine	7.5

Used belt:

Cold engine	2.5
Hot engine	7.0

Torque wrench settings	**Nm**	**lbf ft**
Alternator fixings	25	18
Power steering pump fixings:		
Adjuster clamp bolt	25	18
Adjuster locknut	39	29
Lower mouning bolt	25	18
Wheel nuts:		
Alloy wheels	120	89
Steel wheels	110	81
2.0 litre		
Camshaft cover bolts	8	6
Camshaft housing end cover bolts - X20SE engine	8	6
Camshaft sprocket bolt	45	34
Coolant pump bolts	25	18
Crankshaft pulley bolts	20	15
Crankshaft sprocket bolt:*		
Stage 1	130	96
Stage 2	Angle-tighten a further 40 to 50°	
Spark plugs	25	18
Timing belt cover bolts	6	4
Timing belt tensioner pulley bolt - 1993 onwards models	25	18

Torque wrench settings (continued)

2.2 litre

	Nm	lbf ft
Camshaft cover bolts	8	6
Camshaft sprocket bolt:*		
Stage 1	50	37
Stage 2	Angle-tighten a further 60°	
Stage 3	Angle-tighten a further 15°	
Crankshaft pulley bolts	20	15
Crankshaft sprocket bolt:*		
Stage 1	130	96
Stage 2	Angle-tighten a further 40 to 50°	
Spark plugs	25	18
Timing belt cover bolts	6	4
Timing belt idler pulley:		
Mounting bracket bolts	25	18
Pulley bolt	25	18
Timing belt tensioner bolt	25	18

New bolts should be used

---

1 Auxiliary drivebelt - removal, refitting and adjustment

1 Undo the retaining bolts and remove the undercover from beneath the engine. Proceed as described under the relevant sub-heading.

Alternator drivebelt - pre 1995 2.0 litre engines (C20NE)

2 Remove the cooling fan as described in Section 17.
3 Remove the power steering pump drivebelt as described in this Section.
4 Slacken the alternator upper and lower mounting bolts then pivot the alternator in towards the cylinder block and slip the belt off the pulleys. On some engines, the upper mounting is fitted with a threaded adjuster; on these engines slacken the locknut and back off the adjuster nut to release the drivebelt tension.
5 Manoeuvre the belt into position and seat it on the pulleys. Using the adjuster nut (where fitted) or a piece of wood carefully inserted between the alternator body and cylinder block, position the alternator so that under firm thumb pressure there is about 10 mm of movement at the mid-point on the longest run of the belt. Once the belt is correctly tensioned, hold the alternator in position and tighten its mounting bolts to the specified torque and retighten the adjuster locknut (where fitted) securely. Recheck the drivebelt tension and, if necessary, readjust.
6 Refit the power steering pump drivebelt as described in this Section.
7 Refit the cooling fan as described in Section 17.

Power steering pump drivebelt - pre 1995 2.0 litre engines (C20NE)

8 Slacken the power steering pump lower mounting bolt and loosen the bolt securing the adjuster clamp to the pump bracket.

9 Slacken the adjuster clamp locknut then back off the adjuster nut to release the drivebelt tension. Slip the belt off the pulleys and remove it from the engine.
10 Manoeuvre the new belt into position and seat it on the pulleys.
11 Tension the power steering pump belt using the adjuster nut so that under firm thumb pressure there is about 10 mm of movement at the mid-point on the longest run of the belt. Once the adjuster nut is correctly positioned, tighten the adjuster clamp bolt and the power steering pump lower mounting bolt to their specified torque settings then tighten the adjuster locknut. Refit the undercover and securely tighten its retaining bolts.

Auxiliary drivebelt - 1995 on 2.0 litre engines (X20SE) and all 2.2 litre engines

12 Prior to removal make a note of the correct routing of the belt around the various pulleys. If the belt is to be re-used, also mark the direction of rotation on the belt to ensure the belt is refitted the same way around.
13 Using a suitable spanner or socket fitted to the tensioner pulley centre bolt, lever the tensioner away from the belt until there i sufficient slack to enable the belt to b slipped off the pulleys. Carefully release th tensioner pulley until it is against its stop the remove the belt from the vehicle.
14 Manoeuvre the belt into position, routing correctly around the pulleys; if the original be is being fitted use the marks made prior t removal to ensure it is fitted the correct wa around.
25 Lever the tensioner roller back against spring, and seat the belt on the pulleys Ensure the belt is centrally located on a pulleys then slowly release the tensione pulley until the belt is correctly tensioned. D not allow the tensioner to spring back an stress the belt.
16 Check the position of the drivebe tensioner assembly arm, the arm should be i between the stops on the backplate an should be free to move **(see illustration)**. the tensioner arm is against the stop, the be must be renewed.
17 Refit the undercover and securely tighte its retaining bolts

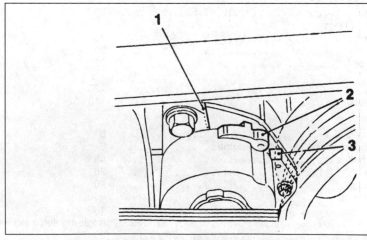

1.16 On 1995 on 2.0 litre engines (X20SE) and all 2.2 litre engines ensure the auxiliary drivebelt tensioner arm indicator (2) is between the stops (1 and 3) on the backplate

2.2 Slowly unscrew the expansion tank cap to release any pressure present in the cooling system

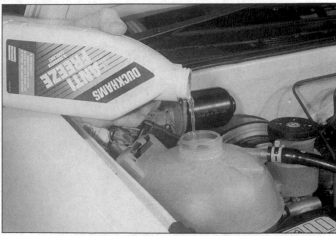

2.6 Add a mixture of water and antifreeze to the expansion tank until the coolant level is slightly above the KALT/COLD mark

2 Coolant - draining and refilling

Draining

⚠️ **Warning: Wait until the engine is cold before starting this procedure. Do not allow antifreeze to come in contact with your skin, or with the painted surfaces of the vehicle. Rinse off spills immediately with plenty of water. Never leave antifreeze lying around in an open container, or in a puddle in the driveway or on the garage floor. Children and pets are attracted by its sweet smell, but antifreeze can be fatal if ingested.**

1 With the engine completely cold, remove the expansion tank filler cap. Turn the cap anti-clockwise, wait until any pressure remaining in the system is released, then unscrew it and lift it off **(see illustration)**.
2 Where necessary, unbolt and remove the engine undercover to improve access to the radiator drain plug.
3 Position a suitable container beneath the radiator then unscrew the drain plug and allow the coolant to drain into the container. Where no drain plug is fitted, slacken the retaining clip and disconnect the bottom hose from the radiator.
4 When the flow of coolant stops, securely tighten the drain plug or reconnect the hose and securely tighten its retaining clip (as applicable).

Filling

5 Before attempting to fill the cooling system, make sure that all hoses and clips are in good condition, and that the clips are tight.
6 Remove the expansion tank filler cap and slowly fill the system until the coolant level reaches the KALT/COLD mark on the side of the expansion tank **(see illustration)**.

7 Once the coolant level is correct, refit the expansion tank cap and tighten securely.
8 Start the engine, and allow it to run until it reaches normal operating temperature (until the cooling fan cuts in and out).
9 Stop the engine, and allow it to cool, then re-check the coolant level **(see illustration)**. Top-up the level if necessary and refit the expansion tank filler cap.

3 Top dead centre (TDC) for No 1 piston (2.0 litre) - locating

1 In its travel up and down its cylinder bore, Top Dead Centre (TDC) is the highest point that each piston reaches as the crankshaft rotates. While each piston reaches TDC both at the top of the compression stroke and again at the top of the exhaust stroke, for the purpose of timing the engine, TDC refers to the piston position (usually number 1) at the top of its compression stroke.
2 Number 1 piston (and cylinder) is at the front (timing belt) end of the engine, and its TDC position is located as follows. Note that the crankshaft rotates clockwise when viewed from the front of the vehicle.

2.9 When the engine is cold, the coolant level should be slightly above the KALT/COLD mark on the side of the tank

3 Disconnect the battery negative terminal. If necessary, remove all the spark plugs to enable the engine to be easily turned over. Continue as described under the relevant sub-heading.

Pre 1993 engines (up to engine number C20NE 14608700)

4 Unclip the timing belt upper outer cover and remove it from the engine (see Section 9).
5 Using a socket and extension bar on the crankshaft sprocket bolt, turn the crankshaft whilst keeping an eye on the camshaft sprocket. Rotate the crankshaft until the timing mark on the camshaft sprocket rim is correctly aligned with the mark on the top of the timing belt inner cover and the notch on the crankshaft pulley rim is aligned with the pointer on the timing belt inner cover **(see illustration)**.
6 With the crankshaft pulley and camshaft sprocket timing marks positioned as described, the engine is positioned with No 1 piston at TDC on its compression stroke.

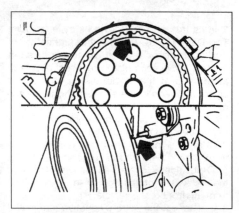

3.5 On pre 1993 engines, align the camshaft sprocket mark with the mark on the top of the inner cover, and the crankshaft pulley notch with the pointer on the inner cover

11A

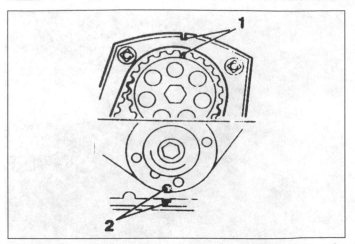

3.8 On 1993 onwards engines, align the camshaft sprocket mark with the mark on the top of the inner cover (1), and the crankshaft sprocket mark with the mark on the inner cover (2)

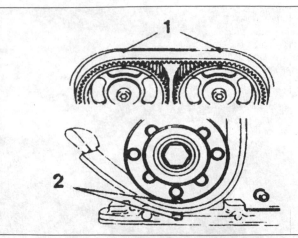

4.6 Align the camshaft sprocket marks with the marks on the top of the camshaft cover (1), and the crankshaft sprocket mark with the mark on the inner cover (2)

1993 on engines (engine number C20NE 14608701 onwards and all X20SE)

7 Remove the timing belt outer cover as described in Section 9.

8 Using a socket and extension bar on the crankshaft sprocket bolt, turn the crankshaft whilst keeping an eye on the camshaft sprocket. Rotate the crankshaft until the timing mark on the camshaft sprocket rim is correctly aligned with the mark on the top of the timing belt inner cover and the timing mark on the crankshaft sprocket rim is aligned with the cutout on the base of the timing belt inner cover **(see illustration)**.

9 With the crankshaft sprocket and camshaft sprocket timing marks positioned as described, the engine is positioned with No1 piston at TDC on its compression stroke.

4 Top dead centre (TDC) for No 1 piston (2.2 litre) - locating

1 In its travel up and down its cylinder bore, Top Dead Centre (TDC) is the highest point that each piston reaches as the crankshaft rotates. While each piston reaches TDC both at the top of the compression stroke and again at the top of the exhaust stroke, for the purpose of timing the engine, TDC refers to the piston position (usually number 1) at the top of its compression stroke.

2 Number 1 piston (and cylinder) is at the front (timing belt) end of the engine, and its TDC position is located as follows. Note that the crankshaft rotates clockwise when viewed from the front of the vehicle.

3 Disconnect the battery negative terminal. If necessary, remove all the spark plugs to enable the engine to be easily turned over.

4 To gain access to the camshaft sprocket timing marks, remove the timing belt outer cover as described in Section 10.

5 Remove the crankshaft pulley as described in Section 8.

6 Using a socket and extension bar on the crankshaft sprocket bolt, rotate the crankshaft until the timing marks on the camshaft sprockets are both at the top and are correctly aligned with the marks on the camshaft cover. With the camshaft sprocket marks correctly positioned, align the mark on the crankshaft sprocket rim with the mark on the timing belt inner cover **(see illustration)**. The engine is now positioned with No 1 piston at TDC on its compression stroke.

5 Camshaft cover (2.0 litre) - removal and refitting

Removal

1 Release the retaining clip(s) and disconnect the breather hose(s) from the camshaft cover.

2 Slacken and remove the retaining bolts, noting the correct fitted location of any clips or brackets retained by the bolts (as applicable) then lift the camshaft cover from the camshaft housing. If the cover is stuck, do not lever between the cover and camshaft housing mating surfaces - if necessary, gently tap the cover sideways to free it. Recover the gasket; if it shows signs of damage or deterioration it must be renewed.

Refitting

3 Prior to refitting, examine the inside of the cover for a build-up of oil sludge or any other contamination, and if necessary clean the cover with paraffin, or a water-soluble solvent. Examine the condition of the crankcase ventilation filter inside the camshaft cover, and clean as described for the inside of the cover if clogging is evident (if desired, the filter can be removed from the cover, after

removing the securing bolts). Dry the cover thoroughly before refitting.

4 Ensure the cover is clean and dry and seat the gasket in the cover recess then refit the cover to the camshaft housing, ensuring the gasket remains correctly seated.

5 Refit the retaining bolts, ensuring all relevant clips/brackets are correctly positioned, and tighten them to the specified torque working in a diagonal sequence.

6 Reconnect the breather hose(s) securely to the cover.

6 Camshaft cover (2.2 litre) - removal and refitting

Removal

1 Slacken the retaining clips and disconnect the breather hoses from the right-hand side of the cover.

2 Undo the retaining screws and remove the spark plug cover. Disconnect the plug caps from the plugs then unclip the HT leads and position them clear of the cover.

3 Disconnect the camshaft sensor wiring connector and unclip the wiring from the camshaft cover.

4 Evenly and progressively slacken and remove the camshaft cover retaining bolts.

5 Lift the camshaft cover away from the cylinder head and recover the cover seal and the sealing rings which are fitted to each of the retaining bolt holes. Examine the seal and sealing rings for signs of wear or damage and renew if necessary.

Refitting

6 Ensure the cover and cylinder head surfaces are clean and dry then fit the camshaft seal securely to the cover groove. Fit the sealing rings to the recesses around ach retaining bolt hole, holding them in osition with a smear of grease.

Carefully manoeuvre the camshaft cover nto position, taking great care to ensure all the ealing rings remain correctly seated. Refit the over retaining bolts and tighten the retaining olts to the specified torque, working in a piral pattern from the centre outwards.

Reconnect the breather hoses, securing hem in position with the retaining clips, and ecurely reconnect the plug caps to the spark lugs.

Reconnect the wiring connector to the amshaft sensor, ensure it is correctly routed nd retained by the cover clips. Refit the park plug cover, tightening its retaining crews securely.

7 Crankshaft pulley (2.0 litre) - removal and refitting

Removal

Remove the auxiliary drivebelt(s) as escribed in Section 1.

On pre 1993 engines (up to engine number C20NE 14608700), position No 1 piston at DC on its compression stroke as described n Section 3.

On all engines, slacken and remove the mall retaining bolts securing the pulley to the rankshaft sprocket and remove the pulley rom the engine. If necessary, prevent crankshaft rotation by holding the sprocket etaining bolt with a suitable socket.

Refitting

Refit the crankshaft pulley and refit its etaining bolts. On pre 1993 engines ensure he camshaft sprocket timing mark is still correctly aligned and align the crankshaft ulley notch with the pointer (see Section 3).

Lock the crankshaft by the method used on emoval, and tighten the pulley retaining bolt o the specified torque setting.

Refit the auxiliary drivebelt(s) as described n Section 1. On early engines, refit the timing elt outer cover ensuring it is clipped securely n position.

8 Crankshaft pulley (2.2 litre) - removal and refitting

Removal

Remove the auxiliary drivebelt as described n Section 1. Prior to removal, mark the direction of rotation on the belt to ensure the elt is refitted the same way around.

Slacken and remove the small retaining olts securing the pulley to the crankshaft sprocket and remove the pulley from the ngine. If necessary, prevent crankshaft otation by holding the sprocket retaining bolt with a suitable socket.

Refitting

3 Ensure the crankshaft sprocket and pulley mating surfaces are clean and dry then refit the pulley, tightening its retaining bolts to the specified torque.

4 Refit the auxiliary drivebelt as described in Section 1, using the mark made prior to removal to ensure the belt is fitted the correct way around.

9 Timing belt covers (2.0 litre) - removal and refitting

Pre 1993 models (up to engine number C20NE 14608700)

Upper outer cover

1 Unclip the retaining clips situated around the cover and manoeuvre the cover away from the engine unit.

2 On refitting ensure the cover is correctly engaged with the other covers and secure it in position with the retaining clips.

Lower outer cover

3 Remove the upper outer cover as described in paragraph 1 then unclip and remove the lower cover.

4 On refitting fit the lower cover to the rear cover, securing it in position with the retaining clips, then refit the upper cover (see paragraph 2).

Inner cover

5 Remove the timing belt as described in Section 11.

6 Remove the camshaft and crankshaft sprockets as described in Section 13.

7 Slacken and remove the bolts securing the cover to the camshaft and oil pump housing then manoeuvre the cover out of position and remove it from the vehicle. With the main inner cover removed, if necessary, the small section can also be removed from the coolant pump.

8 Refitting is the reverse of removal, tightening the cover retaining bolts to the specified torque.

1993 to 1995 models (engine number C20NE 14608701 onwards)

Outer cover

9 Remove the cooling fan and coupling as described in Section 17.

10 Remove the crankshaft pulley as described in Section 7.

11 Unscrew the retaining bolts and remove the cooling fan drive pulley from its spindle.

12 Slacken and remove the retaining bolts then remove the timing belt outer cover from the engine.

13 Refitting is the reverse of removal, tightening the cover retaining bolts to the specified torque.

Inner cover

14 Remove the outer cover as described in paragraphs 9 to 12

15 Remove the timing belt as described in Section 11.

16 Remove the camshaft sprocket, crankshaft sprocket and tensioner pulley as described in Section 13.

17 Slacken and remove the bolts securing the inner cover to the camshaft and oil pump housings. Remove the cover from the engine, taking care not to lose the spacer and rubber grommets from each of the retaining bolt holes.

18 Refitting is the reverse of removal. Ensure the rubber grommets and spacers are correctly fitted to the retaining bolt holes and tighten the bolts to the specified torque.

1995 onwards models (X20SE engine)

Outer cover

19 Remove the auxiliary drive belt as described in Section 1. Where necessary, unscrew the retaining bolt and remove the belt idler pulley (where fitted) from the front of the engine.

20 Remove the crankshaft pulley as described in Section 7.

21 Slacken and remove the retaining bolts and remove the outer cover from the engine.

22 Refitting is the reverse of removal tightening the cover retaining bolts to the specified torque.

Inner cover

23 Remove the outer cover as described in paragraphs 9 to 12.

24 Remove the timing belt as described in Section 11.

25 Remove the camshaft sprocket, crankshaft sprocket and tensioner pulley as described in Section 13.

26 Unclip the crankshaft sensor wiring from the rear of the timing belt inner cover and position, noting its correct routing.

27 Slacken and remove the bolts securing the inner cover to the camshaft and oil pump housings, and remove the cover from the engine.

28 Refitting is the reverse of removal, tightening the bolts to the specified torque. Ensure the crankshaft sensor wiring is correctly routed and clipped securely in position.

10 Timing belt covers (2.2 litre) - removal and refitting

Removal

Outer cover

1 Slacken the retaining clip and disconnect the intake hose from the resonator chamber which is located between the front of the engine and the radiator. Slacken and remove the retaining bolts and spacers and remove the resonator from the rear of the radiator, taking care not to lose the mounting rubbers or washer.

11A

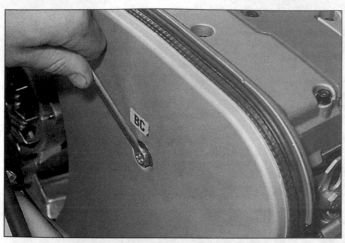

10.3a Unscrew the retaining bolts . . .

10.3b . . . then remove the timing belt outer cover from the engine, complete with seal

2 Remove the auxiliary drivebelt as described in Section 1. Prior to removal, mark the direction of rotation on the belt to ensure the belt is refitted the same way around. Where necessary, unscrew the retaining bolt and remove the belt idler pulley (where fitted) from the front of the engine.

3 Slacken and remove the retaining bolts and remove the cover from the engine unit along with its seal **(see illustrations)**.

Rear cover

4 Remove the timing belt as described in Section 12.

5 Remove the camshaft sprockets, crankshaft sprocket, the timing belt tensioner and the idler pulley assembly as described in Section 14.

6 Undo the retaining bolts and remove the rear cover from the engine unit.

Refitting

7 Refitting is the reverse of removal, tightening all bolts to the specified torque.

---

11 Timing belt (2.0 litre) - removal and refitting

Note: *The timing belt must be removed and refitted with the engine cold.*

Pre 1993 models (up to engine number C20SE 14608700) - engines without a timing belt tensioner pulley

Note: *On these engines Vauxhall specify the use of a special belt tension measuring tool (KM-510-A) to correctly set the timing belt tension.*

Note: *The timing belt tension is altered by rotating the coolant pump in the cylinder block, and a wrench which fits the hexagonal section of the pump housing will be required for the following procedure.*

Removal

1 Remove the cooling fan and coupling as described in Section 17.

2 Remove the timing belt upper outer cover (see Section 9) then position No 1 cylinder at TDC on its compression stroke as described in Section 3.

3 Remove the crankshaft pulley as described in Section 7.

4 Unscrew the retaining bolts and remove the cooling fan drive pulley from its spindle.

5 Release the retaining clips and remove the timing belt lower outer cover (see Section 9).

6 Ensure the camshaft sprocket timing mark is still correctly aligned with the mark on the belt rear cover then fit the adaptor to the coolant pump **(see illustration)**.

7 Loosen the coolant pump retaining bolts then, using a ratchet or extension bar fitted to the adaptor, carefully rotate the pump to relieve the tension in the timing belt.

8 Slide the timing belt off from its sprockets and remove it from the engine. If the belt is to be re-used, use white paint or similar to mark the direction of rotation on the belt. **Do not** rotate the crankshaft until the timing belt has been refitted.

9 If signs of oil contamination are found, trace the source of the oil leak and rectify it, then wash down the engine timing belt area and all related components to remove all traces of oil.

Refitting

10 On reassembly, thoroughly clean the timing belt sprockets then check that the camshaft sprocket timing mark is still correctly aligned with the cover cutout. Temporarily refit the crankshaft pulley to the sprocket and check that the pulley notch is still aligned with the pointer (see Section 3).

11 Fit the timing belt over the crankshaft and camshaft sprockets, ensuring that the belt front run is taut (ie, all slack is on the coolant pump side of the belt), then fit the belt over the coolant pump sprocket. Do not twist the belt sharply while refitting it. Ensure that the belt teeth are correctly seated centrally in the sprockets, and that the timing marks remain in alignment. If a used belt is being refitted, ensure that the arrow mark made on removal points in the normal direction of rotation, as before.

12 Lightly tension the timing belt by rotating the coolant pump and securely tighten the pump retaining bolts.

13 Refit the crankshaft pulley and tighten its retaining bolts to the specified torque.

14 Check the camshaft sprocket and crankshaft pulley timing marks are still correctly aligned. If adjustment is necessary, release the belt tension again then disengage the belt from the sprockets and make any necessary adjustments before retensioning the belt.

15 If the marks are still correctly positioned, rotate the crankshaft smoothly through two complete turns (720°) in the normal direction of rotation to settle the timing belt in position.

16 Check that both the camshaft and crankshaft sprocket timing marks are realigned then tension the timing belt.

17 Ensuring that the front run of the belt between the camshaft and crankshaft sprockets, is taut, fit the measuring tool to the mid-point of the belt run between the coolan

11.6 On engine without a timing belt tensioner pulley fit the adapter to the coolant pump

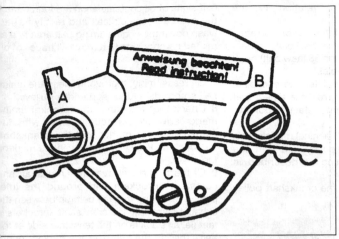

11.17 Fit the special measuring tool to the timing belt making sure that the outside of the belt is correctly positioned against the supports (A and B), and the tool arm (C) Is correctly located between the belt teeth

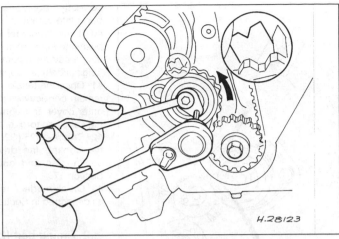

11.34 Tension the timing belt by rotating the tensioner arm fully anti-clockwise until the pointer is positioned as shown

pump and camshaft sprockets. Ensure the belt is correctly engaged with the tool and lightly tap the tool to settle it in position **(see Illustration)**. Read the value on the measuring tool scale and compare it to the values given in the specifications at the start of this Chapter.

18 If adjustment is necessary, slacken the coolant pump retaining bolts and rotate the pump as necessary. Once the tension is correctly set, tighten the coolant pump retaining bolts to the specified torque.

19 Remove the measuring tool from the timing belt then rotate the crankshaft smoothly through another two complete turns (720°) in the normal direction of rotation until the timing marks are correctly realigned.

20 Recheck the belt tension as described in paragraph 17.

21 If adjustment is necessary, repeat the operations described in paragraphs 18 to 20.

22 Once the belt tension is correctly adjusted, ensure the coolant pump retaining bolts are tightened to the specified torque then refit the lower outer timing belt cover and the upper outer cover. Ensure both covers are correctly seated and securely held by all the retaining clips.

23 Refit the cooling fan pulley, tightening its retaining bolts securely.

24 Refit the auxiliary drivebelts as described in Section 1.

25 Refit the cooling fan assembly as described in Section 17.

1993 onwards models (engine number C20NE 14608701 onwards) - engines with a timing belt tensioner pulley

Removal

26 Remove the timing belt outer cover as described in Section 9.

27 Position No 1 cylinder at TDC on its compression stroke as described in Section 3.

28 Slacken the timing belt tensioner pulley bolt. Using an Allen key, rotate the tensioner arm clockwise to its stop, to relieve the tension in the timing belt, and hold it in position by securely tightening the retaining bolt.

29 Slide the timing belt off from its sprockets and remove it from the engine. If the belt is to be re-used, use white paint or similar to mark the direction of rotation on the belt. **Do not** rotate the crankshaft or camshafts until the timing belt has been refitted.

30 If signs of oil contamination are found, trace the source of the oil leak and rectify it, then wash down the engine timing belt area and all related components to remove all traces of oil.

Refitting

31 On reassembly, thoroughly clean the timing belt sprockets and tensioner pulley.

32 Check that the camshaft and crankshaft sprocket timing marks are still correctly aligned with the marks on the rear cover (see Section 3).

33 Fit the timing belt over the crankshaft and camshaft sprockets, ensuring that the belt front run is taut (ie, all slack is on the tensioner side of the belt), then fit the belt over the coolant pump sprocket and tensioner pulley. Do not twist the belt sharply while refitting it. Ensure that the belt teeth are correctly seated centrally in the sprockets, and that the timing marks remain in alignment. If a used belt is being refitted, ensure that the arrow mark made on removal points in the normal direction of rotation, as before.

34 Slacken the timing belt tensioner bolt to release the tensioner spring. Rotate the tensioner arm anti-clockwise until the tensioner pointer is fully over against its stop, without exerting any excess strain on the belt. Hold the tensioner in position and securely tighten its retaining bolt **(see illustration)**.

35 Check the sprocket timing marks are still

correctly aligned. If adjustment is necessary, release the tensioner again then disengage the belt from the sprockets and make any necessary adjustments.

36 Using a socket on the crankshaft sprocket bolt, rotate the crankshaft smoothly through two complete turns (720°) in the normal direction of rotation to settle the timing belt in position.

37 Check that both the camshaft and crankshaft sprocket timing marks are correctly realigned then slacken the tensioner bolt again.

38 If a new timing belt is being fitted, adjust the tensioner so that the pointer is aligned with the cutout on the backplate **(see illustration)**. Hold the tensioner in the correct position and tighten its retaining bolt to the specified torque. Rotate the crankshaft smoothly through another two complete turns in the normal direction of rotation, to bring the sprocket timing marks back into alignment. Check that the tensioner pointer is still aligned with the backplate cutout.

39 If the original belt is being refitted, adjust the tensioner so that the pointer is positioned 4 mm to the left of the cutout on the backplate

11.38 If a new belt is being fitted, position the tensioner so that the pointer is aligned with the backplate cutout

11A

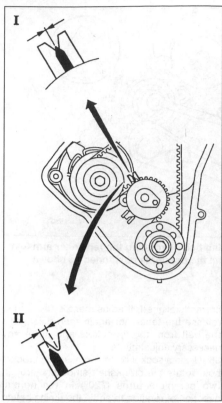

11.39 Timing belt tensioner pointer positions

I   Location if a new belt is being fitted
II Location if the original belt is being re-used (pointer should be 4 mm to the left of the backplate cutout)

(see illustration). Hold the tensioner in the correct position and tighten its retaining bolt to the specified torque. Rotate the crankshaft smoothly through another two complete turns in the normal direction of rotation, to bring the sprocket timing marks back into alignment. Check that the tensioner pointer is still correctly positioned in relation to the backplate cutout.

40 If the tensioner pointer is not correctly positioned in relation to the backplate, repeat the procedure in paragraph 38 (new belt) or 39 (original belt) (as applicable).

41 Once the tensioner pointer and backplate remain correctly aligned, refit the timing belt outer cover and tighten its retaining bolts to the specified torque.

42 On pre-1995 (C20NE engine) models, refit the cooling fan drive pulley and refit the cooling fan and coupling as described in Section 17.

43 On all models, refit the crankshaft pulley as described in Section 7.

12 Timing belt (2.2 litre) - removal and refitting

Note: The timing belt must be removed and refitted with the engine cold.

Removal

1 Remove the crankshaft pulley as described in Section 8.

2 Remove the timing belt outer cover as described in Section 10.

3 Position No 1 cylinder at TDC on its compression stroke as described in Section 4.

4 With the timing marks correctly aligned, slacken the timing belt tensioner bolt. Using an Allen key, rotate the tensioner arm clockwise to its stop, to relieve the tension in the timing belt, and hold it in position by and securely tighten the retaining bolt **(see illustration)**.

5 Slide the timing belt off from its sprockets and remove it from the engine. If the belt is to be re-used, use white paint or similar to mark the direction of rotation on the belt. **Do not** rotate the crankshaft or camshafts until the timing belt has been refitted.

6 If signs of oil contamination are found, trac the source of the oil leak and rectify it, the wash down the engine timing belt area and a related components to remove all traces of oil

Refitting

7 On reassembly, thoroughly clean the timing belt sprockets and tensioner/idler pulleys.

8 Check that the camshaft sprocket timing marks are still correctly aligned with the camshaft cover marks and the crankshaft sprocket mark is still aligned with the mark on the cover.

9 Fit the timing belt over the crankshaft and camshaft sprockets and around the idle pulleys, ensuring that the belt run between the exhaust camshaft and crankshaft sprockets is taut (ie, all slack is on the tensioner side of the belt), then fit the belt over the coolant pump sprocket and tensioner pulley. Do not twist the belt sharply while refitting it. Ensure that the belt teeth are correctly seated centrally in the sprockets, and that the timing marks remain in alignment. If a used belt is being refitted, ensure that the arrow mark made on removal points in the normal direction of rotation, as before.

10 Slacken the timing belt tensioner bolt to release the tensioner spring. Rotate the tensioner arm anti-clockwise until the tensioner pointer is fully over against its stop without exerting any excess strain on the belt. Hold the tensioner in position and securely tighten its retaining bolt **(see illustration)**.

11 Check the sprocket timing marks are still correctly aligned **(see illustration)**. I adjustment is necessary, release the tensioner again then disengage the belt from the sprockets and make any necessary adjustments.

12 Using a socket on the crankshaft sprocket bolt, rotate the crankshaft smoothly through two complete turns (720°) in the normal direction of rotation to settle the timing belt in position.

12.4 Slacken the tensioner pulley bolt (1) and rotate the tensioner arm clockwise using an Allen key in the arm cutout (2)

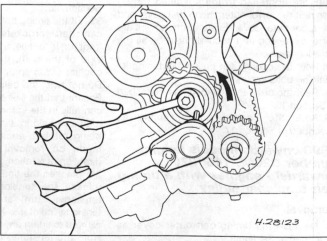

12.10 Tension the timing belt by rotating the tensioner arm fully anti-clockwise until the pointer is positioned as shown

12.11 Check that the sprocket timing marks are still correctly aligned

12.14 If a new belt is being fitted, position the tensioner so that the pointer is aligned with the backplate cutout

3 Check that both the camshaft and crankshaft sprocket timing marks are correctly realigned then slacken the tensioner bolt.

4 If a new timing belt is being fitted, adjust the tensioner so that the pointer is aligned with the cutout on the backplate

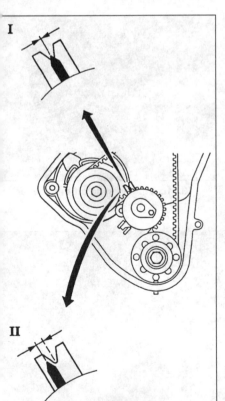

12.15 Timing belt tensioner pointer positions

Location if a new belt is being fitted
Location if the original belt is being re-used (pointer should be 4 mm to the left of the backplate cutout)

(see illustration). Hold the tensioner in the correct position and tighten its retaining bolt to the specified torque. Rotate the crankshaft smoothly through another two complete turns in the normal direction of rotation, to bring the sprocket timing marks back into alignment. Check that the tensioner pointer is still aligned with the backplate cutout.

15 If the original belt is being refitted, adjust the tensioner so that the pointer is positioned 4 mm to the left of the cutout on the backplate **(see illustration)**. Hold the tensioner in the correct position and tighten its retaining bolt to the specified torque. Rotate the crankshaft smoothly through another two complete turns in the normal direction of rotation, to bring the sprocket timing marks back into alignment. Check that the tensioner pointer is still correctly positioned in relation to the backplate cutout.

16 If the tensioner pointer is not correctly positioned in relation to the backplate, repeat the procedure in paragraph 14 (new belt) or 15 (original belt), as applicable.

17 Once the tensioner pointer and backplate remain correctly aligned, refit the timing belt cover and crankshaft pulley as described in Sections 8 and 10.

---

13 Timing belt tensioner and sprockets (2.0 litre) - removal and refitting

Camshaft sprocket

Removal

1 Remove the timing belt as described in Section 7.

2 The camshaft must be prevented from turning as the sprocket bolt is unscrewed, and this can be achieved in one of two ways as follows.

a) *Make up a sprocket-holding tool using two lengths of steel strip (one long, the other short), and three nuts and bolts; one nut and bolt forms the pivot of a forked tool, with the remaining two nuts and bolts at the tips of the 'forks' to engage with the sprocket spokes.*

b) *Remove the camshaft cover as described in Section 5 and hold the camshaft with an open-ended spanner on the flats provided.*

3 Unscrew the retaining bolt and washer and remove the sprocket from the end of the camshaft. If the sprocket locating pin is a loose fit, remove it and store it with the sprocket for safe-keeping.

Refitting

4 Prior to refitting check the oil seal for signs of damage or leakage, if necessary, renewing it.

5 Ensure the locating pin is in position then refit the sprocket, aligning its cutout with the pin. Refit the sprocket retaining bolt and washer.

6 Tighten the sprocket retaining bolt to the specified torque whilst prevent rotation using the method employed on removal.

7 Refit the timing belt as described in Section 11 then (where necessary) refit the camshaft cover as described in Section 5.

Crankshaft sprocket

Note: *A new sprocket retaining bolt must be used on refitting.*

Removal

8 Remove the timing belt as described in Section 11.

9 Slacken the crankshaft sprocket retaining bolt. To prevent crankshaft rotation if the engine is in the vehicle, have an assistant select top gear and apply the brakes firmly. Alternatively retain the sprocket with a length of steel bar; drill two holes in the bar and bolt

11A

13.10a Slacken and remove the retaining bolt and washer . . .

13.10b . . . and remove the crankshaft sprocket

it to the crankshaft pulley retaining bolt threads on the sprocket.

10 Unscrew the retaining bolt and washer then slide the crankshaft sprocket off from the end of the crankshaft **(see illustrations)**. Discard the retaining bolt, a new one must be used on refitting.

11 If necessary, remove the Woodruff key from the crankshaft slot then slide off the spacer **(see illustrations)**.

Refitting

12 Prior to refitting, check the crankshaft oil seal for signs of damage or leakage, if necessary, renewing it.

13 Slide the spacer onto the crankshaft and refit the Woodruff key to the crankshaft slot.

14 Refit the sprocket to the crankshaft, aligning its slot with the Woodruff key.

15 Fit the washer to the new retaining bolt and screw the bolt into position.

16 Lock the crankshaft by the method used on removal, and tighten the sprocket retaining

bolt to the specified stage 1 torque setting then angle-tighten the bolt through the specified stage 2 angle, using a socket and extension bar. It is recommended that an angle-measuring gauge is used during the final stages of the tightening, to ensure accuracy **(see illustrations)**. If a gauge is not

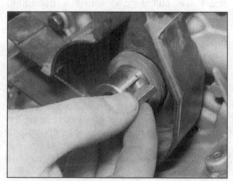

13.11a Remove the Woodruff key from the crankshaft . . .

13.11b . . . and slide off the spacer

available, use white paint to make alignment marks between the bolt head and sprocket prior to tightening; the marks can then be used to check that the bolt has been rotated through the correct angle.

17 Refit the timing belt as described in Section 11.

13.16a Tighten the sprocket retaining bolt to the specified stage 1 torque . . .

13.16b . . . and then through the specified stage 2 angle

14.2 Using an open-ended spanner to retain the camshaft whilst the sprocket retaining bolt is slackened

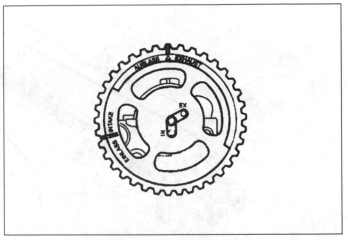

14.7 Ensure the locating pin is engaged in the correct sprocket hole on refitting (see text)

Timing belt tensioner pulley – 1993 onwards models

Removal

8 Remove the timing belt as described in Section 11.

9 Slacken and remove the retaining bolt and remove the tensioner assembly from the engine.

Refitting

10 Fit the tensioner to the engine, making sure that the lug on the backplate is correctly located in the oil pump housing hole. Ensure the tensioner is correctly seated then refit the retaining bolt. Using an Allen key, rotate the tensioner arm clockwise to its stop then securely tighten the retaining bolt.

11 Refit the timing belt as described in Section 11.

14 Timing belt sprockets, tensioner and idler pulleys (2.2 litre) – removal and refitting

Camshaft sprockets

Note: New sprocket retaining bolt(s) will be required on refitting.

Removal

1 Remove the timing belt as described in Section 12.

2 The camshaft must be prevented from turning as the sprocket bolt is unscrewed, and this can be achieved in one of two ways as follows:

a) Make up a sprocket-holding tool using two lengths of steel strip (one long, the other short), and three nuts and bolts; one nut and bolt forms the pivot of a forked tool, with the remaining two nuts and bolts at the tips of the 'forks' to engage with the sprocket spokes.

b) Remove the camshaft cover as described in Section 6 and hold the camshaft with an open-ended spanner on the flats provided (see illustration).

3 Unscrew the retaining bolt and washer and remove the sprocket from the end of the camshaft. If the sprocket locating pin is a loose fit in the camshaft end, remove it and store it with the sprocket for safe-keeping.

4 If necessary, remove the remaining sprocket using the same method (both sprockets are the same).

Refitting

5 Prior to refitting check the oil seal(s) for signs of damage or leakage. If necessary, renew it.

6 Ensure the locating pin is in position in the camshaft end.

7 Both inlet and exhaust camshaft sprockets are the same, but each one is equipped with two locating pin cutouts. If the sprocket is being fitted to the inlet camshaft, engage the locating pin in the IN cutout, and if the sprocket is being fitted to the exhaust camshaft engage the locating pin in the EX (see illustration). Ensure the camshaft locating pin is engaged in the correct sprocket cutout then fit the washer and new retaining bolt.

8 Prevent rotation by the method used on removal, and tighten the sprocket retaining bolt to the specified stage 1 torque setting then angle-tighten the bolt through the specified stage 2 angle, using a socket and extension bar, and finally through the specified stage 3 angle. It is recommended that an angle-measuring gauge is used during the final stages of the tightening, to ensure accuracy. If a gauge is not available, use white paint to make alignment marks between the bolt head and sprocket prior to tightening; the marks can then be used to check that the bolt has been rotated through the correct angle.

9 Refit the timing belt as described in Section 7 then (where necessary) refit the camshaft cover as described in Section 6.

Crankshaft sprocket

Note: A new crankshaft sprocket retaining bolt will be required on refitting.

Removal

10 Remove the timing belt as described in Section 12.

11 Slacken the crankshaft sprocket retaining bolt. To prevent crankshaft rotation, have an assistant select top gear and apply the brakes firmly.

12 Unscrew the retaining bolt and washer then remove the crankshaft sprocket from the end of the crankshaft. If necessary, remove the Woodruff key from the crankshaft end then slide the spacer off of the crankshaft.

Refitting

13 Where necessary, slide the spacer onto the crankshaft then refit the Woodruff key to the crankshaft slot.

14 Align the sprocket groove with the Woodruff key and slide the sprocket into position. Fit the washer and new retaining bolt.

15 Lock the crankshaft by the method used on removal, and tighten the sprocket retaining bolt to the specified stage 1 torque setting then angle-tighten the bolt through the specified stage 2 angle, using a socket and extension bar. It is recommended that an angle-measuring gauge is used during the final stages of the tightening, to ensure accuracy. If a gauge is not available, use white paint to make alignment marks between the bolt head and sprocket prior to tightening; the marks can then be used to check that the bolt has been rotated through the correct angle.

16 Refit the timing belt as described in Section 12.

Tensioner assembly

Removal

17 Remove the timing belt as described in Section 12.

11A

15.5 Radiator upper mounting bracket and fan shroud attachments - 2.0 litre (C20NE) engine

18 Slacken and remove the retaining bolt and remove the tensioner assembly from the engine.

Refitting

19 Fit the tensioner to the engine, making sure that the lug on the backplate is correctly located in the oil pump housing hole. Ensure the tensioner is correctly seated then refit the retaining bolt. Using an Allen key, rotate the tensioner arm clockwise to its stop then securely tighten the retaining bolt.

20 Refit the timing belt as described in Section 12.

Idler pulleys

Removal

21 Remove the timing belt as described in Section 12.

22 Slacken and remove the retaining bolt(s) and remove the idler pulley(s) from the engine. If necessary, unbolt the pulley mounting bracket and remove it from the cylinder block.

Refitting

23 Refit the pulley mounting bracket (where removed) to the cylinder block and tighten its retaining bolts to the specified torque.

24 Refit the idler pulley(s) and tighten the retaining bolt(s) to the specified torque.

25 Refit the timing belt as described in Section 12.

15 Radiator - removal, inspection and refitting

2.0 litre (C20NE)

Removal

1 Disconnect the battery negative lead.

2 Drain the cooling system as described in Section 2.

3 Release the retaining clips and disconnect the coolant hoses from the radiator.

4 On early models, undo the bolts securing the fan shroud to the radiator. Lift the shroud off the radiator and rest it on the fan.

5 Slacken and remove the nuts and bolts securing the radiator upper mounting brackets to the front body panel **(see illustration)**.

6 Check that all pipes and wiring are released, then lift the radiator out from the engine compartment, taking care not to lose the radiator lower mounting rubbers.

Refitting

7 Refitting is a reversal of removal, ensuring that all the mounting rubbers are correctly positioned, and that the upper mounting brackets are correctly engaged with the radiator. On completion, refill the cooling system as described in Section 2.

2.0 litre (X20SE) and 2.2 litre

Removal

8 Disconnect the battery negative lead.

9 Drain the cooling system as described in Chapter 1.

10 Release the retaining clips and disconnect the coolant hoses from the radiator. On 2.2 litre models, disconnect the air hoses from the air intake resonator attached to the fan shroud.

11 Disconnect the electric cooling fan and fan thermo-switch wiring harness plug(s) and release the wiring from any retaining cable ties.

12 Undo the two bolts securing the radiator upper retaining clamp to the body crossmember.

13 Check that all pipes and wiring are released, then lift the radiator and cooling fan assembly out from the engine compartment,

taking care not to lose the radiator lower mounting rubbers.

Refitting

14 Refitting is a reversal of removal, ensuring that all the mounting rubbers are correctly positioned. On completion, refill the cooling system as described in Section 2.

16 Electric cooling fan - removal and refitting

Removal

1 Remove the radiator as described in Section 15.

2 Unscrew the upper mounting bolts securing the fan shroud to the radiator. On 2.2 litre engine models, unscrew the additional bolt securing the air intake resonator to the shroud and remove the resonator. Carefully lift the fan and shroud from the two lower locating lugs and remove the assembly from the radiator.

3 Undo the three mounting nuts and withdraw the motor and fan from the shroud.

4 To remove the fan from the motor, extract the retaining clip from the motor spindle and withdraw the fan.

Refitting

5 Refitting is a reversal of removal.

17 Visco-clutch cooling fan - removal and refitting

Removal

1 Disconnect the battery negative lead.

2 Remove the auxiliary drivebelt(s) as described in Section 1.

3 If required, the cooling fan shroud may be moved out of the way. Undo the bolts securing the shroud to the radiator, then lift it off and rest it on the fan blades.

4 Using an open-ended spanner, hold the visco-clutch hub stationary, then using a wrench and hex bit, slacken and withdraw the Allen bolt from the centre of the hub noting that it has a **left-hand thread**.

5 Remove the fan and hub assembly from the pulley spindle and manoeuvre it out from behind the shroud. The visco-clutch unit may be removed from the fan by slackening and removing the retaining screws.

Refitting

6 Refitting is a reversal of removal, tightening the centre hub bolt securely. Refit the auxiliary drivebelt as described in Section 1.

Chapter 11B
Vauxhall/Opel Frontera diesel 1991 to 1998

Contents

Specifications

Timing belt renewal interval . . . . Every 40 000 miles (65 000 km) or 4 years - whichever comes first

Note: *Although the normal interval for timing belt renewal is 60 000 miles (100 000 km) or 6 years, it is strongly recommended that the interval is reduced on vehicles which are subjected to intensive use, ie, mainly short journeys or a lot of stop-start driving. The actual belt renewal interval is therefore very much up to the individual owner. That being said, it is highly recommended to err on the side of safety, and renew the belt at this earlier interval, bearing in mind the drastic consequences resulting from belt failure.*

Torque wrench settings	Nm	lbf ft
Alternator fixings:		
Lower mounting bolt	40	30
Upper mounting bolt	19	14
Camshaft sprocket bolts:		
Hub-to-camshaft bolt	64	47
Sprocket-to-hub bolts	8	6
Crankshaft pulley bolts:		
Hub-to-crankshaft bolt	186	137
Pulley-to-hub bolt	19	14
Fuel injection pump sprocket nut	64	47
Nudge bar mountings:		
'Soft feel' nudge bar-to-bumper bolts	20	15
'Soft feel' nudge bar-to-chassis bolts	25	18
Steel nudge bar-to-chassis rail bolts	50	37
Power steering pump mounting bolts	37	27
Timing belt backplate bolts	19	14
Timing belt cover bolts	8	6
Timing belt tensioner pulley bolt	76	56
Visco-clutch cooling fan hub nuts	8	6
Wheel nuts:		
Alloy wheels	120	89
Steel wheels	110	81

11B

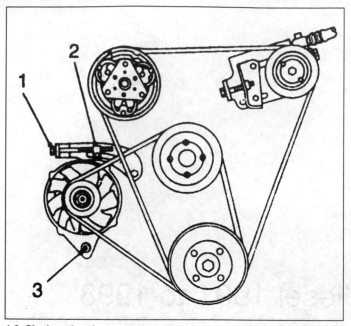

1.2 Slacken the alternator upper and lower mounting bolts (2 and 3) and adjust the belt tension with the adjuster bolt (1)

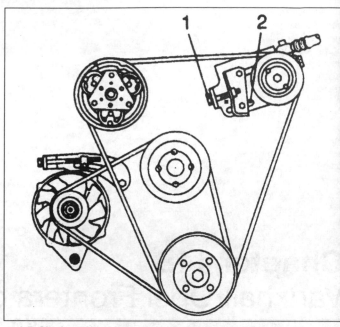

1.5 Slacken the power steering pump mounting bolts (2) and adjust the belt tension with the adjuster bolt (1)

1 Auxiliary drivebelt - removal, refitting and adjustment

Alternator

1 Remove the power steering pump/air conditioning compressor drivebelt as described later in this Section.
2 Slacken the alternator upper and lower mounting bolts then back off the adjuster bolt until the drivebelt can be slipped off the pulleys and removed from the engine **(see illustration)**.
3 Manoeuvre the new belt into position, seating it on the pulleys, and tension it using the adjuster bolt. Adjust the belt tension, so that there is 10 mm of movement in the belt when a force of 98 N (equivalent to 10 kg) is applied to the mid-point on the upper run of the belt the belt. When the belt tension is correctly set, tighten the alternator mounting bolts to the specified torque.
4 Refit the power steering pump/air conditioning compressor drivebelt as described later in this Section.

Power steering pump/air conditioning compressor

5 Slacken the power steering pump mounting bolts then back off the adjuster bolt until the drivebelt can be slipped off the pulleys and removed from the engine **(see illustration)**.
6 Manoeuvre the new belt into position, seating it on the pulleys, and tension it using the adjuster bolt.
7 On models with just power steering, adjust the belt tension so there is 14 to 17 mm of

movement in the belt when a force of 98 N (equivalent to 10 kg) is applied to the mid-point on the upper run of the belt the belt.
8 On models with power steering and air conditioning, adjust the belt tension so that there is 12 to 15 mm of movement in the belt when a force of 98 N (equivalent to 10 kg) is applied to the mid-point on the upper run of the belt the belt.
9 When the belt tension is correctly set, tighten the power steering pump mounting bolts to the specified torque then refit the undercover.

2 Top dead centre (TDC) for No 1 piston - locating

1 In its travel up and down its cylinder bore, Top Dead Centre (TDC) is the highest point that each piston reaches as the crankshaft rotates. While each piston reaches TDC both at the top of the compression stroke and again at the top of the exhaust stroke, for the purpose of timing the engine, TDC refers to the piston position (usually number 1) at the top of its compression stroke.
2 Number 1 piston (and cylinder) is at the front (timing belt) end of the engine, and its TDC position is located as follows. Note that the crankshaft rotates clockwise when viewed from the front of the vehicle.
3 Disconnect the battery negative terminal. To improve access to the crankshaft pulley, unbolt the undercover and remove it from underneath the engine.
4 Undo the retaining bolts and remove the timing belt upper cover to expose the injection

pump timing belt sprocket. Take care not to lose the sealing strip from the rear of the cover.
5 Using a socket and extension bar on the crankshaft pulley bolt, rotate the crankshaft until the TDC notch on the pulley rim is correctly aligned with the pointer on the cover retaining bolt. Note that there are several notches on the pulley rim with the TDC notch being the largest; the other notches are used when setting the injection pump timing. With the TDC notch correctly aligned with the pointer, No 1 and 4 pistons are at TDC **(see illustration)**.
6 To determine which piston is at TDC on its compression stroke, check the position of injection pump sprocket timing hole. If the hole is visible on the left-hand side of the

2.5 Align the crankshaft pulley TDC notch with the pointer (arrowed) to position No 1 and 4 pistons at TDC

sprocket then No 1 piston is at TDC on its compression stroke. If the timing hole is not visible then No 4 cylinder is at TDC on its compression stroke; rotate the crankshaft through a further complete turn (360°) to bring No 1 cylinder to TDC on its compression stroke.

7 With No 1 cylinder at TDC on its compression, the engine can be locked in position by inserting a M8 bolt through the injection pump sprocket timing hole and screwing it into the threaded hole in the backplate.

3 Crankshaft pulley -
removal and refitting

Removal

1 Remove the cooling fan and coupling as described in Section 7.
2 Remove the auxiliary drivebelts as described in Section 1.
3 Slacken and remove the four bolts securing the crankshaft pulley to its hub and remove the pulley from the vehicle. If the locating pin is a loose fit, remove it and store it with the pulley for safe-keeping.

Refitting

4 Ensure the locating pin is in position then refit the pulley, aligning it with the pin. Refit the four retaining bolts and tighten securely.
5 Refit the auxiliary drivebelts as described in Section 1.
6 Refit the cooling fan as described in Section 7.

4 Timing belt covers -
removal and refitting

Upper cover

Removal

1 Unbolt the undercover from underneath the engine unit and remove it from the vehicle.
2 Slacken and remove the retaining bolts then remove the upper cover from the engine, along with its sealing strip. Inspect the sealing strip for signs of wear or damage and renew if necessary.

Refitting

3 Refitting is the reverse of removal, ensuring the sealing strip is correctly positioned. Tighten the cover retaining bolts to the specified torque.

Lower (main) cover

Removal

4 Remove the cooling fan as described in Section 7.
5 Remove the crankshaft pulley as described in Section 3.
6 Remove the upper cover (see paragraph 2) then unbolt the lower cover and remove it from the engine complete with sealing strip. Inspect the sealing strip for signs of damage or deterioration and renew if necessary.

Refitting

7 Ensure the sealing strip is correctly located in the cover groove then apply a smear of sealant to the upper run of the sealing strip which is located in the area underneath the coolant pump.

8 Refit the lower cover to the engine, ensuring the sealing strip remains correctly seated, and tighten its retaining bolts to the specified torque.
9 Refit the upper cover and sealing strip and tighten its retaining bolts to the specified torque.
10 Refit the crankshaft pulley as described in Section 3.
11 Refit the cooling fan as described in Section 7.

5 Timing belt -
removal and refitting

Note: *The timing belt must be removed and refitted with the engine cold. A spring balance or 9 kg weight will be required to tension the belt correctly.*

Removal

1 Position No 1 cylinder at TDC on its compression stroke as described in Section 2.
2 Remove the crankshaft pulley as described in Section 3.
3 Remove the timing belt lower cover as described in Section 4.
4 Lock the camshaft and injection pump sprockets in position by inserting M8 bolts through the sprocket timing holes and screwing them into the threaded holes in the backplate. Check that the crankshaft pulley hub hole/pin is correctly aligned with the TDC pointer on the backplate (see illustration).
5 Undo the retaining screws and remove the timing belt guide plates from the camshaft and injection pump sprockets (see illustration).

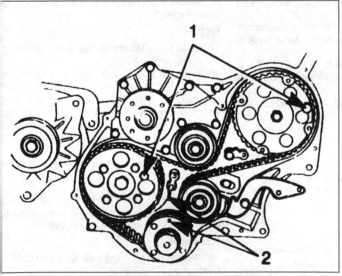

5.4 With No 1 cylinder at TDC on its compression stroke, lock the camshaft and injection pump sprockets in position with M8 bolts (1) and check the crankshaft pulley hub mark is aligned with the pointer (2)

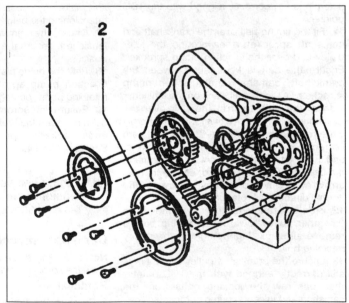

5.5 Undo the retaining screws and remove the camshaft and injection pump sprocket timing belt guides (1 and 2)

5.14 Apply a load of 9 kg to the tensioner pulley lever and securely tighten the pulley bolt

6 Loosen the timing belt tensioner pulley retaining bolt and pivot the pulley away from the belt.

7 Slide the timing belt from its sprockets and remove it from the engine. If the belt is to be re-used, use white paint or similar to mark the direction of rotation on the belt. **Do not** rotate the crankshaft until the timing belt has been refitted.

8 If signs of oil contamination are found, trace the source of the oil leak and rectify it, then wash down the engine timing belt area and all related components to remove all traces of oil.

Refitting

9 On reassembly, thoroughly clean the timing belt sprockets and tensioner/idler pulleys.

10 Ensure that the camshaft and injection pump sprockets are still locked in position and make sure the crankshaft pulley hub hole/pin is still correctly aligned with the TDC pointer.

11 Fit the timing belt over the crankshaft and camshaft sprockets then around the idler pulley and over the injection pump sprocket. Ensure the belt is kept taut between the crankshaft, camshaft and injection pump sprockets (ie, so that all slack on the tensioner side of the belt) then fit the belt over the tensioner pulley. Do not twist the belt sharply while refitting it. Ensure that the belt teeth are correctly seated centrally in the sprockets, and that the timing marks remain in alignment. If a used belt is being refitted, ensure that the arrow mark made on removal points in the normal direction of rotation.

12 Free the tensioner lever and move the tensioner pulley towards the timing belt to remove all slack. Lightly tighten the pulley retaining bolt.

13 Ensure the crankshaft pulley hub mark is still correctly aligned with the TDC pointer then unscrew the locking bolts from the camshaft and injection pump sprockets.

14 Attach the spring balance/weight (as applicable) to the hole in the end of the tensioner pulley lever. With a load of 9 kg applied to the lever hole, slacken the tensioner pulley retaining bolt then securely retighten it **(see illustration)**.

15 Using a socket on the crankshaft pulley hub bolt, rotate the crankshaft 45° in anti-clockwise direction to ensure that all slack is on the tensioner side of the timing belt. With a load of 9 kg applied to the to the hole on the end of the tensioner lever, slacken tensioner pulley retaining bolt again then retighten it to the specified torque setting.

16 Remove the spring balance/weight from the tensioner lever then rotate the crankshaft back to TDC. Check the pulley hub pin/hole is correctly aligned with the TDC pointer and that both the camshaft and injection pump sprocket bolts can be screwed into position. If adjustment is necessary, release the tensioner then disengage the belt from the sprockets and make any necessary adjustments before retensioning the belt.

17 Once the timing belt is correctly tensioned, secure the tensioner lever back in position.

18 Refit the guide plates to the camshaft and injection pump sprockets, tightening their retaining bolts securely.

19 Ensure the sprocket locking bolts have been removed then refit the timing belt covers and crankshaft pulley as described in Sections 3 and 4.

6 Timing belt sprockets, tensioner and idler pulleys - removal and refitting

Camshaft sprocket

Note: *It is likely that a puller will be required to draw the sprocket off the camshaft.*

Removal

1 Remove the timing belt as described in Section 5.

2 Using the sprocket locking bolt to prevent rotation, slacken and remove the centre bolt securing the sprocket hub to the camshaft.

3 Remove the locking bolt then remove the sprocket and hub assembly from the end of the camshaft. If necessary, draw the sprocket off using a suitable puller which engages with the holes in the sprocket. If the Woodruff key is a loose fit in the camshaft end, remove it and store it with the sprocket for safe-keeping.

Refitting

4 Prior to refitting check the oil seal for signs of damage or leakage. If necessary, renew it.

5 Ensure the Woodruff key is in position in the camshaft end.

6 Refit the sprocket assembly, ensuring the hub slot is correctly aligned with the key. Take great care not to damage the oil seal lip as the sprocket is slid into position.

7 Align the sprocket timing hole with the threaded hole in the backplate and screw in the locking bolt. Refit the sprocket hub retaining bolt and washer and tighten it to the specified torque.

8 Refit the timing belt as described in Section 5.

Fuel injection pump sprocket

Note: *It is likely that a puller will be required to draw the sprocket off the pump shaft.*

Removal

9 Remove the timing belt as described in Section 5.

10 Using the sprocket locking bolt to prevent rotation, slacken and remove the sprocket retaining nut and washer.

11 Unscrew the locking bolt then remove the sprocket from the injection pump shaft. If necessary, draw the sprocket off using a suitable puller which engages with the holes in the sprocket. If the Woodruff key is a loose fit, remove it and store it with the sprocket for safe-keeping.

Refitting

12 Ensure the Woodruff key is in position in the pump shaft.

13 Refit the sprocket assembly, aligning its slot with the key, then refit the washer and retaining nut. Align the sprocket timing hole with the threaded hole in the backplate and screw in the locking bolt. The sprocket retaining nut can then be tightened to the specified torque.

14 Refit the timing belt as described in Section 5.

Crankshaft sprocket

Note: *It is likely that a puller will be required to draw the sprocket off the crankshaft.*

Removal

15 Remove the timing belt as described in Section 5.

16 Slacken the crankshaft pulley hub retaining bolt. To prevent crankshaft rotation, have an assistant select top gear and apply the brakes firmly.

7 Unscrew the retaining bolt and remove the crankshaft pulley hub from the end of the crankshaft.

8 Remove the sprocket off from the crankshaft, noting which way around it is fitted; if the sprocket is a tight fit, use a puller to draw it off. If the Woodruff key is a loose fit, remove it and store it with the sprocket.

Refitting

9 Prior to refitting check the oil seal for signs of damage or leakage. If necessary, renew it.

10 Ensure the Woodruff key is in position then slide on the crankshaft sprocket, making sure the sprocket flange is innermost.

11 Refit the crankshaft pulley hub, engaging it with the Woodruff key, and refit the retaining bolt. Lock the crankshaft and tighten the retaining bolt to the specified torque setting.

12 Refit the timing belt as described in Section 5.

Tensioner assembly

Removal

23 Remove the timing belt as described in Section 5.

24 Slacken and remove the retaining bolt and remove the tensioner assembly from the backplate.

Refitting

25 Fit the tensioner to the engine, making sure that its cutout is correctly engaged with the backplate pin. Ensure the tensioner is correctly seated then refit the retaining bolt, tightening by hand only at this stage.

26 Refit the timing belt as described in Section 5.

Idler pulley

Removal

27 Remove the timing belt as described in Section 5.

28 Slacken and remove the retaining bolt and remove the idler pulley from the backplate.

Refitting

29 Refit the idler pulley and securely tighten its retaining bolt.

30 Refit the timing belt as described in Section 5.

7 Viscous-clutch cooling fan - removal and refitting

Removal

1 Disconnect the battery negative lead.

2 Remove the auxiliary drivebelt(s) as described in Section 1. Refer to Section 8 and remove the intercooler hose from the inlet manifold and intercooler.

3 Extract the two upper spring clips securing the fan shroud to the radiator. Lift the shroud upwards to disengage the two lower mounting lugs and rest it on the fan.

4 Unscrew the four nuts securing the fan visco-clutch hub and coolant pump pulley to the pump spindle.

5 Remove the fan and hub assembly from the pump spindle and manoeuvre it out from behind the shroud. The visco-clutch unit may be removed from the fan by slackening and removing the retaining screws.

Refitting

6 Refitting is a reversal of removal, tightening

the four retaining nuts to the specified torque. Refit the auxiliary drivebelt as described in Section 1.

8 Intercooler - removal and refitting

Removal

1 The intercooler is located at the front of the vehicle, behind the radiator grille.

2 Remove the radiator grille as described in Section 9.

3 Slacken the clips and disconnect the two air ducts from the intercooler **(see illustration)**.

4 Disconnect the horn wiring connectors.

5 Undo the bolts and move the bonnet lock vertical stay to one side.

6 Undo the nuts and bolts securing the two upper intercooler mounting brackets and horn mounting brackets to the front body panel, and remove the two horns.

7 Lift the intercooler upwards to disengage the lower mountings from the brackets and remove the intercooler from the vehicle.

8 Withdraw the upper mountings from the intercooler lugs and check the condition of all mounting bushes. Renew any that show signs of deterioration.

Refitting

9 Refitting is a reversal of removal.

9 Radiator grille - removal and refitting

Removal

1 Where fitted, remove the nudge bar as described in Section 10.

2 Undo the screw in the lower centre of the grille panel **(see illustration)**.

3 Using a screwdriver, push down the tag on the upper plastic retaining clips to release the

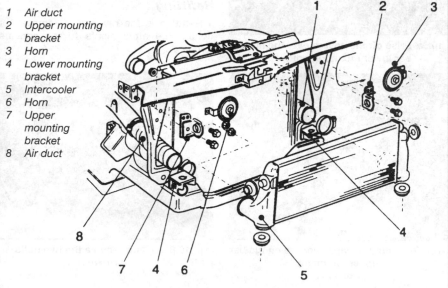

1 Air duct
2 Upper mounting bracket
3 Horn
4 Lower mounting bracket
5 Intercooler
6 Horn
7 Upper mounting bracket
8 Air duct

8.3 Intercooler components and attachments

9.2 Undo the screw (arrowed) in the lower centre of the grille panel

11B

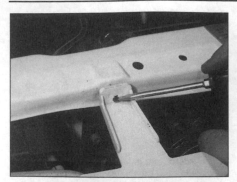

9.3a Push down the tag on the grille plastic retaining clips . . .

9.3b . . . and remove the grille

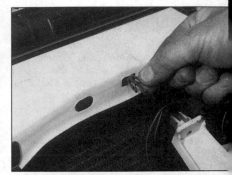

9.4a Withdraw the plastic clips from the body panel . . .

clips from the grille, then withdraw the grille from its location **(see illustrations)**.

Refitting

4 Withdraw the retaining clips from the body panel and refit them to the grille panel, ensuring that the tag on the clip locates fully in the slot on the grille **(see illustrations)**.

5 Locate the grille in position and engage the retaining clips with the openings in the body panel. Push the grille in until the clips lock into place.

6 Refit the centre retaining screw to secure the grille then, where applicable, refit the nudge bar as described in Section 10.

10 Nudge bar -
removal and refitting

Removal
Steel nudge bar

1 Where fitted, disconnect the front fog light or long-range driving light wiring harnesses at the connectors located adjacent to the radiator.

2 Chock the rear wheels then jack up the front of the vehicle and support it on axle stands.

3 Have an assistant support the nudge bar as the mounting bolts are undone.

4 From under the front of the vehicle, undo the bolts securing the nudge bar lower mountings to the chassis rails each side noting the position of any spacers that may be fitted. Withdraw the nudge bar and remove it from the front of the vehicle.

'Soft-feel' nudge bar

5 Where fitted, disconnect the front fog light or long-range driving light wiring harnesses at the connectors located adjacent to the radiator.

6 Using a screwdriver, prise off the covers over the lower mounting bolts each side and undo the two bolts **(see illustrations)**.

7 Similarly, prise out the caps over the two upper bolts securing the nudge bar to the front bumper **(see illustration)**.

8 With an assistant supporting the nudge bar, undo the two upper bolts and lift the nudge bar off the front of the vehicle **(see illustration)**.

Refitting

9 Refitting is the reversal of removal, but tighten the attachments to the specified torque.

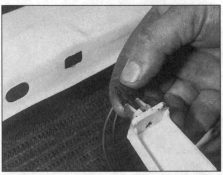

9.4b . . . and refit them to the grille

10.6a Prise off the covers over the nudge bar lower mounting bolts . . .

10.6b . . . then undo the mounting bolts each side

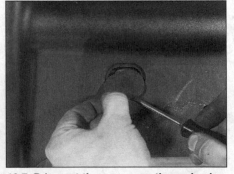

10.7 Prise out the caps over the nudge bar upper mounting bolts . . .

10.8 . . . and remove the two bolts (arrowed)

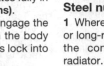

Chapter 12A
Vauxhall Nova &
Opel Corsa petrol 1983 to 1993

Contents

Specifications

Timing belt renewal interval .... Every 36 000 miles (60 000 km) or 4 years - whichever comes first

Torque wrench settings	Nm	lbf ft
Alternator bracket bolts	40	30
Alternator pivot and adjustment bolts	34	25
Camshaft sprocket bolt	45	33
Crankshaft pulley bolt (use locking compound)	55	41
Roadwheel bolts	20	15
Spark plugs	25	18
Temperature gauge transmitter	10	7
Timing belt tensioner bolt	20	15
Water pump bolts	20	15

1 Auxiliary drivebelt - removal, refitting and adjustment

Loosen the alternator mounting bolts and nuts just sufficiently to allow the unit to be pivoted in towards the engine. This will release all tension from the belt which can now be slipped off the respective pulleys. Fit a new belt after checking that it is of the correct type and take up the slack in the belt by swinging the alternator away from the engine and lightly tightening the bolts just to hold it in that position.

2 Although special tools are available for measuring the belt tension a good approximation can be achieved if the belt is tensioned so that there is 13 mm (0.5 in) of movement under firm thumb pressure at the mid-point position on the longest run of belt between pulleys. With the alternator bolts just holding the unit firm, lever the alternator away from the engine using a wooden lever at the mounting bracket end until the correct tension in the belt is reached and then tighten the alternator bolts. On no account apply any loads at the free end of the alternator as serious damage can be caused internally.

12A

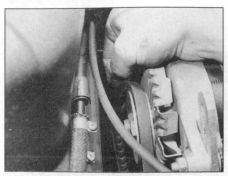

2.3 Disconnect the electrical leads and slip off the drivebelt

2.4 Undo the mounting bolts and remove the alternator

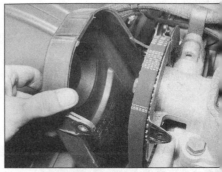

3.3 Remove the timing belt cover

2 Alternator -
removal and refitting

1 Disconnect the battery negative terminal.
2 Make a note of the electrical connections at the rear of the alternator and disconnect the plug, multi-pin connector or terminals as appropriate.
3 Undo and remove the alternator adjustment arm bolt, note the short earth wire. Slacken the lower pivot bolt and swing the alternator in towards the engine. Lift the drivebelt off the alternator pulley **(see illustration)**.
4 Remove the lower pivot bolt and lift the alternator away from the engine **(see illustration)**. Take care not to drop or knock the alternator as this can cause irreparable damage.

5 Refitting the alternator is the reverse of the removal sequence. Tension the drivebelt as described in Section 1.

3 Water pump -
removal and refitting

Removal

1 Drain the cooling system, as described in Section 4, and disconnect the battery negative terminal.
2 Remove the alternator with reference to Section 2.
3 Undo and remove the five small retaining bolts and lift off the timing belt cover **(see illustration)**.

4 Using a spanner or socket on the crankshaft pulley retaining bolt, turn the crankshaft until the notch on the outer edge of the camshaft sprocket is aligned with the groove in the plate behind the sprocket, and at the same time the notch in the crankshaft pulley is in line with the timing pointer. Turn the crankshaft in the normal direction of rotation only, ie clockwise when viewed from the belt cover end.
5 Slacken the three bolts securing the water pump to the cylinder block **(see illustration)**. The pump shaft is eccentric in the pump body, so that by rotating the pump body, the tension in the timing belt can be released. Turn the pump inwards to slacken the timing belt and slip the belt off the pump sprocket **(see illustration)**. Flats are provided on the pump body behind the sprocket and if necessary a large thin spanner can be used to turn the pump.
6 Undo and remove the bolts securing the belt cover backplate to the cylinder block, noting the location of the longer stud bolt. Withdraw the backplate from the engine **(see illustration)**.
7 The three water pump retaining bolts can now be removed and the pump withdrawn from its location **(see illustration)**.

Refitting

8 Before refitting the pump, clean its mounting in the cylinder block. Fit a new O-ring seal to the pump body and apply silicone grease to the seal and to the sealing surface in the block **(see illustration)**. Install

3.5a Slacken the water pump retaining bolts (arrowed) . . .

3.5b . . . and slip the timing belt off the sprockets

3.6 Remove the timing belt cover backplate for access to the pump

3.7 Remove the bolts and withdraw the pump

3.8 Renew the O-ring seal

ne pump and refit the three retaining bolts
nd washers, but only hand tighten them at
his stage.
Refit the timing belt cover backplate and
ecure it with the retaining bolts and stud bolt.
0 Check that the timing mark on the
amshaft sprocket is still aligned with the
otch on the backplate and that the notch on
he crankshaft pulley is in line with the timing
ointer. Now slip the timing belt over the
amshaft and water pump sprockets.
1 Tension the timing belt, as described in
ection 5. When the correct tension on the
ming belt has been achieved, tighten the
hree water pump retaining bolts.
2 Refit the timing belt cover and secure it
ith the five small bolts. Refit the alternator
nd adjust its drivebelt tension, as described
n Sections 1 and 2. Refer to Section 4 and
efill the cooling system, then reconnect the
attery.

4 Cooling system -
   draining and refilling

Draining

Note: *Take care to protect the hands from
scaping steam when removing the expansion
ank filler cap if the system is hot.*

With the car parked on level ground,
nscrew the expansion tank filler cap. If the
ystem is hot unscrew the cap slowly and
llow the pressure in the system to be
eleased before completely removing the cap.
Position a clean container beneath the
ottom hose connection on the left-hand side
f the radiator. Slacken the hose clip, ease the
ose off the outlet and allow the water to drain
nto the container.

Refilling

Before filling the cooling system make sure
hat all the hoses and hose clips are in good
ondition and that the clips are tight.
Remove the filler cap from the expansion
ank. To allow air to escape from the system
s it is being filled, disconnect the lead and
nscrew the temperature gauge transmitter
om the inlet manifold **(see illustration)**.

**5.2a Timing mark on pulley (arrowed) in
line with pointer**

**4.3 Bleed the cooling system through the
temperature gauge transmitter orifice**

5 Pour the coolant into the expansion tank.
When coolant emerges from the temperature
gauge transmitter orifice, refit the hose or
transmitter and ensure that they are secure.
6 Continue adding water until the level in the
expansion tank is just above the KALT mark.
Repeated squeezing of the large coolant
hoses will induce surging of the mixture in the
system which will help to dislodge any air
bubbles. Refit the expansion tank filler cap
and wipe up any spilt coolant.
7 Run the engine at a fast tickover until the
cooling fan motor engages and, particularly if
the system has been disturbed in any way,
examine carefully for leaks. Stop the engine
and allow it to cool before topping-up the
level in the expansion tank if necessary.
Remember that the system must be cold
before an accurate level is indicated in the
expansion tank.

5 Timing belt - removal,
   refitting and adjustment

1.2 and 1.3 litre engines

Note: *1.2 litre engines built from June 1990,
identifiable by the squared off top surfaces of
the timing belt covers, are fitted with a timing
belt automatic tensioner. Refer to the
procedure given below for 1.4 litre engines.*

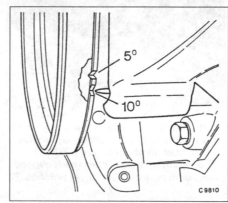

**5.2b Ignition timing pointer aligned with
the crankshaft pulley 10° BTDC notch -
1.4 engines**

5.1 Remove the timing belt cover

1 Undo the five retaining bolts and remove
the belt cover **(see illustration)**.
2 Using a socket or spanner on the
crankshaft until No 1 piston is on the firing
stroke. The notch on the pulley should be in
alignment with the ignition timing pointer **(see
illustrations)** but to ensure that it is No 1
piston that is on the firing stroke and not No 4,
either remove the No 1 spark plug and feel the
compression being generated as the
crankshaft is turned, or remove the distributor
cap and check that the rotor is in alignment
with No 1 spark plug contact in the cap.
3 Although it is possible to slacken the
alternator mountings to push the alternator
towards the engine, access is improved if the
alternator is removed completely (Section 2).
4 Unscrew the crankshaft pulley bolt without
disturbing the set position of the crankshaft.
Withdraw the pulley from the crankshaft. To
prevent the crankshaft rotating as the pulley
bolt is unscrewed, either engage a gear and
apply the brakes, or remove the flywheel
cover plate and lock the flywheel ring gear
with a suitable tool.
5 Refer to Section 4 and drain the cooling
system.
6 Using a socket inserted through the access
holes in the belt cover backplate **(see
illustration)**, slacken the three water pump
retaining bolts just enough to be able to swivel
the pump and release the tension of the
timing belt.
7 If the timing belt is to be used again, note
its running direction before removing it.
8 Take the belt off the sprockets and fit the

**5.6 Slacken the water pump retaining
bolts to release the belt tension**

12A

5.9 A spanner engaged with the flats on the pump can be used to tension the timing belt

5.10 Make a final check that the notch (A) on the sprocket is aligned with the groove (B) in the backplate before finally tensioning the belt

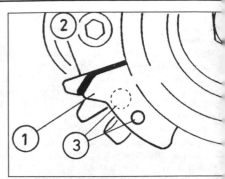

5.14 To lock tensioner for removal/refitting, move indicator arm (1) clockwise until locking rod can be passed through holes (3) in arm and baseplate (2)

new one without moving the set position of the camshaft or crankshaft.

9 Engage the new belt over the sprockets and apply some tension by moving the water pump. Flats are provided on the pump body behind the sprocket and if necessary a large thin spanner can be used to turn the eccentrically mounted pump **(see illustration)**.

10 Refit the crankshaft pulley and then check that the pulley notch is still in alignment with the timing pointer and that the camshaft sprocket mark is aligned with the groove in the plate behind it **(see illustration)**. If not, release the belt tension and readjust the position of the sprockets as necessary.

11 The belt tension should now be adjusted using the official tool (KM 510A). Adjust the tension as necessary by moving the water pump. If the belt is overtight, it will be heard to hum when the engine is running. Gauge readings are:

	New belt	Used belt
1.2 litre	5.5	4.0
1.3 litre	6.0	5.0

When the adjustment is correct, tighten the coolant pump bolts, turn the crankshaft through one full turn, and check the tension

again. Repeat this procedure until the correct tension is obtained.

12 Refit the belt cover and the alternator. Adjust the drivebelt and refill the cooling system, as described in Sections 1 and 4.

1.2 litre engines from 1990 and 1.4 litre engines

13 Remove the timing belt as described above, noting the following points. It may be necessary to remove the air cleaner and intake duct to improve access. The timing belt cover is in two parts, the lower cover being fitted over the water pump; either may be secured by clips or hexagon-headed screws. It is only necessary to drain the cooling system if a leak results from slackening the pump bolts, or from moving the pump (see paragraph 17).

14 To lock the tensioner in its slackest position for removal and refitting, move the tensioner indicator arm clockwise until the holes align in the baseplate and arm, and a close-fitting rod can be passed through them **(see illustration)**; unbolt the tensioner.

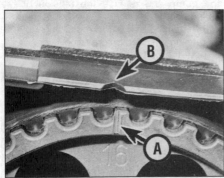

5.15 Camshaft sprocket mark (A) aligned with timing belt rear cover marking (B)

5.21 Timing belt tension is correct when tensioner indicator pointer aligns with baseplate notch centre (A). Note crankshaft sprocket index mark aligned with pump housing/rear cover notches (B)

15 Refit the timing belt so that the front run taut, then remove the tensioner locking ro and check that the index mark on th crankshaft sprocket and the stamped line c the camshaft sprocket are aligned with the respective oil pump housing/timing belt re cover notches **(see illustration)**.

16 Temporarily refit the crankshaft pulle bolt, and remove the spark plugs so th crankshaft can be rotated easily. Turning t water pump is easier if a special spanner used. If the pump cannot be turned to adju the belt tension, it can be freed by light striking it from below using a hammer and long drift. If a coolant leak results fro disturbing the pump, drain the coolin system, remove the pump and renew i O-ring, lubricating it with grease or petroleu jelly (Section 3).

17 Tighten the belt by slackening the thre water pump bolts, and turning the pun clockwise until the holes in the tension indicator arm and baseplate align (th tensioner indicator arm will then have move fully clockwise to its stop).

18 Lightly tighten the pump securing bolt just sufficiently to prevent the pump fro moving.

19 Turn the crankshaft smoothly (or else th belt may jump a tooth) without jerking it moving the water pump, through tw complete revolutions clockwise until th timing marks are again aligned.

20 Slacken the timing belt by turning the wat pump anti-clockwise until the tensioner indicator pointer is in the centre of its basepla notch; the belt tension is then correct.

21 Tighten the pump bolts, turn th crankshaft through two turns clockwise, ar recheck the setting **(see illustration)**. If th pointer and notch are not aligned, th operation must be repeated.

22 Complete the refitting procedure described above.

Chapter 12B
Vauxhall Nova &
Opel Corsa diesel 1983 to 1993

Contents

Specifications

Timing belt renewal interval . . . . Every 36 000 miles (60 000 km) or 4 years - whichever comes first

Note: Although the interval for timing belt renewal is increased for later models, it is strongly recommended that this shorter interval is applied to vehicles which are subjected to intensive use, ie, mainly short journeys or a lot of stop-start driving. The actual belt renewal interval is therefore very much up to the individual owner. That being said, it is highly recommended to err on the side of safety, and renew the belt at this earlier interval, bearing in mind the drastic consequences resulting from belt failure.

Auxiliary drivebelts

Tension (using gauge KM-128-A):
  Alternator:
    New . . . . 440 to 540 N
    Used . . . . 320 to 390 N
  Power steering pump:
    New . . . . 450 N
    Used . . . . 250 to 300 N

Injection pump

Timing setting . . . . 0.50 to 0.60 mm

Torque wrench settings

	Nm	lbf ft
Alternator:		
Adjuster strap nuts and bolts	25	18
Mounting bracket to cylinder block	40	30
Pivot bolt	25	18
Camshaft sprocket bolts	10	7
Crankshaft pulley bolts	20	15
Crankshaft sprocket centre bolt	133 to 161	98 to 119
Fuel injection pump:		
Central vent bolt	20	15
Fuel lines to pump	25	18
Pump to bracket	40	30
Pump to cylinder block/flange	23	17
Sprocket to pump	70	52
Right-hand mounting bracket:		
To cylinder block	45	33
To damping block	45	33
Engine rear suspension bracket:		
To damping block	65	48
To gearbox	90	66
To underbody	75	55
Power steering pump:		
Drivebelt tensioner to pump	40	30
Tension strut to crossmember	60	44
Timing belt cover to cylinder block	8	6
Timing belt guide roller to cylinder block	80	59
Timing belt tensioner roller bolt and nut	19	14
Wheel bolts	90	66

12B

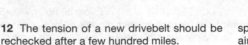

1.7 Tensioning the alternator drivebelt

A   Socket drive in end of adjuster arm   C   Pivot bol
B   Adjuster strap bolt

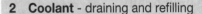

1.8 Using special tool KM-128-A to tension the alternator drivebelt

1   Auxiliary drivebelts - removal, refitting and adjustment

Alternator

Removal and refitting

1 Gain full access to the alternator by jacking up the front right-hand side of the vehicle and supporting it on axle stands.
2 To remove the drivebelt, first slacken the alternator pivot and adjuster bolts.
3 Where fitted, remove the power steering pump drivebelt.
4 Move the alternator towards the engine and slip the drivebelt off its pulleys.
5 Fit the new drivebelt in position over the pulleys and adjust it as follows:

Adjustment

6 Tighten the alternator fastenings slightly, so that the alternator can just be moved by hand.
7 Insert a socket drive in the end of the adjuster arm and use it as a lever to move the alternator away from the engine until the belt tension is correct. Nip the adjuster bolt tight whilst checking the belt tension **(see illustration)**.
8 Vauxhall recommend the use of a special tool (KM-128-A) for tensioning the belt to the specified amount **(see illustration)**. In the absence of this tool, aim for a tension such that the belt can be deflected about 12 mm by firm finger pressure in the middle of its run. The belt tension must, however, be checked with the special tool as soon as possible.
9 Tighten the alternator fastenings to the specified torque setting once the belt tension is correct.
10 Where applicable, refit and tension the steering pump drivebelt.
11 Lower the front of the vehicle, removing the axle stands and jack.

12 The tension of a new drivebelt should be rechecked after a few hundred miles.

Power steering pump

Removal and refitting

13 Gain access to the drivebelt by removing the air cleaner housing assembly.
14 To remove the drivebelt, first loosen the pump pivot and adjuster bolts.
15 Move the pump towards the engine and slip the drivebelt off its pulleys.
16 Fit the new drivebelt in position over the pulleys and adjust it as follows:

Adjustment

17 Tighten the pump fastenings slightly, so that the pump can just be moved by hand.
18 Insert a socket drive in the end of the adjuster arm and use it as a lever to move the pump away from the engine until the belt tension is correct. Nip the adjuster bolt tight whilst checking the belt tension **(see illustration)**.
19 Vauxhall recommend the use of a special tool (KM-128-A) for tensioning the belt to the

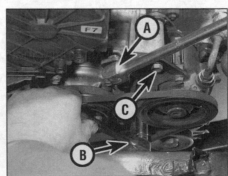

1.18 Tensioning the power steering pump drivebelt

A   Socket drive in end of adjuster arm
B   Adjuster strap bolt
C   Pivot bolt

specified amount. In the absence of this too aim for a tension such that the belt can be deflected approximately 12 mm by firm finge pressure in the middle of its run. The bel tension must, however, be checked with th special tool as soon as possible.
20 Once belt tension is correct, tighten th pump fastenings to the specified torqu setting.
21 Refit the air cleaner housing assembly.
22 The tension of a new drivebelt should b rechecked after a few hundred miles.

2   Coolant - draining and refilling

⚠️ *Warning: Take care to avoi scalding when removing th cooling system expansion tan cap. Place a thick cloth over the cap befor turning it anti-clockwise.*
Caution: Never operate the vehicl with plain water in the cooling system except in an emergency. Apart from the ris of freezing in winter weather, seriou corrosion and rust and scale formation ma occur.
Warning: Antifreeze is poisonous and mus be handled with due care.

Draining

1 The system should only be drained when is cool. If it must be drained hot, take grea care to avoid scalding.
2 Remove the expansion tank cap. If th system is hot, place a thick cloth over the ca before turning it anti-clockwise.
3 Place a container underneath the radiato bottom hose. Disconnect the hose from th radiator and allow the system to drain.
4 A cylinder block drain plug is provided making it possible to drain the cooling syste completely if necessary.

Filling

5 Make sure that all hoses and clips are in good condition. Refit any disturbed hoses and see that their clips are tight. Before refitting the cylinder block drain plug, coat its threads with sealing compound (GM spec. 15 03 166).
6 Fill the system via the expansion tank cap. If new coolant is being put in, start by pouring in the required quantity of neat antifreeze and follow it up with the water.
7 Massage the large coolant hoses to help displace air pockets during filling.
8 Most vehicles will be fitted with a self-venting cooling system this can be recognised by the two small vent hoses which enter the top of the expansion tank. If the system is not self-venting, open the bleed screw on the thermostat elbow during filling and close it when coolant runs out at the bleed screw.
9 When the system appears full, refit the expansion tank cap. Run the engine up to operating temperature, keeping a look-out for coolant leaks, then stop it and allow it to cool. Recheck the coolant level and top-up if necessary.
10 Recheck the tightness of all hose clips when the engine has cooled, and again after a few hundred miles.

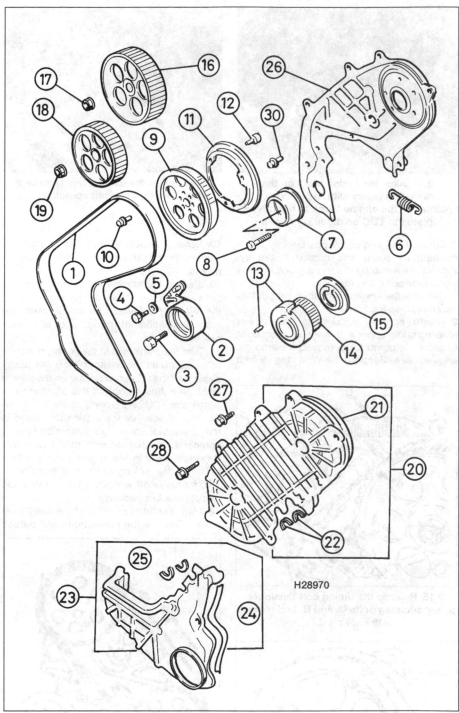

3 Timing belt - removal and refitting

Caution: A timing belt which is damaged, oil-soaked or fuel soaked must be renewed or it will fail, resulting in serious engine damage.

1 The timing belt also drives the oil pump and fuel injection pump **(see illustration)**.

Removal

2 Disconnect the battery earth lead.
3 Gain access to the timing belt cover by first removing the air cleaner housing from its mounting on the right-hand side of the engine bay. Do this by first detaching the outlet tube retaining clamp at the engine manifold. Release the housing inlet scoop from the vehicle front crossmember and manoeuvre it clear of the housing. Disconnect the front retainer at the housing base and pull the housing forward to release it from its rear retainer.
4 Where necessary, release the brake servo vacuum line retaining clamp from the cover and pull the line from the servo unit, moving it to one side. Move any electrical cables clear of the timing belt cover after having released their respective retaining clamps.
5 Remove the upper part of the timing belt cover by undoing its securing bolts (noting their respective lengths) and lifting it from position.
6 Gain access to the side of the engine through the right-hand wheel arch.

3.1 Timing belt and associated components

1 Timing belt	12 Screw	21 Cover seal
2 Tensioner pulley	13 Crankshaft sprocket	22 Cover seal
3 Bolt	14 Locating pin	23 Drivebelt lower front cover
4 Bolt	15 Flange disc	
5 Washer	16 Fuel injection pump sprocket	24 Cover seal
6 Tensioner spring		25 Cover seal
7 Guide roller	17 Nut	26 Drivebelt rear cover
8 Bolt	18 Oil pump sprocket	27 Bolt
9 Camshaft sprocket	19 Nut	28 Screw
10 Bolt	20 Drivebelt upper front cover	29 Screw
11 Sprocket flange		30 Screw

3.11 Align the timing mark on the crankshaft pulley with the reference pointer on the engine block to bring No 1 piston to TDC on the firing stroke

3.12a Insert the locking bolt (arrowed) through the camshaft sprocket . . .

3.12b . . . and insert the locking bolt through the injection pump sprocket

7 Support the engine by positioning a jack beneath its sump and raising it slightly. Protect the sump by placing a piece of thick wood between it and the jack.

8 Remove the engine right-hand mounting assembly, see Section 4.

9 Where applicable, slacken the power steering pump upper and lower retaining bolts to allow the pump to be moved towards the engine, see Section 1. With the V-belt

slackened, detach it from the crankshaft, coolant pump and power steering pump pulleys.

10 Slacken the alternator pivot and retaining bolts and move it towards the engine. With the V-belt slackened, detach it from the crankshaft, coolant pump and alternator pulleys.

11 Turn the crankshaft in the normal direction of rotation until the timing mark on its pulley aligns with the reference pointer on the engine block **(see illustration)**. In this position No 1 piston is at TDC on the firing stroke.

12 Now check that the locking bolt holes in the camshaft and fuel injection pump sprockets are aligned with their respective threaded holes in the engine casing before inserting the locking bolts (bolt sizes M6 x 1.00 for camshaft and M8 x 1.25 for injection pump) **(see illustrations)**.

13 Mark the fitted position of the crankshaft pulley. Remove the pulley bolts and detach

the pulley, tapping its rim to free it i necessary.

14 Remove the lower part of the timing bel cover to fully expose the belt.

15 Release the timing belt tensioner pulle and remove the spring **(see illustration)**.

16 Mark the running direction of the timing belt if it is to be re-used. Also take care not t kink the belt, nor get oil, grease, etc. on it.

17 Unbolt the flange from the camshaf sprocket **(see illustration)**. Slip the belt o the sprocket and then the remaining sprockets to remove it from the engine.

18 If signs of oil contamination are found trace the source of the oil leak and rectify it then wash down the engine timing belt area and all related components to remove a traces of oil.

Refitting

19 Commence refitting by first placing th timing belt over the camshaft sprocket an then the injection pump sprocket, etc. until i is correctly routed **(see illustration)**. Th crankshaft must not be disturbed and th camshaft and fuel injection pump sprocket should still be locked in alignment. Refit th flange to the camshaft sprocket.

20 Remove the camshaft and fuel injectio pump sprocket alignment bolts.

21 Refit the timing belt tensioner spring an check that the tensioner assembly moves free before tightening the tensioner securing bolts t the specified torque setting **(see illustration)**.

3.15 Release the timing belt tensioner pulley securing bolts (A and B) and remove the spring (C)

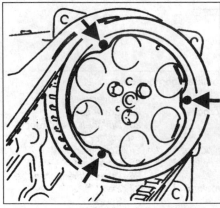

3.17 Remove the camshaft sprocket flange securing screws (arrowed)

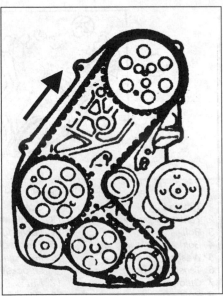

3.19 Ensure the timing belt is correctly routed

Arrow denotes direction of belt travel

3.21 Refit the drivebelt tensioner spring and check that the tensioner assembly moves freely before tightening the tensioner securing bolts

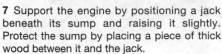

22 Refit the lower part of the timing belt cover to the engine, renewing any damaged sealing strips and tightening the retaining bolts to the specified torque setting.
23 Refit the crankshaft pulley in its previously noted position, tightening its retaining bolts to the specified torque setting.
24 Check the injection pump timing (Section 6).
25 Refit and tension each auxiliary drivebelt, referring to Section 1.
26 Refit the engine right-hand mounting in the reverse sequence to removal, tightening all retaining bolts to the specified torque settings.
27 Refit the upper part of the timing belt cover, renewing any damaged sealing strips and tightening the retaining bolts to the specified torque setting.
28 Refit all other removed components.
29 Remove the jack from beneath the engine and reconnect the battery earth lead.

4 Engine/transmission mountings - removal and refitting

1 The flexible mountings can be renewed if they have deteriorated. To facilitate removal, take the weight of the engine/transmission on a hoist, or use a jack with a protective wooden block from below. Only remove and refit one mounting at a time (see illustration).
2 With the mounting refitted, only nip up the retaining bolts at first, then tighten them to the specified torque.
3 Lower the hoist or jack and check that the mounting is not under strain. Slacken and retighten the bolts as necessary.

5 Valve timing - checking and adjustment

Note: When carrying out the following procedure, refer to the illustrations referred to in Section 3 on timing belt removal and refitting.

Checking

1 Disconnect the battery earth lead.
2 Gain access to the timing belt cover by first removing the air cleaner housing from its mounting on the right-hand side of the engine bay. Do this by first detaching the outlet tube retaining clamp at the engine manifold. Release the box inlet scoop from the vehicle front crossmember and manoeuvre it clear of the housing. Disconnect the front retainer at the housing base and pull the housing forward to release it from its rear retainer.
3 Where necessary, release the brake servo vacuum line retaining clamp from the cover

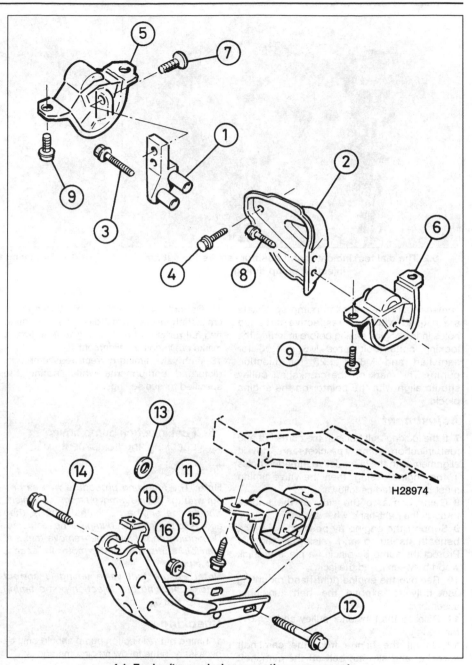

4.1 Engine/transmission mounting components

1 Right-hand mounting bracket	9 Screw
2 Left-hand mounting bracket	10 Rear mounting bracket
3 Screw	11 Flexible block - rear mounting
4 Screw	12 Screw
5 Flexible block - right-hand mounting	13 Washer
6 Flexible block - left-hand mounting	14 Screw
7 Screw	15 Screw
8 Screw	16 Nut

and pull the line from the servo unit, moving it to one side. Move any electrical cables clear of the drivebelt cover after having released their respective retaining clamps.
4 Remove the upper part of the belt cover by undoing its securing bolts (noting their respective lengths) and lifting it from position.

5 Turn the crankshaft in the normal direction of rotation until the timing mark on its pulley aligns with the reference pointer on the engine block. In this position No 1 piston is at TDC on the firing stroke.
6 Now check that the valve timing is correct by ensuring that the locking bolt holes in the

12B

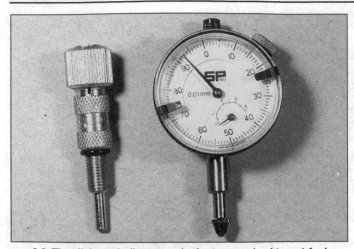

6.2 The dial test indicator and adaptor required to set fuel injection pump timing

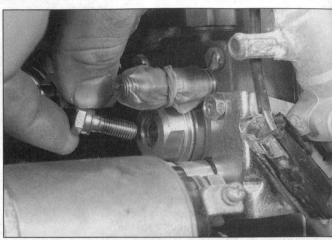

6.7 Removing the central plug from the injection pump

camshaft and fuel injection pump sprockets are aligned with their respective threaded holes in the engine casing before inserting the locking bolts (bolt sizes M6 x 1.00 for camshaft and M8 x 1.25 for injection pump). The mark on the crankshaft pulley should align with the pointer on the engine block.

Adjustment

7 If the locking bolt holes in the camshaft and fuel injection pump sprockets are not in alignment with their respective threaded holes in the engine casing, then the valve timing must be adjusted as follows.

8 Gain access to the side of the engine through the right-hand wheelarch.

9 Support the engine by positioning a jack beneath its sump and raising it slightly. Protect the sump by placing a piece of thick wood between it and the jack.

10 Remove the engine right-hand mounting assembly to expose the belt tensioner assembly.

11 Release the tensioner pulley and remove the spring.

12 Unbolt the flange from the camshaft sprocket and slip the belt off the camshaft and injection pump sprockets.

13 Rotate the camshaft and fuel injection pump sprockets by the least amount until the locking bolt holes are aligned with their respective threaded holes in the engine casing. Insert the locking bolts. The mark on the crankshaft pulley should still align with the pointer on the engine block.

14 Place the timing belt over the injection pump and camshaft sprockets.

15 Remove the sprocket locking bolts.

16 Refit the tensioner spring and check that the tensioner assembly moves freely before first tightening the tensioner roller bolt and then the nut to the specified torque setting.

17 Confirm valve timing by turning the crankshaft in the normal direction of rotation two full turns and rechecking that all timing marks are in correct alignment.

18 With valve timing correct, reassemble all disturbed components whilst noting the specified torque settings.

6 Fuel injection pump timing - checking and adjustment

Note: *The following procedure was carried out with the engine removed from the vehicle. Should the engine be in the vehicle, then access to the injection pump will be restricted. Depending on vehicle type, remove the inlet manifold and/or the starter motor for access to the pump.*

Note: *Ensure that valve timing is correct before checking fuel injection pump timing (see Section 5).*

Checking

1 Timing of the injection pump should only be necessary in the following circumstances:

a) When fitting a new or overhauled pump
b) If the timing is suspected of being wrong
c) If the timing belt has been re-tensioned o[r] renewed

2 Obtain a dial test indicator (DTI) an[d] adapter **(see illustration)**. The manufacture[r] specifies the use of an adapter which screw[s] into, and seals, the plug hole.

3 Disconnect the battery earth lead.

4 Clean around the injection pipe unions [at] the pump and cylinder head.

5 Disconnect Nos 1 and 2 injection pipe[s] from the injectors and the pump and remov[e] them from the engine. Be prepared for fue[l] spillage during subsequent operations.

6 Blank off all exposed pipe connections [to] prevent the ingress of dirt and moisture.

7 Remove the central plug from the injectio[n] pump **(see illustration)**.

8 Turn the crankshaft in the normal directio[n] of rotation until the timing mark on its pulle[y] aligns with the reference pointer on the engin[e] block **(see illustration)**. In this position No [1] piston is at TDC on the firing stroke.

9 Deactivate the cold start lever by using [a] screwdriver as shown **(see illustration)**.

10 Fit the adapter and dial test indicator wit[h] the indicator probe entering the central plu[g]

6.8 The timing mark on the crankshaft pulley aligned with the reference pointer on the engine block

6.9 Deactivating the cold start lever with screwdriver

6.10 The adaptor and dial test indicator fitted to the injection pump

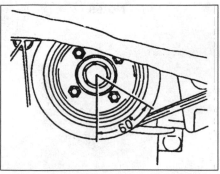

6.11 Turn the crankshaft in the normal direction of rotation to approximately 60° before TDC (No 1 firing)

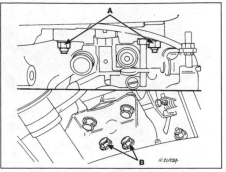

6.14 The fuel injection pump securing nuts (A) and pump bracket bolts (B)

ole and contacting the pump piston **(see illustration)**.

1 Turn the crankshaft in the normal direction of rotation to approximately 60° before TDC (No 1 firing) **(see illustration)**. At this point, the injection pump piston will be at bottom dead centre (BDC).

2 Zero the indicator, checking its adjustment by rotating the crankshaft slightly in either direction to ensure BDC.

3 Bring the engine back to TDC (No 1 firing). When the timing mark on the pulley is aligned with the reference pointer, the dial test indicator should show a lift corresponding to

the desired timing setting - see the *Specifications* at the start of this Chapter.

Adjustment

14 If adjustment is necessary, loosen the two nuts which secure the injection pump and the two bolts which secure the pump bracket **(see illustration)**.

15 Loosen Nos 3 and 4 injection pipes at the injectors and pump.

16 Rotate the pump until the dial test indicator shows the desired lift, then tighten the loosened nuts and bolts to the specified torque settings. Rotating the top of the pump

towards the engine will lower the lift value, whereas rotating the pump in the opposite direction will raise the lift value.

17 Repeat the checking procedure.

18 With the pump timing correct, remove the DTI and adapter then refit the plug to the pump.

19 Remove any blanking materials and reconnect all injection pipe unions, working in the reverse sequence to removal and tightening them to the specified torque settings.

20 Refit any other disturbed components, start the engine and check for fuel leaks.

Notes

Chapter 13
Vauxhall/Opel Omega petrol 1994 to 1998

Contents

Specifications

Timing belt renewal interval .... Every 36 000 miles (60 000 km) or 4 years - whichever comes first
Note: *Although the interval for timing belt renewal is increased for later models, it is strongly recommended that this shorter interval is applied to vehicles which are subjected to intensive use, ie, mainly short journeys or a lot of stop-start driving. The actual belt renewal interval is therefore very much up to the individual owner. That being said, it is highly recommended to err on the side of safety, and renew the belt at this earlier interval, bearing in mind the drastic consequences resulting from belt failure.*

Torque wrench settings

	Nm	lbf ft
2.0 litre SOHC engine		
Coolant pump	25	28
Camshaft cover bolts	8	6
Camshaft sprocket bolt	45	33
Crankshaft pulley bolts	20	15
Crankshaft sprocket bolt:*		
Stage 1	130	96
Stage 2	Angle-tighten a further 40 to 50°	
Inlet manifold nuts and bolts	22	16
Roadwheel bolts	110	81
Spark plug heatshields	25	18
Spark plugs	25	18
Timing belt cover bolts:		
Outer cover	4	3
Rear cover	6	4
Timing belt tensioner bolt	20	15

13

Torque wrench settings (continued)

	Nm	lbf ft
2.0 litre DOHC engine		
Camshaft cover bolts	8	6
Camshaft sprocket bolt:*		
Stage 1	50	37
Stage 2	Angle-tighten a further 60°	
Stage 3	Angle-tighten a further 15°	
Coolant pump	25	28
Crankshaft pulley bolts	20	15
Crankshaft sprocket bolt:*		
Stage 1	130	96
Stage 2	Angle-tighten a further 40 to 50°	
Inlet manifold nuts and bolts	22	16
Roadwheel bolts	110	81
Spark plugs	25	18
Timing belt cover bolts:		
Outer cover	6	4
Rear cover	8	6
Timing belt idler pulley:		
Mounting bracket bolts	25	18
Pulley bolt	25	18
Timing belt tensioner bolt	20	15
2.5 and 3.0 litre engine		
Auxiliary drivebelt tensioner mounting bolts	35	26
Camshaft cover bolts	8	6
Camshaft sprocket bolt:*		
Stage 1	50	37
Stage 2	Angle-tighten a further 60°	
Stage 3	Angle-tighten a further 15°	
Coolant pump	25	28
Coolant pump pulley bolts:*		
Stage 1	8	6
Stage 2	Angle-tighten a further 30°	
Stage 3	Angle-tighten a further 30°	
Crankshaft pulley bolts	20	15
Crankshaft sprocket bolt:*		
Stage 1	250	185
Stage 2	Angle-tighten a further 45°	
Stage 3	Angle-tighten a further 15°	
EGR pipe union nuts	25	18
EGR valve adaptor bolts	8	6
EGR valve bolts	20	15
Inlet manifold nuts and bolts:		
Flange to cylinder head bolts	20	15
Lower section:		
Retaining bolts	20	15
Fuel pipe adaptor mounting bolts	8	6
Upper section retaining bolts	8	6
Power steering pump pulley bolts:*		
Stage 1	20	15
Stage 2	Angle-tighten a further 30°	
Stage 3	Angle-tighten a further 15°	
Roadwheel bolts	110	81
Spark plugs	25	18
Timing belt cover bolts:		
Outer cover	8	6
Rear cover:		
M6 bolts	8	6
M8 threaded stud	10	7
Timing belt lower guide pulley bolt	40	30
Timing belt tensioner pulley/upper guide pulley assembly:		
Backplate-to-cylinder head bolts	40	30
Guide pulley bolt	40	30
Tensioner pulley nut	20	15

Use new bolts

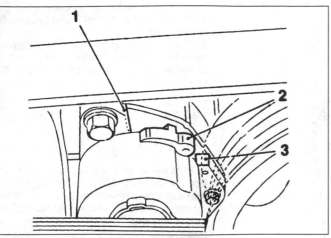

1.5 On 2.0 litre engines check that the drivebelt tensioner arm indicator (2) is correctly positioned between the stops (1 and 3) on the backplate

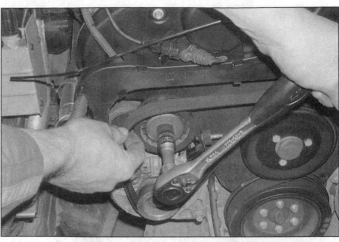

1.8 Lever the tensioner away from the belt then slip the belt off from its pulleys (2.5 litre engine shown)

1 Auxiliary drivebelt - removal, refitting and adjustment

2.0 litre engine

Prior to removal make a note of the correct routing of the belt around the various pulleys. If the belt is to be re-used, also mark the direction of rotation on the belt to ensure the belt is refitted the same way around.

Using a suitable spanner or socket fitted to the tensioner pulley centre bolt, lever the tensioner away from the belt until there is sufficient slack to enable the belt to be slipped off from the pulleys. Carefully release the tensioner pulley until it is against its stop then remove the belt from the vehicle. If necessary, the tensioner can be locked in the released position by aligning the arm hole with the hole in the backplate and inserting a suitable tool/pin.

Manoeuvre the belt into position, routing it correctly around the pulleys; if the original belt is being fitted use the marks made prior to removal to ensure it is fitted the correct way around.

Lever the tensioner roller back against is spring, and seat the belt on the pulleys. Ensure the belt is centrally located on all pulleys then slowly release the tensioner pulley until the belt is correctly tensioned. Do not allow the tensioner to spring back and stress the belt.

Check the position of the drivebelt tensioner assembly arm in relation to the backplate. The arm indicator should be in between the stops on the backplate and should be free to move. (see illustration).

2.5 and 3.0 litre engine

Remove the multi-ram air intake system pre-volume chamber and the secondary air injection system front connecting pipe as described in Sections 22 and 23.

7 Prior to removal make a note of the correct routing of the belt around the various pulleys. If the belt is to be re-used, also mark the direction of rotation on the belt to ensure the belt is refitted the same way around.

8 Using a suitable spanner or socket fitted to the tensioner pulley centre bolt, lever the tensioner away from the belt until there is sufficient slack to enable the belt to be slipped off from the pulleys (see illustration). Carefully release the tensioner pulley until it is against its stop then remove the belt from the vehicle.

9 Manoeuvre the belt into position, routing it correctly around the pulleys; if the original belt is being fitted use the marks made prior to removal to ensure it is fitted the correct way around.

10 Lever the tensioner roller back against is spring, and seat the belt on the pulleys. Ensure the belt is centrally located on all pulleys then slowly release the tensioner pulley until the belt is correctly tensioned. Do

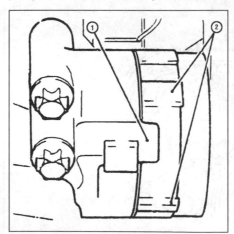

1.11 On 2.5 and 3.0 litre engines ensure the stop (1) on the drivebelt tensioner mounting plate is in between the lugs (2) on the arm

not allow the tensioner to spring back and stress the belt.

11 Check the position of the drivebelt tensioner assembly arm in relation to the backplate. The stop on the tensioner mounting plate should be positioned between the lugs on the arm and the arm should be free to move (see illustration).

12 Refit the secondary air injection system connecting pipe and the multi-ram air intake system pre-volume chamber as described in Sections 22 and 23.

2 Top dead centre (TDC) for No 1 piston (2.0 litre SOHC) - locating

1 In its travel up and down its cylinder bore, Top Dead Centre (TDC) is the highest point that each piston reaches as the crankshaft rotates. While each piston reaches TDC both at the top of the compression stroke and again at the top of the exhaust stroke, for the purpose of timing the engine, TDC refers to the piston position (usually number 1) at the top of its compression stroke.

2 Number 1 piston (and cylinder) is at the front (timing belt) end of the engine, and its TDC position is located as follows. Note that the crankshaft rotates clockwise when viewed from the front of the vehicle.

3 Disconnect the battery negative terminal. If necessary, remove all the spark plugs to enable the engine to be easily turned over.

4 To gain access to the camshaft sprocket timing mark, remove the timing belt outer cover as described in Section 11.

5 Using a socket and extension bar on the crankshaft sprocket bolt, turn the crankshaft whilst keeping an eye on the camshaft sprocket. Rotate the crankshaft until the timing mark on the camshaft sprocket is correctly aligned with the cutout on the top of the timing belt rear cover and the mark on the

13

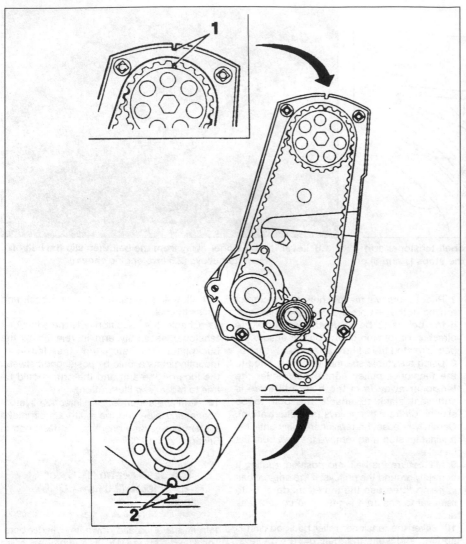

2.5 Align the camshaft sprocket timing mark with the cutout on the timing belt cover (1) and align the crankshaft sprocket mark with the cutout on the oil pump housing (2) to position No1 piston at TDC on its compression stroke

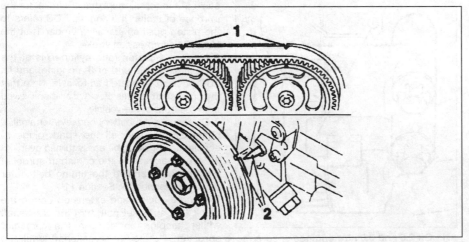

3.5 Align the camshaft sprocket timing marks with the cutout on the camshaft cover (1) and align the crankshaft pulley notch with the pointer (2) to position No 1 piston at TDC on its compression stroke

crankshaft sprocket rim is correctly aligne
with the cutout on the oil pump housing (se
illustration).

6 With the crankshaft pulley and camsha
sprocket timing marks positioned a
described, the engine is positioned with No
piston at TDC on its compression stroke.

3 Top dead centre (TDC) for No 1 piston (2.0 litre DOHC) - locating

1 In its travel up and down its cylinder bore
Top Dead Centre (TDC) is the highest poin
that each piston reaches as the cranksha
rotates. While each piston reaches TDC bot
at the top of the compression stroke an
again at the top of the exhaust stroke, for th
purpose of timing the engine, TDC refers
the piston position (usually number 1) at th
top of its compression stroke.

2 Number 1 piston (and cylinder) is at th
front (timing belt) end of the engine, and i
TDC position is located as follows. Note tha
the crankshaft rotates clockwise when viewe
from the front of the vehicle.

3 Disconnect the battery negative terminal.
necessary, remove all the spark plugs t
enable the engine to be easily turned over.

4 To gain access to the camshaft sprocke
timing marks, remove the timing belt oute
cover as described in Section 12.

5 Using a socket and extension bar on th
crankshaft sprocket bolt, rotate the cranksha
until the timing marks on the camsha
sprockets are both at the top and are correctl
aligned with the marks on the camshaft cove
With the camshaft sprocket marks correctl
positioned, align the notch on the cranksha
pulley rim with the pointer **(see illustration**
The engine is now positioned with No 1 pisto
at TDC on its compression stroke. **Note:** *If th
crankshaft pulley has been removed, use th
mark on the crankshaft sprocket rim. The mar
should be aligned with the cutout on the o
pump housing (see Section 15).*

4 Top dead centre (TDC) for No 1 piston (2.5 and 3.0 litre) - locating

1 In its travel up and down its cylinder bore
Top Dead Centre (TDC) is the highest poin
that each piston reaches as the cranksha
rotates. While each piston reaches TDC bot
at the top of the compression stroke an
again at the top of the exhaust stroke, for th
purpose of timing the engine, TDC refers
the piston position (usually number 1) at th
top of its compression stroke.

2 Number 1 piston (and cylinder) is at th
front (timing belt) end of the right-han
cylinder bank, and its TDC position is locate
as follows. Note that the crankshaft rotate
clockwise when viewed from the front of th
vehicle.

4.5a Align the relevant camshaft sprockets timing marks with the cutouts on the timing belt rear cover (arrowed) on both the right-hand . . .

4.5b . . . and left-hand cylinder heads (arrowed) . . .

3 Disconnect the battery negative terminal. If necessary, remove all the spark plugs to enable the engine to be easily turned over.

4 Remove the timing belt outer cover to gain access to the camshaft sprocket timing marks (see Section 13).

5 Using a socket and extension bar on the crankshaft sprocket bolt, rotate the crankshaft until the relevant timing marks on the camshaft sprockets are all at the top and are correctly aligned with the marks on the timing belt rear cover. Each sprocket has two timing marks the correct mark to use is as follows (see illustrations).

Camshaft	Timing mark to be used
Right-hand cylinder head exhaust	1
Right-hand cylinder head inlet	2
Left-hand cylinder head inlet	3
Left-hand cylinder head exhaust	4

6 With the camshaft sprocket marks correctly positioned, align the notch on the crankshaft pulley rim with the pointer on the oil pump housing **(see illustration)**. The engine is now positioned with No 1 piston at TDC on its compression stroke. **Note:** *If the crankshaft pulley has been removed, use the mark on the crankshaft sprocket rim. The mark should be aligned with the cutout on the base of the oil pump housing (see Section 16).*

5 Camshaft cover (2.0 litre SOHC) - removal and refitting

Removal

1 Release the retaining clip and disconnect the breather hose from the camshaft cover.

2 Slacken and remove the retaining bolts, noting the correct fitted location of any clips or brackets retained by the bolts (as applicable) then lift the camshaft cover from the camshaft housing. If the cover is stuck, do not lever between the cover and camshaft housing mating surfaces - if necessary, gently tap the cover sideways to free it. Recover the gasket; if it shows signs of damage or deterioration it must be renewed.

Refitting

3 Prior to refitting, examine the inside of the cover for a build-up of oil sludge or any other contamination, and if necessary clean the cover with paraffin, or a water-soluble solvent. Examine the condition of the crankcase ventilation filter inside the camshaft cover, and clean as described for the inside of the cover if clogging is evident (if desired, the filter can be removed from the cover, after removing the securing bolts). Dry the cover thoroughly before refitting.

4 Ensure the cover is clean and dry and seat the gasket in the cover recess then refit the cover to the camshaft housing, ensuring the gasket remains correctly seated.

5 Refit the retaining bolts, ensuring all relevant clips/brackets are correctly positioned, and tighten them to the specified torque working in a diagonal sequence.

6 Reconnect the breather hose securely to the cover.

6 Camshaft cover (2.0 litre DOHC) - removal and refitting

Removal

1 Slacken the retaining clips and disconnect the breather hoses from the camshaft cover **(see illustration)**.

2 Undo the retaining screws and remove the spark plug cover. Disconnect the plug caps from the plugs then unclip the HT leads and position them clear of the cover **(see illustrations)**.

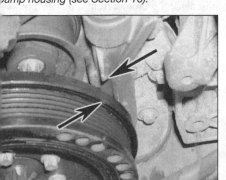

4.6 . . . and the crankshaft pulley notch with the pointer on the oil pump housing (arrowed) to position No 1 piston at TDC on its compression stroke

6.1 Release the retaining clips and disconnect the breather hoses from the camshaft cover

6.2a Remove the spark plug cover . . .

13

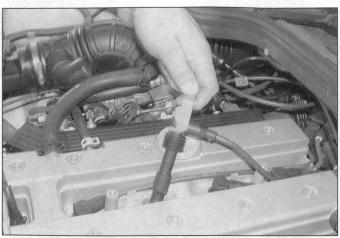

6.2b . . . and disconnect the plug caps from the spark plugs

7.6 Disconnecting the wiring connector from the engine management ECU

3 Slacken the nut securing the engine wiring harness tray to the timing belt cover upper fixing then free the tray from the front of the cover and position it clear

4 Disconnect the camshaft sensor wiring connector and unclip the wiring from the camshaft cover.

5 Evenly and progressively slacken and remove the camshaft cover retaining bolts.

6 Lift the camshaft cover away from the cylinder head and recover the cover seal and the sealing rings which are fitted to each of the retaining bolt holes. Examine the seal and sealing rings for signs of wear or damage and renew if necessary.

Refitting

7 Ensure the cover and cylinder head surfaces are clean and dry then fit the camshaft seals securely to the cover grooves. Fit the sealing rings to the recesses around each retaining bolt hole, holding them in position with a smear of grease.

8 Apply a smear of suitable sealant (Vauxhall/Opel recommend the use of sealant 15 03 295 - available from a dealer) to the areas of the cylinder head surface around the front inlet and exhaust camshaft bearing caps, and also to the semi-circular cutouts on the rear of the head.

9 Carefully manoeuvre the camshaft cover into position, taking great care to ensure all the sealing rings remain correctly seated. Refit the cover retaining bolts and tighten the retaining bolts to the specified torque, working in a spiral pattern from the centre outwards.

10 Reconnect the breather hoses, securing them in position with the retaining clips, and securely reconnect the plug caps to the spark plugs.

11 Reconnect the camshaft sensor wiring connector then refit the spark plug cover and securely tighten its retaining screws. Clip the wiring tray back into position and securely tighten its retaining nut.

7 Camshaft covers (2.5 and 3.0 litre) - removal and refitting

Removal

1 Remove the inlet manifold as described in Section 21.

Right-hand cover

2 Disconnect the plug caps from the plugs then unclip the HT leads and position them clear of the cover.

3 Evenly and progressively slacken an remove the camshaft cover retaining bolts.

4 Lift the camshaft cover away from th cylinder head and recover the cover seals an the sealing rings which are fitted to each o the retaining bolt holes. Examine the seal an sealing rings for signs of wear or damage an renew if necessary.

Left-hand cover

5 To improve access, remove the windscree wiper arms and the water deflector panel (se Section 24). Access can be further improve by disconnecting the engine wiring harness a follows.

6 Remove the cover from the relay box in th left-hand corner of the engine compartmen Lift out the engine management electroni control unit (ECU) then release the retainin clip and disconnect its wiring connector (se illustration). The ECU can be left in positio in the box.

7 Trace the engine wiring harness back fro the left-hand cylinder head to the engin compartment relay box. Unclip the injectio system relay connectors from the box the disconnect the harness connector and fre the sealing grommet from the relay box (se illustrations).

7.7a Unclip the injection system relays . . .

7.7b . . . then disconnect the wiring connector . . .

7.7c . . . and free the wiring harness from the relay box

7.8a Disconnect the harness connectors located at the rear of the battery

7.8b Where the engine harness is connected to the fusible link housing, remove the fusible link . . .

7.8c . . . then unclip the connector from the housing

7.8d Once all the wiring has been disconnected, position the harness clear of the cylinder head

7.10a Lift the retaining tab (arrowed) . . .

7.10b . . . and rotate the oil filler neck anti-clockwise to free it from the left-hand camshaft cover

Disconnect the harness connectors which are located at the rear of the battery then disconnect the camshaft sensor and left-hand cylinder bank knock sensor wiring connectors. Free the engine wiring harness auxiliary connections from the battery positive terminal and position the harness clear of the cylinder head. On some models the harness is connected to the fusible link housing instead of the battery terminal; where this is the case, remove the fusible link and unclip the connector from the housing **(see illustrations)**.

9 On models with air conditioning, unbolt the air conditioning pipe/hose bracket from the front of the cylinder head and position the hose/pipe to one side.

10 Lift the oil filler neck retaining tab then twist the neck anti-clockwise and remove it from the top of the cover **(see illustrations)**. Recover the neck sealing ring and discard it; a new one should be used on refitting.

11 Remove the cover as described in paragraphs 3 and 4 **(see illustration)**.

Refitting

Right-hand cover

12 Ensure the cover and cylinder head surfaces are clean and dry then fit the seals securely to the cover grooves. Fit the sealing rings to the recesses around each retaining bolt hole, holding them in position with a smear of grease **(see illustrations)**.

13 Apply a smear of suitable sealant (Vauxhall/Opel recommend the use of sealant 15 03 295 - available from a dealer) to the

7.11 Removing the left-hand camshaft cover

7.12a Fit the new seals securely to the cover grooves . . .

7.12b . . . and install the sealing rings in the bolt hole grooves

13

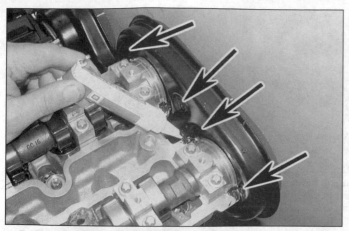

7.13a Apply sealant to the areas at the sides of the camshaft front bearing caps (arrowed) . . .

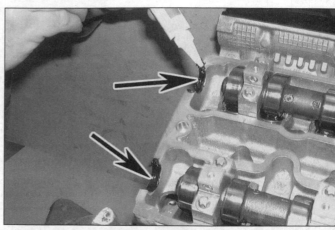

7.13b . . . and also to the semi-circular cut-outs (arrowed) on the rear of the cylinder head

areas of the cylinder head surface around the front inlet and exhaust camshaft bearing caps, and also to the semi-circular cutouts on the rear of the head **(see illustrations)**.

14 Carefully manoeuvre the camshaft cover into position, taking great care to ensure all the sealing rings remain correctly seated.

15 Refit the cover retaining bolts and tighten the retaining bolts to the specified torque, working in a spiral pattern from the centre outwards.

16 Securely reconnect the plug caps to the spark plugs making sure the HT leads are clipped securely in position.

17 Refit the inlet manifold as described in Section 21.

Left-hand cover

18 Refit the cover as described in paragraphs 12 to 15.

19 Fit a new sealing ring to the filler neck then refit the neck to the cover making sure its retaining tab is correctly engaged with the cover retaining bolt.

20 Where necessary, refit the air conditioning pipe/hose retaining clip and securely tighten its retaining bolt.

21 Refit the windscreen wiper motor water deflector panel and wiper arms as described in Section 24. Where necessary, reconnect the engine wiring harness making sure the wiring is correctly routed and all connectors are securely connected.

8 Crankshaft pulley (2.0 litre SOHC) - removal and refitting

Removal

1 Remove the auxiliary drivebelt as described in Section 1. Prior to removal, mark the direction of rotation on the belt to ensure the belt is refitted the same way around.

2 Slacken and remove the small retaining bolts securing the pulley to the crankshaft sprocket and remove the pulley from the engine. If necessary, prevent crankshaft rotation by holding the sprocket retaining bolt with a suitable socket.

Refitting

3 Seat the crankshaft pulley on the sprocket and tighten its retaining bolts to the specified torque.

4 Refit the auxiliary drivebelt as described in Section 1 using the mark made prior to removal to ensure the belt is fitted the correct way around.

9 Crankshaft pulley (2.0 litre DOHC) - removal and refitting

Removal

1 Remove the auxiliary drivebelt as described in Section 1. Prior to removal, mark the direction of rotation on the belt to ensure the belt is refitted the same way around.

2 Using a socket and extension bar on the crankshaft sprocket bolt, turn the crankshaft until the notch on the pulley rim is correctly aligned with the pointer on the cover **(see illustration)**.

3 Slacken and remove the small retaining bolts securing the pulley to the crankshaft sprocket and remove the pulley from the engine. If necessary, prevent crankshaft rotation by holding the sprocket retaining bolt with a suitable socket.

Refitting

4 Check that the crankshaft sprocket mark is still aligned with the mark on the oil pump housing then manoeuvre the crankshaft pulley into position. Align the notch on the pulley rim with the pointer then seat the pulley on the sprocket and tighten its retaining bolts to the specified torque.

5 Refit the auxiliary drivebelt as described in Section 1 using the mark made prior to removal to ensure the belt is fitted the correct way around.

10 Crankshaft pulley (2.5 and 3.0 litre) - removal and refitting

Removal

1 Remove the auxiliary drivebelt as described in Section 1. Prior to removal, mark the direction of rotation on the belt to ensure the belt is refitted the same way around.

2 Using a socket and extension bar on the crankshaft sprocket bolt, turn the crankshaft until the notch on the pulley rim is correctly aligned with the pointer on the cover.

3 Slacken and remove the small retaining bolts securing the pulley to the crankshaft sprocket and remove the pulley from the engine. If necessary, prevent crankshaft rotation by holding the sprocket retaining bolt with a suitable socket.

Refitting

4 Check that the crankshaft sprocket mark is still aligned with the mark on the oil pump housing then manoeuvre the crankshaft pulley into position. Align the notch on the pulley rim with the pointer then seat the pulley on the sprocket and tighten its retaining bolts to the specified torque.

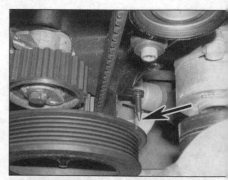

9.2 Align the crankshaft pulley notch with the pointer on the cover (arrowed - shown with timing belt outer cover removed)

12.2a Undo the retaining nut and free the wiring tray from the outer cover . . .

12.2b . . . then unclip the cover . . .

Refit the auxiliary drivebelt as described in Section 1 using the mark made prior to removal to ensure the belt is fitted the correct way around.

11 Timing belt covers (2.0 litre SOHC) - removal and refitting

Outer cover

Removal

Remove the crankshaft pulley as described in Section 8.
Undo the retaining bolt and free the wiring harness guide from the top of the timing belt cover.
Undo the remaining retaining bolts then unclip the timing belt outer cover and remove it from the engine.

Refitting

Refitting is the reverse of removal, ensuring the auxiliary drivebelt is fitted the same way round as it was prior removal.

Rear cover

Removal

Remove the camshaft and crankshaft timing belt sprockets and the timing belt tensioner as described in Section 17.

6 Free the crankshaft sensor wiring from the base of the timing belt rear cover, noting its correct routing.
7 Slacken and remove the bolts securing the rear cover to the camshaft housing and oil pump housing and remove the cover from the engine.

Refitting

8 Refitting is the reverse of removal, tightening the cover retaining bolts to the specified torque. Ensure the crankshaft sensor wiring is correctly routed before refitting the timing belt components.

12 Timing belt covers (2.0 litre DOHC) - removal and refitting

Outer cover

Removal

1 Remove the auxiliary drivebelt as described in Section 1. Prior to removal, mark the direction of rotation on the belt to ensure the belt is refitted the same way around.
2 Slacken and remove the nut securing the engine wiring harness tray to the outer cover upper mounting and free the tray assembly from the timing belt cover. Unclip the cover

12.2c . . . and free the wiring and coolant hose and remove the tray from the engine compartment

from the tray then free the wiring harness and coolant hose and remove the tray from the engine compartment (see illustrations).
3 Slacken and remove the retaining bolts, along with their washers and outer rubber spacers, then remove the outer cover from the engine unit along with its seal. Once the cover has been removed, recover inner rubber spacers from the mountings (see illustrations).

Refitting

4 Ensure the inner rubber spacers are correctly fitted to each of the mountings then manoeuvre the cover into position (see illustration).

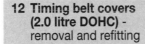

12.3a Slacken and remove the cover retaining bolts (upper bolt shown) and recover the outer rubber spacers . . .

12.3b . . . then remove the outer cover from the engine

12.4 Ensure the inner rubber spacers are correctly fitted to the mountings before installing the outer cover . . .

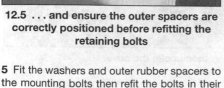

12.5 . . . and ensure the outer spacers are correctly positioned before refitting the retaining bolts

13.4a Retain the coolant pump shaft with an open-ended spanner then undo the retaining bolts . . .

13.4b . . . and remove the pulley from the engine

5 Fit the washers and outer rubber spacers to the mounting bolts then refit the bolts in their original locations and tighten them to the specified torque **(see illustration)**.

6 Seat the wiring harness correctly in the tray then refit the tray cover. Clip the tray securely onto the timing belt cover and securely tighten its retaining nut.

7 Refit the auxiliary drivebelt as described in Section 1 using the mark made prior to removal to ensure the belt is fitted the correct way around.

Rear cover

Removal

8 Remove the timing belt as described in Section 15.

9 Remove the camshaft sprockets, crankshaft sprocket, the timing belt tensioner and the idler pulley assembly as described in Section 18.

10 Unbolt the camshaft sensor from the cylinder head.

11 Undo the retaining bolts, noting their correct fitted locations, and remove the rear cover from the engine unit.

Refitting

12 Refitting is the reverse of removal, tightening all bolts to the specified torque (where given).

---

13 Timing belt covers (2.5 and 3.0 litre) - removal and refitting

Outer cover

Note: *New coolant pump and power steering pump pulley bolts will be required on refitting.*

Removal

1 Remove the multi-ram air intake system pre-volume chamber assembly as described in Section 22.

2 Remove the secondary air injection system front connecting pipe as described in Section 23.

3 Remove the auxiliary drivebelt as described in Section 1. Prior to removal, mark the direction of rotation on the belt to ensure the belt is refitted the same way around.

4 Slacken and remove the coolant pump drivebelt pulley retaining bolts whilst retaining the pump shaft with an open-ended spanner. Remove the pulley and discard the bolts; new ones must be used on refitting **(see illustrations)**.

5 Insert a socket and extension bar in through the one of the power steering pump pulley holes and locate it on a pump mounting bolt to prevent rotation. Slacken and remove the pulley retaining bolts and remove the pulley, noting which way around it is fitted **(see**

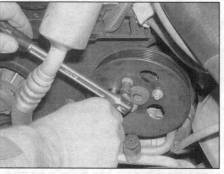

13.5a Insert a socket and extension bar through the power steering pump pulley then undo the retaining bolts . . .

13.7a Unclip the front . . .

illustrations). Discard the bolts; new ones must be used on refitting.

6 Disconnect the right-hand cylinder bank knock sensor wiring connector and unclip it from the front of the timing belt cover.

7 Unclip the covers from the front and right-hand end of the wiring harness tray which runs across the front of the timing belt cover. Disconnect the wiring connector from the EGR valve and position the wiring harness clear of the timing belt cover then undo the retaining bolts and remove the tray from the belt cover **(see illustrations)**.

8 Slacken and remove the retaining bolts and remove the auxiliary drivebelt tensioner

13.5b . . . and remove the pulley from the pump

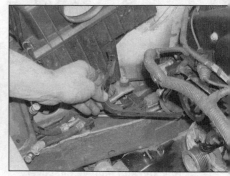

13.7b . . . and right-hand covers and position the wiring harness clear of the tray

13.7c Undo the retaining bolts and remove the tray from the timing belt cover

13.8 Undo the retaining bolts and remove the auxiliary drivebelt tensioner

13.9 Removing the timing belt outer cover

assembly from the right-hand cylinder head (see illustration).

Slacken and remove the retaining bolts then remove the outer cover from the engine unit along with its seal (see illustration).

Refitting

10 Ensure the seal is firmly fixed to the cover prior to refitting. If necessary, glue it in position with a suitable adhesive (Vauxhall/Opel recommend the use of adhesive 08 983 341). Refit the cover to the engine and tighten its retaining bolts to the specified torque.

11 Refit the auxiliary drivebelt tensioner and tighten its retaining bolts to the specified torque.

12 Refit the wiring harness tray onto the cover and securely tighten its retaining bolts. Seat the wiring correctly in the tray then clip in the front and right-hand covers.

13 Refit the drivebelt pulleys to the coolant and power steering pump then fit the new retaining bolts. Tighten the pulley bolts to the specified stage 1 torque then angle-tighten through the specified stage 2 and 3 angles. It is recommended that an angle-measuring gauge is used during the final stages of the tightening, to ensure accuracy.

14 Refit the auxiliary drivebelt as described in

Section 1 using the mark made prior to removal to ensure the belt is fitted the correct way around.

15 Refit the air injection system connecting pipe and the air intake pre-volume chamber as described in Sections 23 and 22.

Rear cover

Removal

16 Remove the timing belt as described in Section 16.

17 Remove the camshaft sprockets, the timing belt tensioner pulley/upper guide pulley assembly and the lower guide pulley as described in Section 19.

18 Drain the cooling system and remove the coolant pump (see Sections 25 and 26).

19 Undo the retaining bolts, noting the correct fitted location of the threaded stud, and remove the rear cover from the engine unit (see illustration).

Refitting

20 Refit the rear cover to the engine and tighten its retaining bolts and the threaded stud to their specified torque settings.

21 Refit the coolant pump as described in Section 26.

22 Refit the guide pulley, tensioner assembly, camshaft sprockets and crankshaft sprocket

as described in Section 19 then refit the timing belt as described in Section 16.

23 On completion, refill the cooling system as described in Section 25.

14 Timing belt (2.0 litre SOHC) - removal and refitting

Note: The timing belt must be removed and refitted with the engine cold.

Removal

1 Disconnect the battery negative terminal then remove the timing belt outer cover as described in Section 11. **Note:** *On models with a Vauxhall anti-theft warning system (ATWS), the battery negative terminal must be disconnected within 15 seconds of the ignition being switched off to prevent the alarm system being triggered.*

2 Position No 1 cylinder at TDC on its compression stroke as described in Section 2.

3 Slacken the timing belt tensioner bolt. Using an Allen key, rotate the tensioner arm clockwise to its stop, to relieve the tension in the timing belt, and hold it in position by securely tighten the retaining bolt (see illustration).

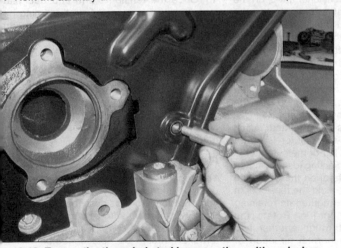

13.19 Ensure the threaded stud is correctly positioned when refitting the timing belt rear cover

14.3 Slacken the timing belt tensioner bolt (1) and rotate the tensioner clockwise using an Allen key in the arm cutout (2)

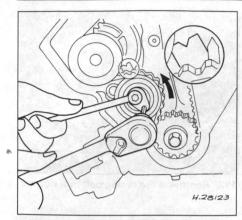

14.8 Tension the belt by rotating the tensioner arm fully anti-clockwise until the pointer is positioned as shown

4 Slide the timing belt off from its sprockets and remove it from the engine. If the belt is to be re-used, use white paint or similar to mark the direction of rotation on the belt. **Do not** rotate the crankshaft or camshaft until the timing belt has been refitted.

5 If signs of oil contamination are found, trace the source of the oil leak and rectify it, then wash down the engine timing belt area and all related components to remove all traces of oil.

Refitting

6 On reassembly, thoroughly clean the timing belt sprockets then check that the camshaft sprocket timing mark is still correctly aligned with the rear cover cutout and the crankshaft sprocket mark is still aligned with the mark on the oil pump housing.

7 Fit the timing belt over the crankshaft and camshaft sprockets, ensuring that the belt left-hand run is taut (ie, all slack is on the tensioner pulley side of the belt), then fit the belt over the coolant pump sprocket and tensioner pulley. Do not twist the belt sharply while refitting it. Ensure that the belt teeth are correctly seated centrally in the sprockets, and that the timing marks remain in alignment. If a used belt is being refitted, ensure that the arrow mark made on removal points in the normal direction of rotation, as before.

8 Slacken the timing belt tensioner bolt to release the tensioner spring. Rotate the tensioner arm anti-clockwise until the tensioner pointer is fully over against its stop, without exerting any excess strain on the belt **(see illustration)**. Hold the tensioner in position and securely tighten its retaining bolt.

9 Check the sprocket timing marks are still correctly aligned. If adjustment is necessary, release the tensioner again then disengage the belt from the sprockets and make any necessary adjustments.

10 Using a socket on the crankshaft sprocket bolt, rotate the crankshaft smoothly through two complete turns (720°) in the normal direction of rotation to settle the timing belt in position.

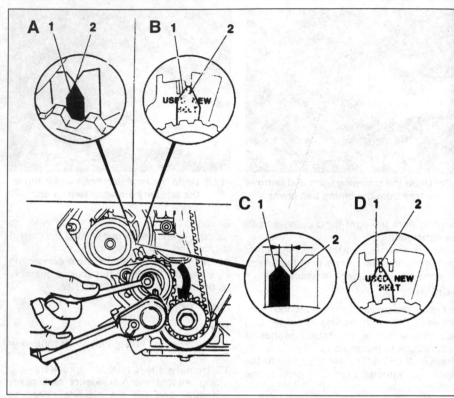

14.12 Ensure the timing belt tensioner arm (1) is correctly position in relation to the backplate cutout/marking (2) as described in text

A Correct position for new belt - engines with an unmarked tensioner
B Correct position for new belt - engines with a marked tensioner
C Correct position for used belt - engines with an unmarked tensioner
D Correct position for used belt - engines with a marked tensioner

11 Check that both the camshaft and crankshaft sprocket timing marks are correctly realigned then slacken the tensioner bolt again.

12 If a new timing belt is being fitted, adjust the tensioner so that the pointer is aligned with either the cutout or NEW marking (depending on type of tensioner fitted) on the backplate **(see illustration)**. Hold the tensioner in the correct position and tighten its retaining bolt to the specified torque. Rotate the crankshaft smoothly through another two complete turns in the normal direction of rotation, to bring the sprocket timing marks back into alignment. Check that the tensioner pointer is still aligned with the backplate cutout/marking (as applicable).

13 If the original belt is being refitted, adjust the tensioner so that the pointer is either positioned 4 mm to the left of the cutout or is aligned with the USED marking (depending on the type of tensioner fitted) on the backplate **(see illustration 14.12)**. Hold the tensioner in the correct position and tighten its retaining bolt to the specified torque. Rotate the crankshaft smoothly through another two complete turns in the normal direction of rotation, to bring the sprocket timing marks back into alignment. Check that the tensioner

pointer is still correctly positioned in relatio to the backplate cutout/marking (a applicable).

14 If the tensioner pointer is not correctl positioned in relation to the backplate, repea the procedure in paragraph 12 (new belt) or 1 (original belt).

15 Once the tensioner arm and backplat remain correctly aligned, refit the timing bel cover and crankshaft pulley as described i Sections 8 and 11.

15 Timing belt (2.0 litre DOHC) - removal and refitting

Note: The timing belt must be removed an refitted with the engine cold.

Removal

1 Disconnect the battery negative termina then position No 1 cylinder at TDC on it compression stroke as described in Section 3 **Note**: On models with a Vauxhall anti-thef warning system (ATWS), the battery negativ terminal must be disconnected withi 15 seconds of the ignition being switched o to prevent the alarm system being triggered.

Remove the crankshaft pulley as described Section 9.

Check the camshaft sprocket timing marks re correctly aligned with the camshaft cover arks and the crankshaft sprocket timing ark is aligned with the cutout on the oil ump housing.

Slacken the timing belt tensioner bolt **(see lustration 14.3)**. Using an Allen key, rotate ne tensioner arm clockwise to its stop, to lieve the tension in the timing belt, and hold in position by and securely tighten the taining bolt.

Slide the timing belt off from its sprockets nd remove it from the engine. If the belt is to e re-used, use white paint or similar to mark ne direction of rotation on the belt. **Do not** otate the crankshaft or camshafts until the ming belt has been refitted.

6 If signs of oil contamination are found, trace the source of the oil leak and rectify it, then wash down the engine timing belt area and all related components to remove all traces of oil.

Refitting

7 On reassembly, thoroughly clean the timing belt sprockets and tensioner/idler pulleys.
8 Check that the crankshaft sprocket timing mark is still aligned with the cutout on the oil pump housing and the camshaft sprocket marks are aligned with the marks on the camshaft cover. If the camshaft cover has been removed, align the sprocket marks with the lugs on the top of the camshaft front bearing caps **(see illustration)**.
9 Fit the timing belt over the crankshaft and camshaft sprockets and around the idler pulleys, ensuring that the belt left-hand run is

taut (ie, all slack is on the tensioner side of the belt), then fit the belt over the coolant pump sprocket and tensioner pulley. Do not twist the belt sharply while refitting it. Ensure that the belt teeth are correctly seated centrally in the sprockets, and that the timing marks remain in alignment. If a used belt is being refitted, ensure that the arrow mark made on removal points in the normal direction of rotation, as before.
10 Slacken the timing belt tensioner bolt to release the tensioner spring. Rotate the tensioner arm anti-clockwise until the tensioner pointer is fully over against its stop, without exerting any excess strain on the belt **(see illustration 14.8)**. Hold the tensioner in position and securely tighten its retaining bolt.
11 Check the sprocket timing marks are still correctly aligned. If adjustment is necessary, release the tensioner again then disengage the belt from the sprockets and make any necessary adjustments.
12 Using a socket on the crankshaft sprocket bolt, rotate the crankshaft smoothly through two complete turns (720°) in the normal direction of rotation to settle the timing belt in position.
13 Check that both the camshaft and crankshaft sprocket timing marks are correctly realigned then slacken the tensioner bolt again.
14 If a new timing belt is being fitted, adjust the tensioner so that the pointer is aligned with either the cutout or NEW marking (depending on type of tensioner fitted) on the backplate **(see illustration 14.12)**. Hold the tensioner in the correct position and tighten its retaining bolt to the specified torque. Rotate the crankshaft smoothly through another two complete turns in the normal direction of rotation, to bring the sprocket timing marks back into alignment. Check that the tensioner pointer is still aligned with the backplate cutout/marking (as applicable).
15 If the original belt is being refitted, adjust the tensioner so that the pointer is either positioned 4 mm to the left of the cutout or is aligned with the USED marking (depending on the type of tensioner fitted) on the backplate **(see illustration 14.12)**. Hold the tensioner in the correct position and tighten its retaining bolt to the specified torque. Rotate the crankshaft smoothly through another two complete turns in the normal direction of rotation, to bring the sprocket timing marks back into alignment. Check that the tensioner pointer is still correctly positioned in relation to the backplate cutout/marking (as applicable).
16 If the tensioner pointer is not correctly positioned in relation to the backplate, repeat the procedure in paragraph 14 (new belt) or 15 (original belt).
17 Once the tensioner pointer and backplate remain correctly aligned, refit the timing belt cover and crankshaft pulley as described in Sections 9 and 12.

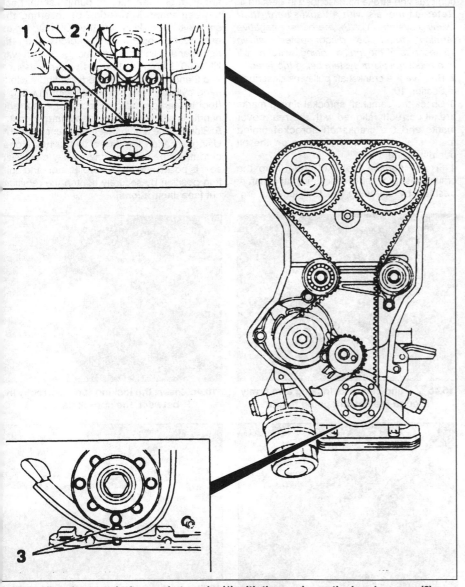

15.8 Align the camshaft sprocket marks (1) with the marks on the bearing caps (2) or cover and ensure the crankshaft sprocket timing mark is correctly aligned with the oil pump cutout (3)

13

16 Timing belt (2.5 and 3.0 litre) - removal and refitting

Note: Accurate adjustment of the timing belt requires the use of the following Vauxhall service tools; camshaft sprocket locking tools (KM-800-1 and KM-800-2), crankshaft sprocket locking tool (KM-800-10), timing belt locating wedge (KM-800-30) and a camshaft sprocket timing gauge (KM-800-20) (see illustration).

Note: There are two different types of timing belt and tensioner assembly available for this engine and it is essential that the timing belt is of the correct type for the tensioner. A modified tensioner assembly and timing belt were fitted as standard to later (1997 model year onwards) engines. The modified tensioner assembly can be identified by checking the letter stamped on the tensioner pulley/upper guide roller backplate; the original tensioner is marked with D and the modified assembly marking has an E in it (EA or EB) (see illustration 16.15). It is most important to check the tensioner backplate marking before ordering a timing belt since the modified tensioner and belt can also be installed on early (pre 1997 model year) engines. See your Vauxhall/Opel dealer for further details.

Note: The timing belt must be removed and refitted with the engine cold.

Removal

1 Disconnect the battery negative lead then position No1 cylinder at TDC on its

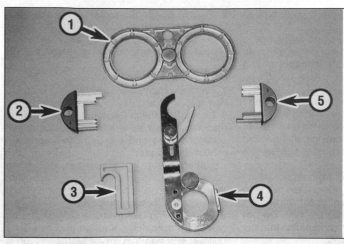

16.0 Vauxhall timing belt service tools

1 *Timing gauge (KM-800-20)*
2 *Sprocket locking tool (KM-800-1)*
3 *Timing belt wedge (KM-800-30)*
4 *Crankshaft locking tool (KM-800-10)*
5 *Sprocket locking tool (KM-800-2)*

compression stroke as described in Section 4.

Note: On models with a Vauxhall anti-theft warning system (ATWS), the battery negative terminal must be disconnected within 15 seconds of the ignition being switched off to prevent the alarm system being triggered.

2 Remove the crankshaft pulley as described in Section 10.

3 Check the camshaft sprocket timing marks are all correctly aligned with the rear cover marks and the crankshaft sprocket timing mark is aligned with the cutout on the oil pump housing.

4 Fix the service tool (KM-800-10) to the crankshaft sprocket and lock the crankshaft in position by clamping the tool locking arm

firmly around the coolant pump flange. Lock the camshafts in position by inserting the service tools making sure the TOP marking on each tool is uppermost; the sprockets on the right-hand cylinder head must be locked with KM-800-1 (tool is stamped with numbers 1 and 2 and handle is coloured red) and the left-hand cylinder head sprockets with KM-800-2 (tool is stamped with numbers 3 and 4 and handle is coloured green) (see illustrations).

5 Slacken the timing belt tensioner pulley nut. Using an Allen key fitted to the hexagonal cutout, rotate the tensioner pulley clockwise so it is positioned just before its stop and hold it in position by securely tighten the retaining nut (see illustrations).

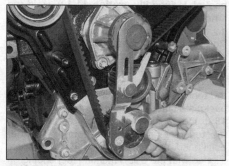

16.4a If the service tools are available, firmly attach the crankshaft locking tool to the sprocket . . .

16.4b . . . and clamp its locking arm firmly around the coolant pump flange

16.4c Insert the locking tools correctly in between the sprockets . . .

16.4d . . . making sure their TOP markings are uppermost

16.5a Slacken the tensioner pulley retaining nut . . .

16.5b . . . then rotate the pulley clockwise, positioning it just before its stop, and secure it by retightening the nut

16.6a Slacken the retaining bolts securing the upper guide pulley . . .

16.6b . . . and lower guide pulley in position then slide the belt off the sprockets

16.10a Ensure the right-hand cylinder head camshaft sprocket markings (1 and 2) . . .

6 Slacken the retaining bolts for the timing belt upper and lower guide pulleys **(see illustrations)**.

7 Slide the timing belt off from its sprockets and remove it from the engine. If the new belt is not being fitted straight away, rotate the crankshaft **backwards** by approximately 60°; this will position the pistons approximately halfway up the bores reducing the risk of the valves contacting the pistons should the camshafts move.

8 If signs of oil contamination are found, trace the source of the oil leak and rectify it, then wash down the engine timing belt area and all related components to remove all traces of oil.

Refitting

Note: *There are two different types of timing belt and tensioner assembly - see note at the beginning of the Section.*

9 On reassembly, thoroughly clean the timing belt sprockets and tensioner/guide pulleys.

10 Check that the crankshaft sprocket timing mark is still aligned with the cutout on the oil pump housing and the camshaft sprocket marks are aligned with the marks on the rear cover (see Section 4) **(see illustrations)**. If the crankshaft was moved back 60°, rotate it to TDC to bring the marks into alignment.

16.10b . . . and the left-hand cylinder head camshaft markings (3 and 4) are all correctly aligned with the rear cover cutouts (arrowed) . . .

11 Lock the camshaft sprockets and crankshaft sprocket in position as described in paragraph 4.

12 Examine the fitting marks on the outer face of the timing belt. The arrows on the belt must point in the direction of rotation and the double line on the belt should be aligned with the crankshaft sprocket mark. The four single lines on the belt will then align with the camshaft sprocket timing marks if the belt is correctly installed.

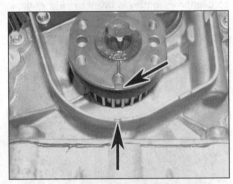

16.10c . . . and the crankshaft sprocket timing mark is correctly aligned with the oil pump housing cutout (arrowed)

13 Ensure the arrows on the belt are pointing in the correct direction of rotation then align the double line on the belt with the crankshaft sprocket timing mark and engage the belt with the sprocket. If the locating wedge (KM-800-30) is available secure the belt in position by inserting the wedge in between the right-hand side of the belt and the rear cover **(see illustrations)**.

14 Check the identification marking stamped onto the tensioner pulley/upper guide pulley

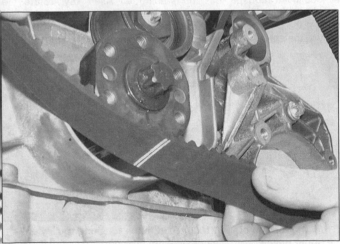

16.13a Align the double line on the timing belt with the crankshaft sprocket timing mark

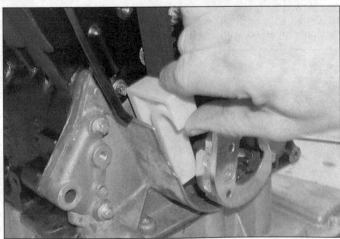

16.13b If the service tool is available secure the belt in position with the wedge

13

16.15 Checking the marking (location arrowed) on the tensioner/upper guide pulley backplate to identify which type of tensioner assembly is fitted to your engine - see text

16.16a On engines with a modified tensioner, work around in a clockwise direction and engage the belt first with the right-hand cylinder head sprockets . . .

16.16b . . . and then the left-hand head sprockets (directional fitting arrows arrowed), making sure the fitting lines are all correctly aligned with the sprockets . . .

16.16c . . . and finally over the lower guide pulley

16.18a Remove all slack from the left-hand run of the belt by rotating the lower guide pulley whilst making sure the sprocket timing marks remain in alignment (timing gauge shown) . . .

backplate (see Note at the start of the Section).

15 On early engines with the original tensioner (marked with a D - **see illustration**), fit the timing belt over the lower guide pulley then around the left-hand cylinder head camshaft sprockets making sure the belt fitting marks are correctly aligned with the sprocket marks. Fit the belt around the upper guide pulley then over the right-hand cylinder camshaft, again making sure the fitting marks are correctly aligned, and the tensioner pulley. Do not twist the belt sharply while refitting it.

16 On all engines fitted with the modified tensioner (marked with an E - **see illus-**

tration 16.15), fit the belt behind the tensioner pulley and then over the right-hand cylinder head camshaft sprockets ensuring that the fitting marks are both correctly aligned with the sprocket marks. Fit the belt around the upper guide pulley then over the left-hand cylinder camshaft sprockets, again making sure the fitting marks are correctly aligned, and finally over the lower guide pulley (**see illustrations**). Do not twist the belt sharply while refitting it.

17 On all engines, ensure that the belt teeth are correctly seated centrally in the sprockets

and the sprocket timing marks/belt fitting marks are correctly aligned. If adjustment is necessary, disengage the belt from the sprockets and make any necessary adjustments.

18 Slacken the lower guide pulley retaining bolt. Rotate the pulley anti-clockwise to remove all slack from the left-hand run of the belt without placing any excess strain on the belt. Ensure that all the sprocket timing marks remain in alignment as the pulley is moved; remove the locking tools and use the timing gauge (KM-800-20) to check the sprocket mark positions. Once the pulley is correctly positioned, hold it stationary and tighten its retaining bolt to the specified torque (**see illustrations**).

19 Slacken the upper guide pulley retaining bolt. Rotate the pulley anti-clockwise to remove all slack from the top run of the belt without placing any excess strain on the belt. Ensure that all the sprocket timing marks remain in alignment as the pulley is moved. Once the pulley is correctly positioned, hold it stationary and tighten its retaining bolt to the specified torque (**see illustration**).

20 Slacken the timing belt tensioner pulley nut then, using an Allen key, rotate the tensioner arm anti-clockwise until the gap between the tensioner plate and its stop is 0.5 to 1.5 mm (**see illustration**). Hold the

16.18b . . . then hold the pulley stationary and tighten its retaining bolt to the specified torque

16.19 Remove all slack from the top run of the belt then hold the upper pulley stationary and tighten its retaining bolt to the specified torque

16.20 Rotate the tensioner pulley anti-clockwise until the gap (arrowed) is 0.5 to 1.5 mm then securely tighten its retaining nut

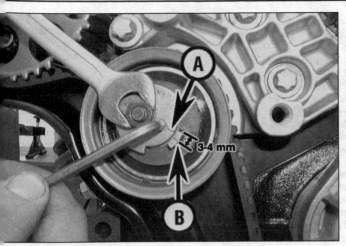

16.23 Adjust the tensioner pulley so that its index mark (A) is positioned 3 to 4 mm above backplate mark (B) then tighten its retaining nut to the specified torque

17.2 Using a home-made sprocket holding tool to retain the camshaft sprocket whilst the bolt is slackened

tensioner pulley in this position and securely tighten its retaining nut.

21 Remove all the service tools then, using a socket on the crankshaft sprocket bolt, rotate the crankshaft smoothly through two complete turns (720°) in the normal direction of rotation to settle the timing belt in position.

22 Check that all the camshaft and crankshaft sprocket timing marks are correctly realigned then slacken the tensioner nut again. **Note:** *The belt fitting lines will not be realigned with the sprocket marks; they serve no purpose once the belt has been installed.*

23 Using an Allen key, position the tensioner pulley so that the index mark on the tensioner plate is positioned 3 to 4 mm above the mark on the backplate stop **(see illustration)**. Hold the tensioner correctly in position and tighten its retaining nut to the specified torque.

24 Rotate the crankshaft smoothly through another two complete turns (720°) in the normal direction of rotation to bring the sprocket timing marks back into alignment.

25 Lock the crankshaft in position (tool KM-800-10) and check the camshaft sprocket

17.5 Refit the camshaft sprocket making sure the locating pin (1) engages with the sprocket hole (2)

timing marks are correctly positioned using the timing gauge (KM-800-20).

26 If the service tools are not available, ensure the crankshaft sprocket timing mark is correctly aligned with the cutout on the oil pump housing and all the camshaft sprocket timing marks are exactly aligned with the cutouts on the rear cover.

27 If adjustment is necessary repeat the operations described in paragraphs 18 to 26.

28 Once the timing marks are all correctly aligned, refit the timing belt cover and crankshaft pulley as described in Sections 10 and 13.

17 Timing belt tensioner and sprockets (2.0 litre SOHC) - removal and refitting

Camshaft sprocket

Removal

1 Remove the timing belt as described in Section 14.

2 The camshaft must be prevented from turning as the sprocket bolt is unscrewed, and this can be achieved in one of two ways as follows.

a) *Make up a sprocket-holding tool using two lengths of steel strip (one long, the other short), and three nuts and bolts; one nut and bolt forms the pivot of a forked tool, with the remaining two nuts and bolts at the tips of the 'forks' to engage with the sprocket spokes as shown* **(see illustration)**.

b) *Remove the camshaft cover as described in Section 5 and hold the camshaft with an open-ended spanner on the flats provided.*

3 Unscrew the retaining bolt and washer and remove the sprocket from the end of the camshaft.

Refitting

4 Prior to refitting check the oil seal for signs of damage or leakage, if necessary, renewing it.

5 Refit the sprocket to the end of the camshaft, aligning its cutout with the camshaft locating pin, then refit the retaining bolt and washer **(see illustration)**.

6 Tighten the sprocket retaining bolt to the specified torque whilst prevent rotation using the method employed on removal.

7 Refit the timing belt as described in Section 14 then (where necessary) refit the camshaft cover as described in Section 4.

Crankshaft sprocket

Note: *A new crankshaft sprocket retaining bolt will be required on refitting.*

Removal

8 Remove the timing belt as described in Section 14.

9 The crankshaft must be prevented from turning as the sprocket bolt is unscrewed (the bolt is very tight), and this can be achieved in one of the following ways.

a) *Use the holding tool described in paragraph 2 securing the tool to the sprocket with two bolts screwed into opposite pulley retaining bolt holes.*

b) *On manual transmission models have an assistant select top gear and apply the brakes firmly.*

10 Unscrew the retaining bolt and washer and remove the crankshaft sprocket from the end of the crankshaft. Discard the bolt; a new one must be used on refitting. If necessary, remove the sprocket Woodruff key from the crankshaft end and slide off the spacer.

Refitting

11 Slide the spacer (where removed) onto the crankshaft then refit the Woodruff key to the crankshaft slot.

12 Align the sprocket with the key and slide it

13

into position, ensuring the sprocket flange is facing outwards. Fit the washer and new retaining bolt.

13 Lock the crankshaft by the method used on removal, and tighten the sprocket retaining bolt to the specified stage 1 torque setting then angle-tighten the bolt through the specified stage 2 angle, using a socket and extension bar. It is recommended that an angle-measuring gauge is used during the final stages of the tightening, to ensure accuracy. If a gauge is not available, use white paint to make alignment marks between the bolt head and sprocket prior to tightening; the marks can then be used to check that the bolt has been rotated through the correct angle.

14 Refit the timing belt as described in Section 14.

Tensioner assembly

Removal

15 Remove the timing belt as described in Section 14.

16 Slacken and remove the retaining bolt and remove the tensioner assembly from the engine.

Refitting

17 Fit the tensioner to the engine, making sure that the lug on the backplate is correctly located in the oil pump housing hole. Ensure the tensioner is correctly seated then refit the retaining bolt. Using an Allen key, rotate the tensioner arm clockwise to its stop then securely tighten the retaining bolt.

18 Refit the timing belt as described in Section 14.

---

18 Timing belt sprockets, tensioner and idler pulleys (2.0 litre DOHC) - removal and refitting

---

Camshaft sprockets

Note: *New sprocket retaining bolt(s) will be required on refitting.*

Removal

1 Remove the timing belt as described in Section 15.

2 The camshaft must be prevented from turning as the sprocket bolt is unscrewed, and this can be achieved in one of two ways.

a) *Make up a sprocket-holding tool using two lengths of steel strip (one long, the other short), and three nuts and bolts; one nut and bolt forms the pivot of a forked tool, with the remaining two nuts and bolts at the tips of the 'forks' to engage with the sprocket spokes* **(see illustration 17.2)**.

b) *Remove the camshaft cover as described in Section 6 and hold the camshaft with an open-ended spanner on the flats provided* **(see illustration)**.

3 Unscrew the retaining bolt and washer and remove the sprocket from the end of the camshaft. If the sprocket locating pin is a loose fit in the camshaft end, remove it and store it with the sprocket for safe-keeping.

4 If necessary, remove the remaining sprocket using the same method.

Refitting

5 Prior to refitting check the oil seal(s) for signs of damage or leakage, if necessary renewing it.

6 Ensure the locating pin is in position in the camshaft end.

7 Note that both inlet and exhaust camshaft sprockets are the same but each one is equipped with two locating pin cutouts. If the sprocket is being fitted to the inlet camshaft engage the locating pin in the IN cutout, and if the sprocket is being fitted to the exhaust camshaft engage the locating pin in the EX cutout **(see illustration)**.

8 Ensure the camshaft locating pin is engaged in the correct sprocket cutout then fit the washer and new retaining bolt.

9 Retain the sprocket by the method used on removal, and tighten the new sprocket retaining bolt to the specified stage 1 torque setting then angle-tighten the bolt through the specified stage 2 angle, using a socket and extension bar, and finally through the specified stage 3 angle. It is recommended that an angle-measuring gauge is used during the final stages of the tightening, to ensure accuracy. If a gauge is not available, use white paint to make alignment marks between the bolt head and sprocket prior to tightening; the marks can then be used to check that the bolt has been rotated through the correct angle.

10 Refit the timing belt as described in Section 15 then (where necessary) refit the camshaft cover as described in Section 6.

Crankshaft sprocket

Note: *A new crankshaft sprocket retaining bolt will be required on refitting.*

Removal

11 Remove the timing belt as described in Section 15.

12 The crankshaft must be prevented from turning as the sprocket bolt is unscrewed (the bolt is very tight), and this can be achieved in one of the following ways.

a) *Use the holding tool described in paragraph 2 securing the tool to the sprocket with two bolts screwed into opposite pulley retaining bolt holes.*

b) *On manual transmission models have an assistant select top gear and apply the brakes firmly.*

13 Unscrew the retaining bolt and washer and remove the crankshaft sprocket from the end of the crankshaft. Discard the bolt; a new one must be used on refitting. If necessary, remove the sprocket Woodruff key from the crankshaft end and slide off the spacer.

Refitting

14 Slide the spacer (where removed) onto the crankshaft then refit the Woodruff key to the crankshaft slot.

15 Align the sprocket with the key and slide it into position, ensuring the sprocket flange is facing outwards. Fit the washer and new retaining bolt.

18.2 Using an open-ended spanner to retain the camshaft sprocket whilst the sprocket bolt is slackened

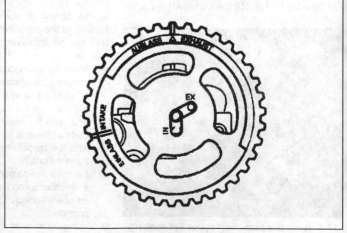

18.7 Ensure the locating pin is engaged in the correct sprocket hole on refitting (see text)

5 Lock the crankshaft by the method used in removal, and tighten the sprocket retaining bolt to the specified stage 1 torque setting then angle-tighten the bolt through the specified stage 2 angle, using a socket and extension bar. It is recommended that an angle-measuring gauge is used during the final stages of the tightening, to ensure accuracy. If a gauge is not available, use white paint to make alignment marks between the bolt head and sprocket prior to tightening; the marks can then be used to check that the bolt has been rotated through the correct angle.
7 Refit the timing belt as described in Section 15.

Tensioner assembly

Removal

8 Remove the timing belt as described in Section 15.
9 Slacken and remove the retaining bolt and remove the tensioner assembly from the engine.

Refitting

0 Fit the tensioner to the engine, making sure that the lug on the backplate is correctly located in the oil pump housing hole. Ensure the tensioner is correctly seated then refit the retaining bolt. Using an Allen key, rotate the tensioner arm clockwise to its stop then securely tighten the retaining bolt.
1 Refit the timing belt as described in Section 15.

Idler pulleys

Removal

22 Remove the timing belt as described in Section 15.
23 Slacken and remove the retaining bolt(s) and remove the idler pulley(s) from the engine. If necessary, unbolt the pulley mounting bracket and remove it from the cylinder block.

Refitting

24 Refit the pulley mounting bracket (where removed) to the cylinder block and tighten its retaining bolts to the specified torque.

19.2a Using a home-made tool to prevent rotation as the camshaft sprocket bolt is slackened

25 Refit the idler pulley(s) and tighten the retaining bolt(s) to the specified torque.
26 Refit the timing belt as described in Section 15.

19 Timing belt sprockets, tensioner and guide pulleys (2.5 and 3.0 litre) - removal and refitting

Camshaft sprockets

Note: *New sprocket retaining bolt(s) will be required on refitting.*

Removal

1 Remove the timing belt as described in Section 16. Once the belt has been removed, rotate the crankshaft **backwards** by approximately 60°; this will position the pistons approximately halfway up the bores reducing the risk of the valves contacting the pistons.
2 The camshaft must be prevented from turning as the sprocket bolt is unscrewed, and this can be achieved in one of two ways.
a) *Make up a sprocket-holding tool using two lengths of steel strip (one long, the other short), and three nuts and bolts; one nut and bolt forms the pivot of a forked tool, with the remaining two nuts and*

19.2b If the camshaft cover has been removed, the camshaft can be held with an open-ended spanner on the flats provided

bolts at the tips of the 'forks' to engage with the sprocket spokes (see illustration).
b) *Remove the camshaft cover as described in Section 7 and hold the camshaft with an open-ended spanner on the flats provided (see illustration).*

3 Unscrew the retaining bolt and washer and remove the sprocket from the end of the camshaft (see illustrations). If the sprocket locating pin is a loose fit in the camshaft end, remove it and store it with the sprocket for safe-keeping.
4 If necessary, remove the remaining sprocket(s) using the same method.

Refitting

5 Prior to refitting check the oil seal(s) for signs of damage or leakage, if necessary renew them.
6 Ensure the locating pin is in position in the camshaft end.
7 Note that there are two pairs of camshaft sprockets, one for the right-hand cylinder head and the other for the left-hand cylinder head; the right-hand cylinder head sprockets carry the identification marks 1 and 2 and the left-hand cylinder head sprockets the marks 3 and 4. The inlet and exhaust camshaft sprockets on each head are the same but each one is equipped with two locating pin

19.3a Unscrew the retaining bolt and washer . . .

19.3b . . . and remove the sprocket from the camshaft

13

19.7a Right-hand cylinder head camshaft sprocket. Ensure timing mark and slot 1 are used on the exhaust camshaft and 2 on the inlet camshaft

19.7b Left-hand cylinder head camshaft sprocket. Ensure timing mark and slot 3 are used on the inlet camshaft and 4 on the exhaust camshaft

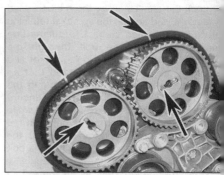

19.8a Ensure the locating pins are engaged in the correct sprocket slots (arrowed) . . .

cutouts and two timing marks. On refitting is vital that the sprocket locating pin is engaged in the correct sprocket slot as follows and the correct timing mark is used **(see illustrations)**.

Camshaft   **Sprocket slot/timing mark number to be used**

Right-hand cylinder head exhaust   1
Right-hand cylinder head inlet   2
Left-hand cylinder head inlet   3
Left-hand cylinder head exhaust   4

8 Ensure the camshaft locating pin is engaged in the correct sprocket cutout then fit the washer and new retaining bolt **(see illustrations)**.

9 Retain the sprocket by the method used on removal, and tighten the sprocket retaining bolt to the specified stage 1 torque setting then angle-tighten the bolt through the specified stage 2 angle, using a socket and extension bar, and finally through the specified stage 3 angle **(see illustrations)**. It is recommended that an angle-measuring gauge is used during the final stages of the tightening, to ensure accuracy. If a gauge is not available, use white paint to make alignment marks between the bolt head and sprocket prior to tightening; the marks can then be used to check that the bolt has been rotated through the correct angle.

10 Ensure the relevant camshaft sprocket timing marks are all correctly aligned with the cutouts on the rear cover then carefully rotate the crankshaft in the normal direction of rotation until the sprocket mark is correctly realigned with the notch on the oil pump housing.

11 Refit the timing belt as described in Section 16 then (where necessary) refit the camshaft cover as described in Section 7.

Crankshaft sprocket

Note: *A new crankshaft sprocket retaining bolt will be required on refitting.*

Removal

12 Remove the timing belt as described in Section 16.

13 The crankshaft must be prevented from turning as the sprocket bolt is unscrewed (the bolt is very tight), and this can be achieved in one of the following ways.

a) *Use the holding tool described in paragraph 2 securing the tool to the sprocket with two bolts screwed into opposite pulley retaining bolt holes* **(see illustration)**.

19.8b . . . and the relevant sprocket timing marks are correctly aligned with the rear cover cutouts (arrowed)

19.9a Retaining the sprocket/camshaft then tighten the retaining bolt first to the stage 1 torque . . .

19.9b . . . and then through the specified stage 2 and 3 angles

19.13 Home-made tool for preventing crankshaft rotation as the sprocket bolt is slackened

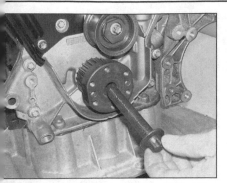

19.14a Unscrew the retaining bolt . . .

19.14b . . . then slide off the crankshaft sprocket . . .

19.14c . . . and, if necessary, withdraw the spacer from the oil seal

On manual transmission models have an assistant select top gear and apply the brakes firmly.

4 Unscrew the retaining bolt and remove the crankshaft sprocket from the end of the crankshaft. Discard the bolt; a new one must be used on refitting. If necessary, slide the spacer out from the oil seal and remove it from the crankshaft; if the outer surface of the spacer is damaged it should be renewed **(see illustrations)**.

Refitting

5 Prior to refitting, examine the oil seal for signs of damage or deterioration and renew if necessary.

6 Slide the spacer (where removed) onto the crankshaft and into position taking care not to damage the oil seal lip.

7 Align the sprocket with the crankshaft slot and slide it into position, ensuring the sprocket flange is facing outwards. Fit the new retaining bolt.

8 Lock the crankshaft by the method used in removal, and tighten the sprocket retaining bolt to the specified stage 1 torque setting then angle-tighten the bolt through the specified stage 2 angle, using a socket and extension bar, and finally through the specified stage 3 angle. It is recommended that an angle-measuring gauge is used during the final stages of the tightening, to ensure accuracy **(see illustrations)**. If a gauge is not available, use white paint to make alignment marks between the bolt head and sprocket

prior to tightening; the marks can then be used to check that the bolt has been rotated through the correct angle.

19 Refit the timing belt as described in Section 16.

Tensioner pulley/upper guide pulley assembly

Note: *The tensioner pulley/upper guide pulley assembly must be renewed as a complete unit. It is not possible to renew the individual components of the assembly separately.*

Removal

20 Remove the timing belt as described in Section 16.

21 Slacken and remove the retaining bolts securing the backplate to the cylinder head

19.18a Tighten the crankshaft sprocket bolt to the specified stage 1 torque setting . . .

and remove the assembly from the engine **(see illustrations)**.

Refitting

22 Fit the tensioner pulley/upper guide pulley assembly to the cylinder head and tighten its retaining bolts to the specified torque.

23 Refit the timing belt as described in Section 16. If a new tensioner assembly has been fitted, fit a new timing belt ensuring it is of the correct type for the tensioner.

Lower guide pulley

Removal

24 Remove the timing belt as described in Section 16.

25 Slacken and remove the retaining bolt and remove the lower guide pulley and its spacer from the engine **(see illustration)**.

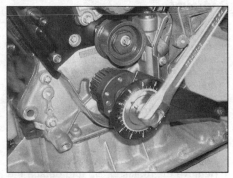

19.18b . . . then tighten it through the specified stage 2 and 3 angles

19.21a Undo the retaining bolts (arrowed) . . .

19.21b . . . and remove the tensioner pulley/upper guide pulley assembly from the cylinder head

19.25 Unscrew the retaining bolt and remove the lower guide pulley and its spacer (arrowed) from the engine

13

Refitting

26 Position the spacer behind the guide pulley then refit the pulley retaining bolt, tightening it lightly only at this stage.
27 Refit the timing belt as described in Section 16.

20 Airflow meter (2.5 and 3.0 litre) - removal and refitting

Removal

1 Ensure the ignition is switched off then disconnect the wiring connectors from the airflow meter and intake air temperature sensor.
2 Slacken the retaining clips then detach the intake duct from the airflow meter and air cleaner housing and remove it from the vehicle.
3 Slacken the retaining clip then remove the airflow meter from the vehicle. Inspect the meter for signs of damage and renew if necessary.

Refitting

4 Refitting is the reverse of removal, ensuring the intake ducts are correctly engaged with the meter recesses.

21 Inlet manifold (2.5 and 3.0 litre) - removal and refitting

Removal

1 Disconnect the battery negative terminal.
Note: *On models with a Vauxhall anti-theft warning system (ATWS), the battery negative terminal must be disconnected within 15 seconds of the ignition being switched off to prevent the alarm system being triggered.*
2 Slacken the retaining clip and disconnect the inlet hose from the idle speed adjuster **(see illustration)**.
3 Slacken the retaining clips securing the intake ducts to the throttle housing and intake pre-volume valve and remove both ducts.
4 Remove the retaining clip and detach the accelerator cable from the throttle cam balljoint then unclip the cable from its mounting bracket. On models with cruise control it will also be necessary to remove the second retaining clip and detach the cruise control cable **(see illustrations)**.
5 Clamp the coolant hoses which are connected to the throttle housing then release the retaining clips and disconnect both hoses **(see illustration)**. Wipe away any spilt coolant.
6 Disconnect the wiring connectors from the throttle valve potentiometer, the idle speed adjuster, the inlet manifold switchover valve solenoid and the exhaust gas recirculation (EGR) valve.
7 Unscrew the union nut and disconnect the pipe from the EGR valve then unscrew the retaining bolt and free the pipe bracket from the valve **(see illustrations)**. Where

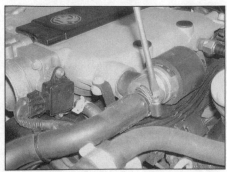

21.2 Slacken the retaining clip and detach the air hose from the idle speed adjuster valve

21.4a Remove the retaining and detach the accelerator inner cable from the throttle cam

21.4b On models with cruise control prise off the second retaining clip . . .

21.4c . . . and free the cruise control cable from the throttle cam and bracket

21.5 Release the retaining clips and detach the coolant hoses (arrowed) from the throttle housing

21.7a Unscrew the union nut and free the EGR pipe from the EGR valve

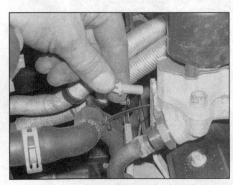

21.7b . . . then remove the bracket retaining bolt

21.8 Unscrew the union nut and disconnect the braking system servo unit hose

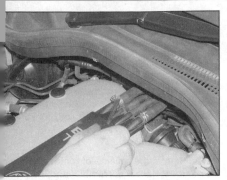

21.9 Release the retaining clips and disconnect the vacuum and breather hoses from the rear of the manifold

21.10 Undo the retaining bolts and free the hose/wiring brackets from the manifold

21.11a Remove the caps then unscrew the retaining bolts . . .

necessary, disconnect the connector and free the knock sensor wiring connector from the EGR valve bracket.

8 Unscrew the union nut and disconnect the braking system servo unit vacuum hose from the manifold upper section **(see illustration)**.

9 Make a note of the correct fitted locations of the vacuum/breather hoses connected to the rear of the manifold upper section then release the retaining clips (where fitted) and disconnect them **(see illustration)**.

10 Unscrew the retaining bolts and detach the hose/wiring brackets from the corners of the manifold upper section **(see illustration)**.

11 Remove the caps from the top of the manifold then slacken and remove the upper section retaining bolts. Lift off the manifold upper section, disconnecting the vacuum hoses from the manifold switchover solenoid valve as they become accessible **(see illustrations)**. Remove the sealing rings from the top of manifold lower section and discard them; new ones should be used on refitting. *Caution: Take great care not to allow any foreign object to drop down into the cylinder head intake ports.*

Refitting

12 Refitting is the reverse of removal noting the following.

a) *Ensure all the mating surfaces are clean and dry and the new seals/sealing rings*

are correctly seated in their recesses **(see illustration)**. *Tighten all the manifold retaining bolts evenly and progressively to their specified torque settings.*

b) *Ensure that all relevant hoses are reconnected to their original positions, and are securely held (where necessary) by their retaining clips.*

c) *Ensure the EGR valve and pipe mating surfaces are clean and dry and apply a smear of high-temperature grease to the threads of the union nut (Vauxhall/Opel recommend the use of assembly paste 19 48 569 - available from a dealer). Reconnect the pipe to the valve and tighten its union nut to the specified torque.*

d) *On completion, adjust the accelerator cable as described in Section 27.*

22 Multi-ram air intake system (2.5 and 3.0 litre) - component removal and refitting

Pre-volume chamber assembly

Removal

1 Remove the airflow meter as described in Section 20.

2 Slacken the retaining clip and disconnect

the idle speed adjuster hose from the intake duct.

3 Slacken the retaining clips securing the intake ducts to the throttle housing and switchover valve and remove both ducts from the engine compartment.

4 Disconnect the wiring connector and vacuum hose from the intake duct switchover valve solenoid valve on the rear of the chamber.

5 Unscrew the mounting nuts then free the chamber assembly from its lower mounting rubber and manoeuvre it out of position **(see illustration)**.

Refitting

6 Refitting is the reverse of removal ensuring the chamber is correctly engaged with its lower mounting rubber.

23 Secondary air injection system (2.5 and 3.0 litre) - component removal and refitting

Front connecting pipe

Removal

1 Remove the multi-ram air intake system pre-volume chamber as described in Section 22.

2 Release the retaining clip and disconnect

21.11b . . . and remove the manifold upper section

21.12 On refitting be sure to renew all manifold seals and sealing rings

22.5 Removing the pre-volume chamber assembly

13

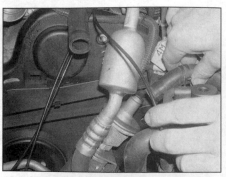

23.2 Disconnect the air hose from the non-return valve on the front connecting pipe

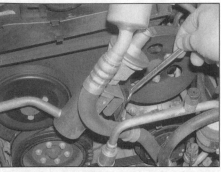

23.3a Slacken and remove the left-hand . . .

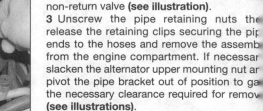

the air hose from the front connecting pip non-return valve (see illustration).

3 Unscrew the pipe retaining nuts the release the retaining clips securing the pip ends to the hoses and remove the assemb from the engine compartment. If necessar slacken the alternator upper mounting nut ar pivot the pipe bracket out of position to ga the necessary clearance required for remov (see illustrations).

Refitting

4 Refitting is the reverse of removal ensurin the hose are correctly and secure reconnected.

24 Wiper motor water deflector panel - removal and refitting

23.3b . . . and right-hand retaining nuts then (if necessary) slacken the alternator mounting nut and pivot the bracket (arrowed) clear of the pipe . . .

23.3c . . . to allow the front connecting pipe to be removed from the engine

Removal

1 Remove both wiper arms.

2 Release the rubber weatherstrip from th rear of the engine compartment bulkhea (see illustration).

3 Slacken and withdraw the screws securin the ends of the water deflector panel to th bodywork (see illustration).

4 Lift the lower edge of the windscree sealing strip, then release the press stud clip securing the edge of the water deflector pan to the bodywork. Unclip and remove the pan (see illustrations).

Refitting

5 Refitting is a reversal of removal. Refit th wiper arms.

25 Coolant - draining and refilling

24.2 Release the rubber weatherstrip from the rear of the engine compartment bulkhead

24.3 Slacken and withdraw the screws securing the ends of the water deflector panel to the bodywork

Draining

⚠ *Warning: Wait until the engine i cold before starting this procedure. Do not allow antifreeze to come in contact with your skin, or with the painted surfaces of the*

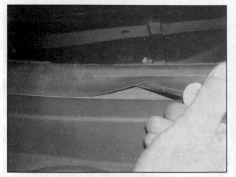

24.4a Lift the lower edge of the windscreen sealing strip . . .

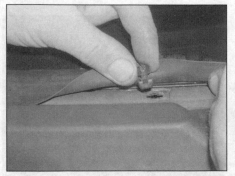

24.4b . . . then release the press stud clips securing the edge of the water deflector panel to the bodywork

24.4c Unclip and remove the water deflector panel

25.3 Open the drain plug at the base of the radiator (arrowed)

vehicle. Rinse off spills immediately with plenty of water. Never leave antifreeze lying around in an open container, or in a puddle in the driveway or on the garage floor. Children and pets are attracted by its sweet smell, but antifreeze can be fatal if ingested.

1 With the engine completely cold, remove the expansion tank filler cap. Turn the cap anti-clockwise, wait until any pressure remaining in the system is released, then unscrew it and lift it off.
2 Where applicable, remove the engine undershield, then position a suitable container beneath the left-hand side of the radiator.
3 Open the drain plug at the base of the radiator, and allow the coolant to drain into the container (see illustrations).
4 When the flow of coolant stops, close the drain plug securely.

Refilling

5 Before attempting to fill the cooling system, make sure that all hoses and clips are in good condition, and that the clips are tight. Note that an antifreeze mixture must be used all year round, to prevent corrosion of the engine components.
6 Remove the expansion tank filler cap, and top the level up to the KALT/COLD mark.

6-cylinder engine models

7 Disconnect the heater supply (upper) hose from the bulkhead connection.
8 Pour coolant into the disconnected heater

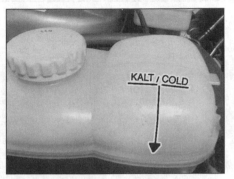

25.9 Slowly fill the system via the expansion tank filler neck, until the coolant level again reaches the KALT/COLD mark on the side of the expansion tank

hose with the aid of a funnel, until no more coolant will flow in, then reconnect the heater hose to the bulkhead connection and tighten the clip securely.
9 Slowly fill the system via the expansion tank filler neck, until the coolant level again reaches the KALT/COLD mark on the side of the expansion tank (see illustration).

All models

10 Refit and tighten the expansion tank filler cap.
11 Start the engine, and allow it to run until it reaches normal operating temperature (until the cooling fan cuts in and out). The cooling system will bleed automatically as the engine warms up.
12 Stop the engine, and allow it to cool, then re-check the coolant level. Top-up the level if necessary and refit the expansion tank filler cap. Where applicable, refit the engine undershield.

---

26 Coolant pump -
removal and refitting

Models with 4-cylinder engines

1 Drain the cooling system as described in Section 25.
2 Remove the camshaft timing belt tensioner

pulley, as described in Section 17 or 18, as applicable.
3 Release the crankshaft sensor wiring from the timing belt cover, noting its routing ensure correct refitting.
4 Progressively slacken and remove the water pump retaining bolts. Note that the bolts are of different lengths; make a note of the fitted position of each bolt to ensure correct refitting.
5 Lift the coolant pump away from the engine and recover the seal.

Refitting

6 Refit the coolant pump by following the removal procedure in reverse, noting these points:
a) Use a new coolant pump sealing ring.
b) Coat the new sealing ring and the pump mating surface with silicon grease before fitting.
c) The lug on the side of the coolant pump flange must be aligned with the corresponding recess in the cylinder block.
d) Tighten the coolant pump securing bolts to the specified torque.
e) Refit the timing belt tensioner pulley, according to the information given in Section 17 or 18 (as applicable).
f) On completion, refill the cooling system.

Models with 6-cylinder engines

Removal

7 Drain the cooling system as described in Section 25.
8 Remove the camshaft timing belt front cover, as described in Section 13. Note that this entails the removal of the auxiliary drivebelt (see Section 1) and the coolant pump pulley.
9 Progressively slacken and remove the water pump retaining bolts (see illustration). Note that the bolts are of different lengths; make a note of the fitted position of each bolt to ensure correct refitting.
10 Lift the coolant pump away from the engine and recover the seal (see illustrations).

26.9 Progressively slacken and remove the water pump retaining bolts

26.10a Lift the coolant pump away from the engine . . .

26.10b . . . and recover the seal

13

Refitting

11 Refit the coolant pump by following the removal procedure in reverse, noting these points:

a) Use a new coolant pump sealing ring..
b) Coat the new sealing ring and the pump mating surface with silicon grease before fitting.
c) Tighten the coolant pump securing bolts to the specified torque.
d) Refit the timing belt cover, coolant pump pulley and auxiliary drivebelt, according to the information given in Section 13 and Section 1 (as applicable).
e) On completion, refill the cooling system.

27 Accelerator cable - adjustment

1 Working in the engine compartment, slide off the adjustment clip from accelerator outer cable.

2 With the clip removed, ensure that the throttle cam is fully against its stop. Gently pull the cable out of its grommet until all free play is removed from the inner cable.

3 With the cable held in this position, refit the spring clip to the last exposed outer cable groove in front of the rubber grommet. When the clip is refitted and the outer cable released, there should be only a small amount of free play in the inner cable.

4 Have an assistant depress the accelerator pedal, and check that the throttle cam opens fully and returns smoothly to its stop.

Section 14A
Vauxhall/Opel Vectra petrol 1995 to 1998

Contents

Specifications

Timing belt renewal interval . . . . Every 40 000 miles (65 000 km) or 4 years - whichever comes first
Note: *Although the interval for timing belt renewal is increased for later models, it is strongly recommended that this shorter interval is applied to vehicles which are subjected to intensive use, ie, mainly short journeys or a lot of stop-start driving. The actual belt renewal interval is therefore very much up to the individual owner. That being said, it is highly recommended to err on the side of safety, and renew the belt at this earlier interval, bearing in mind the drastic consequences resulting from belt failure.*

Torque wrench settings

	Nm	lbf ft
SOHC engine		
Alternator fixings:		
Alternator to bracket bolts	35	26
Alternator bracket to cylinder block bolts	35	26
Support bracket bolts	18	13
Engine torque support rod bolts	60	44
Camshaft cover bolts	8	6
Camshaft sprocket bolt	45	33
Coolant pump bolts	8	6
Crankshaft pulley bolt: *		
Stage 1	55	41
Stage 2	Angle-tighten a further 45°	
Stage 3	Angle-tighten a further 15°	
Engine/transmission mounting bolts:		
Front (left- and right-hand) mounting:		
Bracket-to-engine/transmission bolts	60	44
Mounting-to-bracket/subframe nuts	45	33
Rear mounting:		
Mounting-to-bracket bolts	45	33
Mounting-to-subframe bolts	20	15
Bracket-to-transmission bolts	60	44
Torque support rod bolts	60	44
Inlet manifold nuts and bolts	22	16
Power steering pump to bracket:		
1.6 litre petrol engine models	20	15
1.8 and 2.0 litre petrol engine models	25	18
Power steering pump pulley: *		
Stage 1	20	15
Stage 2	Angle-tighten 30°	
Stage 3	Angle-tighten 45°	
Power steering pump tensioner	40	30
Roadwheel bolts	110	81
Spark plugs	25	18
Timing belt cover bolts:		
Upper and lower covers	4	3
Rear cover	12	9
Timing belt tensioner bolt	20	15

14A

Torque wrench settings (continued)

	Nm	lbf ft

1.6 litre DOHC engine

	Nm	lbf ft
Alternator fixings:		
Alternator to bracket bolts	35	26
Alternator bracket to cylinder block bolts	35	26
Support bracket bolts	18	13
Engine torque support rod bolts	60	44
Camshaft cover bolts	8	6
Camshaft sprocket bolt: *		
Stage 1	50	37
Stage 2	Angle-tighten a further 60°	
Stage 3	Angle-tighten a further 15°	
Crankshaft pulley bolt: *		
Stage 1	95	70
Stage 2	Angle-tighten a further 30°	
Stage 3	Angle-tighten a further 15°	
Engine/transmission mounting bolts:		
Front (left- and right-hand) mounting:		
Bracket-to-engine/transmission bolts	60	44
Mounting-to-bracket/subframe nuts	45	33
Rear mounting:		
Mounting-to-bracket bolts	45	33
Mounting-to-subframe bolts	20	15
Bracket-to-transmission bolts	60	44
Torque support rod bolts	60	44
Inlet manifold nuts and bolts:		
Upper manifold nuts and bolts	8	6
Lower manifold nuts and bolts	20	15
Power steering pump to bracket:		
1.6 litre petrol engine models	20	15
1.8 and 2.0 litre petrol engine models	25	19
Power steering pump pulley: *		
Stage 1	20	15
Stage 2	Angle-tighten 30°	
Stage 3	Angle-tighten 45°	
Power steering pump tensioner	40	30
Roadwheel bolts	110	81
Spark plugs	25	19
Timing belt cover bolts:		
Upper and lower covers	4	3
Rear cover	6	4
Timing belt idler pulley bolt	25	18
Timing belt tensioner bolt	20	15

1.8 and 2.0 litre DOHC engines

	Nm	lbf ft
Alternator fixings:		
Alternator to bracket bolts	35	26
Alternator bracket to cylinder block bolts	35	26
Support bracket bolts	18	13
Engine torque support rod bolts	60	44
Camshaft cover bolts	8	6
Camshaft sprocket bolt: *		
Stage 1	50	37
Stage 2	Angle-tighten a further 60°	
Stage 3	Angle-tighten a further 15°	
Crankshaft pulley bolts	20	15
Crankshaft sprocket bolt: *		
Stage 1	130	96
Stage 2	Angle-tighten a further 40 to 50°	
Engine/transmission front mounting fasteners:		
Bracket-to-engine/transmission bolts	60	44
Mounting-to-bracket/subframe nuts	45	33
Engine/transmission rear mounting bolts:		
Mounting-to-bracket bolts	45	33
Mounting-to-subframe bolts	20	15
Bracket-to-transmission bolts	60	44
Inlet manifold nuts and bolts	22	16

Torque wrench settings

	Nm	lbf ft
1.8 and 2.0 litre DOHC engines (continued)		
Power steering pump to bracket:		
1.6 litre petrol engine models	20	15
1.8 and 2.0 litre petrol engine models	25	19
Power steering pump pulley: *		
Stage 1	20	15
Stage 2	Angle-tighten 30°	
Stage 3	Angle-tighten 45°	
Power steering pump tensioner	40	30
Roadwheel bolts	110	81
Spark plugs	25	19
Timing belt cover bolts	6	4
Timing belt idler pulley:		
Pulley bolt	25	18
Mounting bracket bolts	25	18
Timing belt tensioner bolt	20	15

Note: *The manufacturer states that all fasteners secured by the angle-tightening method must be renewed as a matter of course.*

1 Auxiliary drivebelt - removal, refitting and adjustment

1 To remove the drivebelt, first remove the air cleaner housing as described in Section 15.
2 On models with air conditioning, it will be necessary to remove the engine/transmission right-hand front mounting in order to allow the belt to be removed/refitted (see Section 14).
Note: *If the belt is being removed as part of another repair procedure (ie timing belt renewal) and is not to be renewed, the mounting can be left in position. Simply release the tensioner then disengage the belt from the pulleys and position it clear of the engine.*
3 Prior to removal, make a note of the correct routing of the belt around the various pulleys. If the belt is to be re-used, also mark the direction of rotation on the belt to ensure the belt is refitted the same way around.
4 Using a suitable spanner or socket fitted to the tensioner pulley centre bolt, lever the tensioner away from the belt until there is sufficient slack to enable the belt to be slipped off the pulleys. Carefully release the tensioner pulley until it is against its stop then remove the belt from the vehicle.
5 Manoeuvre the belt into position, routing it correctly around the pulleys; if the original belt is being fitted use the marks made prior to removal to ensure it is fitted the correct way around.
6 Lever the tensioner roller back against is spring, and seat the belt on the pulleys. Ensure the belt is centrally located on all pulleys then slowly release the tensioner pulley until the belt is correctly tensioned. **Do not** allow the tensioner to spring back and stress the belt.
7 Check the position of the drivebelt tensioner assembly arm, the arm should be in between the stops on the backplate and should be free to move **(see illustration)**. If the tensioner arm is against the stop, the belt must be renewed.
8 On models equipped with air conditioning, refit the engine mounting as described in Section 14.
9 On all models, refit the air cleaner housing as described in Section 15.

2 Top dead centre (TDC) for No 1 piston (SOHC) - locating

1 In its travel up and down its cylinder bore, Top Dead Centre (TDC) is the highest point that each piston reaches as the crankshaft rotates. While each piston reaches TDC both

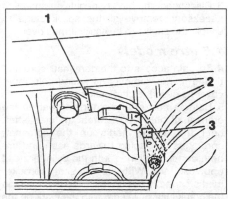

1.7 Check the auxiliary drivebelt tensioner arm indicator (2) is correctly positioned between the stops (1 and 3) on the backplate

at the top of the compression stroke and again at the top of the exhaust stroke, for the purpose of timing the engine, TDC refers to the piston position (usually number 1) at the top of its compression stroke.
2 Number 1 piston (and cylinder) is at the right-hand (timing belt) end of the engine, and its TDC position is located as follows. Note that the crankshaft rotates clockwise when viewed from the right-hand side of the car.
3 Disconnect the battery negative terminal. If necessary, remove all the spark plugs to enable the engine to be easily turned over.
4 To gain access to the camshaft sprocket timing mark, remove the timing belt upper cover as described in Section 8.
5 Using a socket and extension bar on the crankshaft pulley bolt, turn the crankshaft whilst keeping an eye on the camshaft sprocket. Rotate the crankshaft until the timing mark on the camshaft sprocket is correctly aligned with the cut-out on the top of the timing belt rear cover and the notch on the crankshaft pulley rim is correctly aligned with the pointer on the timing belt lower cover (**see illustrations**).
6 With the crankshaft pulley and camshaft sprocket timing marks positioned as described, the engine is positioned with No 1 piston at TDC on its compression stroke.

2.5a Align the camshaft sprocket timing mark with the cut-out on the timing belt cover . . .

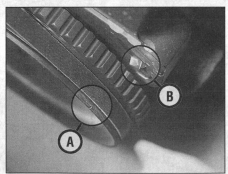

2.5b . . . and align the crankshaft pulley notch with the timing belt pointer to position No 1 piston at TDC on its compression stroke

14A

3 Top dead centre (TDC) for No 1 piston (DOHC) - locating

1 In its travel up and down its cylinder bore, Top Dead Centre (TDC) is the highest point that each piston reaches as the crankshaft rotates. While each piston reaches TDC both at the top of the compression stroke and again at the top of the exhaust stroke, for the purpose of timing the engine, TDC refers to the piston position (usually number 1) at the top of its compression stroke.

2 Number 1 piston (and cylinder) is at the right-hand (timing belt) end of the engine, and its TDC position is located as follows. Note that the crankshaft rotates clockwise when viewed from the right-hand side of the car.

3 Disconnect the battery negative terminal. If necessary, remove all the spark plugs to enable the engine to be easily turned over.

1.6 litre models

4 To gain access to the camshaft sprocket timing marks, remove the timing belt upper cover as described in Section 9.

5 Using a socket and extension bar on the crankshaft pulley bolt, rotate the crankshaft until the timing marks on the camshaft sprockets are facing towards each and are both correctly aligned with the cylinder head upper surface. With the camshaft sprocket marks correctly positioned, align the notch on the crankshaft pulley rim with the mark on the timing belt lower cover (see illustration). The engine is now positioned with No 1 piston at TDC on its compression stroke.

1.8 and 2.0 litre models

6 To gain access to the camshaft sprocket timing marks, remove the timing belt outer cover as described in Section 9.

7 Using a socket and extension bar on the crankshaft sprocket bolt, rotate the crankshaft until the timing marks on the camshaft

3.5 On 1.6 litre engines align the camshaft sprocket timing marks (A) with the cylinder head upper surface (B) as shown to position No 1 cylinder at TDC on its compression stroke

sprockets are both at the top and are correctly aligned with the marks on the camshaft cover. With the camshaft sprocket marks correctly positioned, align the notch on the crankshaft pulley rim with the pointer on the cover (see illustration). The engine is now positioned with No 1 piston at TDC on its compression stroke.

4 Camshaft cover (SOHC) - removal and refitting

Removal

1 Release the retaining clips and disconnect the breather hoses from the camshaft cover (see illustrations).

2 Slacken and remove the retaining bolts, noting the correct fitted location of any clips or brackets retained by the bolts (as applicable) then lift the camshaft cover from

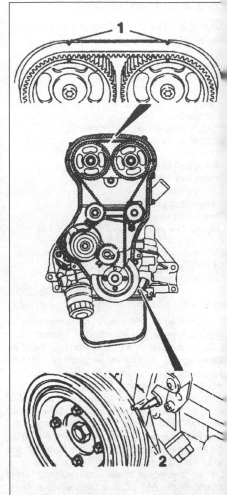

3.7 On 1.8 and 2.0 litre engines align the camshaft sprocket timing marks with the marks (1) on the cylinder head cover, and the crankshaft pulley notch with the pointer (2) to position No 1 cylinder at TDC on its compression stroke

4.1a Slacken the retaining clips and disconnect the large . . .

4.1b . . . and small breather hose from the rear of the camshaft cover

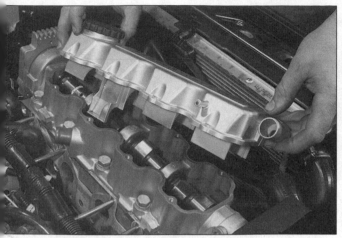

4.2 Removing the camshaft cover from the engine

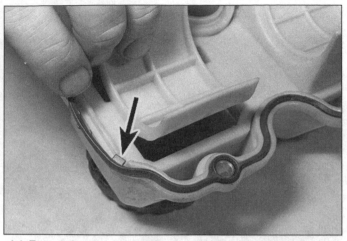

4.4 Ensure the gasket is correctly located in the camshaft cover recess

he camshaft housing **(see illustration)**. If the cover is stuck, do not lever between the cover and camshaft housing mating surfaces - if necessary, gently tap the cover sideways to ee it. Recover the gasket; if it shows signs of amage or deterioration it must be renewed.

Refitting

Prior to refitting, examine the inside of the cover for a build-up of oil sludge or any other contamination, and if necessary clean the cover with paraffin, or a water-soluble solvent. Examine the condition of the crankcase ventilation filter inside the camshaft cover, nd clean as described for the inside of the cover if clogging is evident (if desired, the filter an be removed from the cover, after emoving the securing bolts). Dry the cover horoughly before refitting.

Ensure the cover is clean and dry and seat he gasket in the cover recess then refit the cover to the camshaft housing, ensuring the gasket remains correctly seated **(see illustration)**.

5 Refit the retaining bolts, ensuring all relevant clips/brackets are correctly positioned, and tighten them to the specified torque working in a diagonal sequence **(see illustration)**.
6 Reconnect the breather hoses securely to the cover.

---

5 Camshaft cover (DOHC) - removal and refitting

1.6 litre models

Removal

1 Remove the upper section of the inlet manifold as described in Section 16.
2 Disconnect the plug caps from the spark plugs and position them clear of the cover.
3 Release the retaining clips and disconnect the breather hoses from the left-hand end of the camshaft cover **(see illustration)**.

4.5 On refitting ensure the wiring and HT lead clips (arrowed) are fitted to the correct bolts

4 Evenly and progressively slacken and remove the camshaft cover retaining bolts **(see illustration)**.
5 Lift the camshaft cover away from the cylinder head and recover the covers' seals and the sealing rings which are fitted to each of the retaining bolt holes **(see**

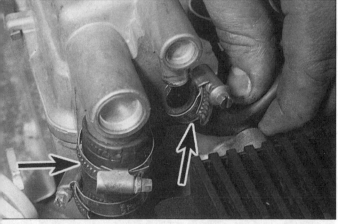

5.3 On 1.6 litre engines slacken the retaining clips and disconnect the breather hoses (arrowed) from the left-hand end of the camshaft cover

5.4 Unscrew the retaining bolts . . .

14A

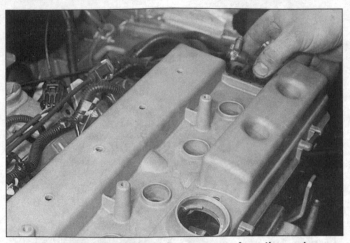

5.5 . . . and lift the camshaft cover away from the engine

5.6a Ensure the seals are correctly seated in the cover recesses . . .

illustration). Examine the seals and sealing rings for signs of wear or damage and renew if necessary.

Refitting

6 Ensure the cover and cylinder head surfaces are clean and dry then fit the camshaft seals securely to the cover grooves. Fit the sealing rings to the recesses around each retaining bolt hole, holding them in position with a smear of grease **(see illustrations)**.

7 Apply a smear of suitable sealant areas of the cylinder head surface around the right-hand end inlet and exhaust camshaft bearing caps and also to the semi-circular cut-outs on the left-hand end of the head.

8 Carefully manoeuvre the camshaft cover into position, taking great care to ensure all the sealing rings remain correctly seated. Refit the cover retaining bolts and tighten the retaining bolts to the specified torque, working in a spiral pattern from the centre outwards.

9 Reconnect the breather hose, securing them in position with the retaining clips, and securely reconnect the plug caps to the spark plugs.

10 Refit the inlet manifold upper section as described in Section 16.

1.8 and 2.0 litre models

Removal

11 Slacken the retaining clips and disconnect the breather hoses from the rear of the cover **(see illustration)**.

12 Undo the retaining screws and remove the spark plug cover. Disconnect the plug caps from the plugs then unclip the HT leads and position them clear of the cover.

13 Disconnect the camshaft sensor wiring connector and unclip the wiring from the camshaft cover.

14 Evenly and progressively slacken and remove the camshaft cover retaining bolts.

15 Lift the camshaft cover away from the

cylinder head and recover the cover's sea and the sealing rings which are fitted to eac of the retaining bolt holes. Examine th seal and sealing rings for signs of wear c damage and renew if necessary.

Refitting

16 Refit the cover as described i paragraphs 6 to 9, remembering to reconnec the camshaft sensor wiring.

6 Crankshaft pulley (SOHC) - removal and refitting

Note: A new pulley retaining bolt will b required on refitting.

Removal

1 Apply the handbrake, then jack up the fron of the car and support it on axle stands Remove the right-hand roadwheel.

5.6b . . . and fit the sealing rings to the recess around each retaining bolt hole

5.11 On 1.8 and 2.0 litre engines release the retaining clips and disconnect the breather hoses (arrowed) from the rear of the cove

.5 Refit the crankshaft pulley aligning the cut-out with the raised notch on the crankshaft sprocket (arrowed)

6.6 Fit the new retaining bolt and tighten it as described in text

Remove the auxiliary drivebelt as described n Section 1. Prior to removal, mark the irection of rotation on the belt to ensure the elt is refitted the same way around.

Slacken the crankshaft pulley retaining bolt. o prevent crankshaft rotation on manual ansmission models, have an assistant select op gear and apply the brakes firmly. On utomatic transmission models prevent otation by removing one of the torque onverter retaining bolts and bolting the riveplate to the transmission housing using a etal bar, spacers and suitable bolts.

Unscrew the retaining bolt and washer and emove the crankshaft pulley from the end of e crankshaft, taking care not to damage the rankshaft sensor.

Refitting

Refit the crankshaft pulley, aligning the ulley cut-out with the raised notch on the ming belt sprocket, then fit the washer and ew retaining bolt **(see illustration)**.

Lock the crankshaft by the method used on emoval, and tighten the pulley retaining bolt the specified stage 1 torque setting then ngle-tighten the bolt through the specified tage 2 angle, using a socket and extension ar, and finally through the specified stage 3 ngle. It is recommended that an angle-easuring gauge is used during the final tages of the tightening, to ensure accuracy see illustration). If a gauge is not available, se white paint to make alignment marks etween the bolt head and pulley prior to ghtening; the marks can then be used to heck that the bolt has been rotated through e correct angle.

Refit the auxiliary drivebelt as described in ection 1 using the mark made prior to moval to ensure the belt is fitted the correct ay around.

Refit the roadwheel then lower the car to e ground and tighten the wheel bolts to the pecified torque.

7 Crankshaft pulley (DOHC) - removal and refitting

1.6 litre models

Note: *A new pulley retaining bolt will be required on refitting.*

Removal

1 Apply the handbrake, then jack up the front of the car and support it on axle stands. Remove the right-hand roadwheel.

2 Remove the auxiliary drivebelt as described in Section 1. Prior to removal, mark the direction of rotation on the belt to ensure the belt is refitted the same way around.

3 Slacken the crankshaft pulley retaining bolt. To prevent crankshaft rotation on manual transmission models, have an assistant select top gear and apply the brakes firmly. On automatic transmission models prevent rotation by removing one of the torque converter retaining bolts and bolting the driveplate to the transmission housing using a metal bar, spacers and suitable bolts.

4 Unscrew the retaining bolt and washer and remove the crankshaft pulley from the end of the crankshaft, taking care not to damage the crankshaft sensor.

Refitting

5 Refit the crankshaft pulley, aligning the pulley cut-out with the raised notch on the timing belt sprocket, then fit the washer and new retaining bolt.

6 Lock the crankshaft by the method used on removal, and tighten the pulley retaining bolt to the specified stage 1 torque setting then angle-tighten the bolt through the specified stage 2 angle, using a socket and extension bar, and finally through the specified stage 3 angle. It is recommended that an angle-measuring gauge is used during the final stages of the tightening, to ensure accuracy. If a gauge is not available, use white paint to make alignment marks between the bolt head

and pulley prior to tightening; the marks can then be used to check that the bolt has been rotated through the correct angle.

7 Refit the auxiliary drivebelt as described in Section 1 using the mark made prior to removal to ensure the belt is fitted the correct way around.

8 Refit the roadwheel then lower the car to the ground and tighten the wheel bolts to the specified torque.

1.8 and 2.0 litre models

Removal

9 Carry out the operations described in paragraphs 2 and 3.

10 Using a socket and extension bar on the crankshaft sprocket bolt, turn the crankshaft until the notch on the pulley rim is correctly aligned with the pointer on the cover.

11 Slacken and remove the small retaining bolts securing the pulley to the crankshaft sprocket and remove the pulley from the engine. If necessary, prevent crankshaft rotation by holding the sprocket retaining bolt with a suitable socket.

Refitting

12 Check that the crankshaft sprocket mark is still aligned with the mark on the housing then manoeuvre the crankshaft pulley into position. Align the notch on the pulley rim with the pointer then seat the pulley on the sprocket and tighten its retaining bolts to the specified torque.

13 Carry out the operations described in paragraphs 7 and 8.

8 Timing belt covers (SOHC) - removal and refitting

Upper cover

Removal

1 Remove the air cleaner housing as described in Section 15.

14A

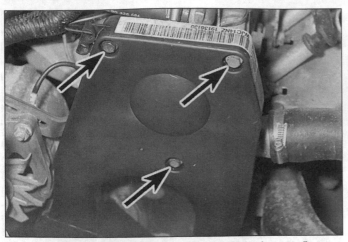

8.3 Timing belt upper cover retaining bolts (arrowed)

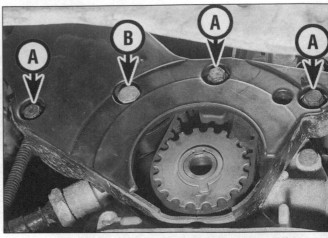

8.6 Timing belt lower cover retaining bolts (A)
B Timing belt tensioner bolt

2 Remove the auxiliary drivebelt as described in Section 1. Prior to removal, mark the direction of rotation on the belt to ensure the belt is fitted the same way around on refitting.
3 Undo the retaining screws then unclip the timing belt upper cover and remove it from the engine **(see illustration)**.

Refitting

4 Refitting is the reverse of removal, ensuring the auxiliary drivebelt is fitted the same way around as it was prior removal.

Lower cover

Removal

5 Remove the crankshaft pulley (see Section 6).
6 Remove the upper cover (see paragraphs 1 and 3) then undo the retaining screws and remove the lower cover from the engine **(see illustration)**.

Refitting

7 Refitting is the reverse of removal, using a new crankshaft pulley retaining bolt.

Rear cover

Removal

8 Remove the camshaft and crankshaft timing belt sprockets and the timing belt tensioner as described in Section 12.

9 Slacken and remove the bolts securing the rear cover to the camshaft housing and oil pump housing, and remove the cover from the engine **(see illustration)**.

Refitting

10 Refitting is the reverse of removal, tightening the cover retaining bolts to the specified torque.

9	Timing belt covers (DOHC) - removal and refitting

1.6 litre models

Upper cover

1 Remove the air cleaner housing as described in Section 15.
2 Undo the retaining screws then unclip the upper cover from the rear cover and remove it from the engine compartment **(see illustration)**.
3 Refitting is the reverse of removal, tightening the retaining bolts to the specified torque.

Lower cover

4 Remove the upper cover as described in paragraphs 1 and 2.

8.9 Slacken and remove the retaining bolts and remove the timing belt rear cov◄

5 Remove the crankshaft pulley as describe in Section 7.
6 Undo the retaining bolts then unclip th cover from the rear cover and manoeuvre out of position **(see illustrations)**.
7 Refitting is the reverse of remova tightening the cover bolts to the specifie torque.

Rear cover

8 Remove the timing belt as described Section 11.
9 Remove the camshaft sprocke crankshaft sprocket, the timing belt tension

9.2 Removing the timing belt upper cover - 1.6 litre engine

9.6a Timing belt lower cover upper retaining bolt (arrowed) . . .

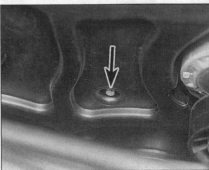

9.6b . . . and lower retaining bolt (arrowe - 1.6 litre engine

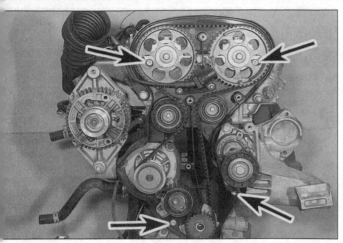

9.10 Timing belt rear cover retaining bolt locations - 1.6 litre engine (shown with timing belt and sprockets still fitted)

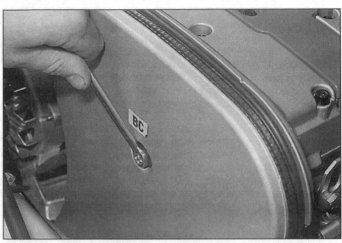

9.15a On 1.8 and 2.0 litre engines undo the timing belt cover retaining bolts . . .

and the rear idler pulley as described in Section 13.

10 Undo the retaining bolts and remove the rear cover from the engine unit **(see illustration)**.

11 Refitting is the reverse of removal, tightening the cover bolts to the specified torque.

1.8 and 2.0 litre models

Outer cover

12 Remove the air cleaner housing as described in Section 15.

13 Remove the auxiliary drivebelt as described in Section 1. Prior to removal, mark the direction of rotation on the belt to ensure the belt is refitted the same way around.

14 Slacken and remove the bolt securing the torque support rod to the engine bracket then unbolt the bracket and remove it from the right-hand end of the engine.

15 Slacken and remove the retaining bolts, along with their washers and rubber spacers, and remove the cover from the engine unit along with its seal **(see illustrations)**.

16 Refitting is the reverse of removal, ensure the cover seal is correctly fitted **(see illustration)**. Tighten all bolts to the specified torque.

Rear cover

17 Remove the timing belt as described in Section 11.

18 Remove the camshaft sprockets, crankshaft sprocket, the timing belt tensioner and the idler pulley assembly as described in Section 13.

19 Unbolt the camshaft sensor from the cylinder head.

20 Unbolt the torque support rod bracket from the end of the cylinder head.

21 Undo the retaining bolts and remove the rear cover from the engine unit.

22 Refitting is the reverse of removal, tightening all bolts to the specified torque.

10 Timing belt (SOHC) - removal and refitting

Note: *The timing belt must be removed and refitted with the engine cold.*

Removal

1 Remove the timing belt upper cover as described in Section 8.

2 Position No 1 cylinder at TDC on its compression stroke as described in Section 2.

3 Remove the crankshaft pulley as described in Section 6.

4 Unbolt the timing belt lower cover and remove it from the engine (see Section 8).

5 Insert a suitable tool (such as a pin punch) into the hole in the timing belt tensioner arm, then lever the arm clockwise to its stop, and lock it in position by inserting the tool into the corresponding hole in the tensioner backplate

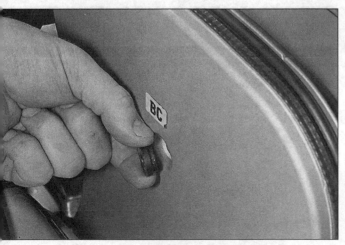

9.15b . . . and recover the rubber spacers

9.16 On refitting ensure the seal is correctly fitted to the outer cover

14A

10.5a Insert a tool (such as a punch) into the hole (arrowed) in the tensioner arm . . .

10.5b . . . then lever the arm clockwise and lock the tensioner in position by locating the tool in the backplate hole

10.7a Slacken the coolant pump bolts . . .

10.7b . . . and relieve the timing belt tension by rotating the pump with a suitable adapter

(see illustrations). Leave the tool in position to lock the tensioner in position until the belt is refitted.

6 Check the camshaft and crankshaft sprocket timing marks are correctly aligned with the marks on the belt rear cover and oil pump housing.

7 Slacken the coolant pump retaining bolts then, using an open-ended spanner, carefully rotate the pump to relieve the tension in the timing belt. Adapters to fit the pump are available from most tool shops and allow the pump to be easily turned using a ratchet or extension bar **(see illustrations).**

8 Slide the timing belt off from its sprocket and remove it from the engine **(see illustration).** If the belt is to be re-used, use white paint or similar to mark the direction of rotation on the belt. **Do not** rotate the crankshaft until the timing belt has been refitted.

9 If signs of oil contamination are found, trace the source of the oil leak and rectify it, then wash down the engine timing belt area and all related components to remove all traces of oil.

Refitting

10 On reassembly, thoroughly clean the timing belt sprockets then check that the camshaft sprocket timing mark is still correctly aligned with the cover cut-out and the crankshaft sprocket mark is still aligned with the mark on the oil pump housing **(see illustration).**

11 Fit the timing belt over the crankshaft and camshaft sprockets, ensuring that the belt front run is taut (ie, all slack is on the tensioner pulley side of the belt), then fit the belt over

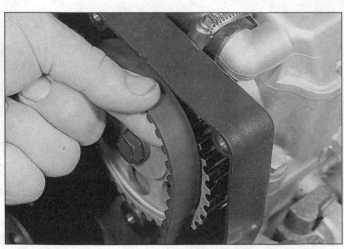

10.8 Slip the timing belt off from the sprockets and remove it from the engine

10.10 Ensure the timing mark on the crankshaft sprocket is correctly aligned with the mark on the oil pump housing

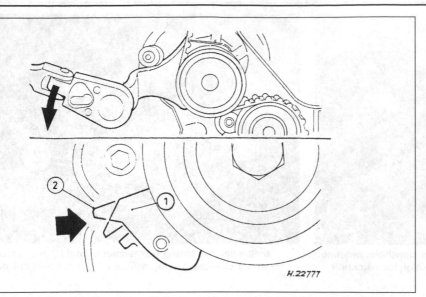

10.16 Rotate the coolant pump until the tensioner arm pointer (1) is correctly aligned with the cut-out (2) on the backplate

he coolant pump sprocket and tensioner ulley. Do not twist the belt sharply while efitting it. Ensure that the belt teeth are orrectly seated centrally in the sprockets, nd that the timing marks remain in alignment. a used belt is being refitted, ensure that the rrow mark made on removal points in the ormal direction of rotation, as before.

2 Carefully remove the punch from the ming belt tensioner to release the tensioner pring.

3 Check the sprocket timing marks are still orrectly aligned. If adjustment is necessary, ck the tensioner in position again then disengage the belt from the sprockets and make any necessary adjustments.

14 If the marks are still correctly positioned, tension the timing belt by rotating the coolant pump whilst observing the movement of the tensioner arm. Position the pump so that the tensioner arm is fully over against its stop, without exerting any excess strain on the belt, then tighten the coolant pump retaining bolts.

15 Temporarily refit the crankshaft pulley bolt then rotate the crankshaft smoothly through two complete turns (720°) in the normal direction of rotation to settle the timing belt in position.

16 Check that both the camshaft and crankshaft sprocket timing marks are realigned then slacken the coolant pump bolts. Adjust the pump so that the tensioner arm pointer is aligned with the cut-out on the backplate then tighten the coolant pump bolts to the specified torque **(see illustration)**. Rotate the crankshaft smoothly through another two complete turns in the normal direction of rotation, to bring the sprocket timing marks back into alignment. Check that the tensioner arm pointer is still aligned with the backplate cut-out.

17 If the tensioner arm is not correctly aligned with the backplate, repeat the procedure in paragraph 16.

18 Once the tensioner arm and backplate remain correctly aligned, ensure the coolant pump bolts are tightened to the specified torque, then refit the timing belt covers and crankshaft pulley as described in Sections 6 and 8.

11 Timing belt (DOHC) - removal and refitting

Note: *The timing belt must be removed and refitted with the engine cold.*

Removal

1 Position No 1 cylinder at TDC on its compression stroke as described in Section 3.

2 Remove the crankshaft pulley as described in Section 7.

3 On 1.6 litre models, unbolt the timing belt lower cover and remove it from the engine (see Section 9).

4 On 1.6 litre models, check the camshaft sprocket timing marks are correctly aligned with the cylinder head surface and the crankshaft sprocket timing mark is aligned with the mark on the cover. Undo the two bolts securing the camshaft sensor to the cylinder head and position it clear of the engine **(see illustrations)**.

5 On 1.8 and 2.0 litre models, check the camshaft sprocket timing marks are correctly aligned with the camshaft cover marks and the

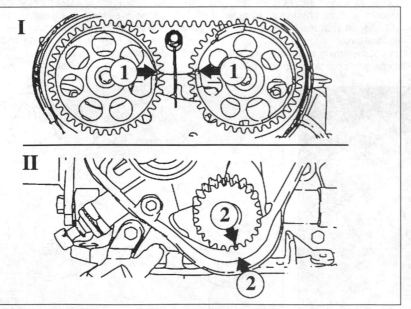

11.4a Camshaft (1) and crankshaft sprocket (2) timing marks - 1.6 litre engine

Camshaft sprocket timing marks aligned with the cylinder head upper surface
Crankshaft sprocket timing mark aligned with mark on oil pump housing

11.4b On 1.6 litre engines unbolt the camshaft sensor and position it clear of the timing belt

14A

11.5 On 1.8 and 2.0 litre engines ensure the camshaft sprocket marks are correctly aligned with the marks on the camshaft cover (arrowed)

11.6 Slacken the timing belt tensioner bolt (1) and rotate the tensioner clockwise using an Allen key in the arm cut-out (2)

11.7 Removing the timing belt

crankshaft sprocket timing mark is aligned with the pointer on the cover (see illustration).
6 On all models, slacken the timing belt tensioner bolt. Using an Allen key, rotate the tensioner arm clockwise to its stop, to relieve the tension in the timing belt, hold it in position and securely tighten the retaining bolt (see illustration).

7 Slide the timing belt off from its sprockets and remove it from the engine (see illustration). If the belt is to be re-used, use white paint or similar to mark the direction of rotation on the belt. Do not rotate the crankshaft or camshafts until the timing belt has been refitted.
8 If signs of oil contamination are found, trace the source of the oil leak and rectify it, then wash down the engine timing belt area and all related components to remove all traces of oil.

Refitting

9 On reassembly, thoroughly clean the timing belt sprockets and tensioner/idler pulleys.
10 Check that the camshaft sprocket timing marks are still correctly aligned with the cylinder head surface (1.6 litre models) or the camshaft cover marks (1.8 and 2.0 litre models) and the crankshaft sprocket mark is still aligned with the mark on the cover (see illustration).
11 Fit the timing belt over the crankshaft and camshaft sprockets and around the idler

pulleys, ensuring that the belt front run is tau (ie, all slack is on the tensioner side of th belt), then fit the belt over the coolant pum sprocket and tensioner pulley. Do not twis the belt sharply while refitting it. Ensur that the belt teeth are correctly seate centrally in the sprockets, and that the timin marks remain in alignment. If a used belt i being refitted, ensure that the arrow mar made on removal points in the norma direction of rotation, as before.
12 Slacken the timing belt tensioner bo to release the tensioner spring. Rotat the tensioner arm anti-clockwise until th tensioner pointer is fully over against its stor without exerting any excess strain on the bel Hold the tensioner in position and securel tighten its retaining bolt (see illustration).
13 Check the sprocket timing marks are sti correctly aligned. If adjustment is necessar release the tensioner again then disengag the belt from the sprockets and make an necessary adjustments.
14 Using a socket on the crankshaf

11.10 Crankshaft sprocket (A) and belt cover (B) timing marks - 1.6 litre engine

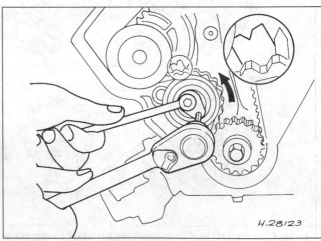

11.12 Tension the belt by rotating the tensioner arm fully anti-clockwise until the pointer is positioned as shown

11.16 If a new belt is being fitted, position the tensioner so that the pointer is aligned with the backplate cut-out

pulley/sprocket bolt (as applicable), rotate the crankshaft smoothly through two complete turns (720°) in the normal direction of rotation to settle the timing belt in position.

15 Check that both the camshaft and crankshaft sprocket timing marks are correctly realigned then slacken the tensioner bolt again.

16 If a new timing belt is being fitted, adjust the tensioner so that the pointer is aligned with the cut-out on the backplate **(see illustration)**. Hold the tensioner in the correct position and tighten its retaining bolt to the specified torque. Rotate the crankshaft smoothly through another two complete turns in the normal direction of rotation, to bring the sprocket timing marks back into alignment. Check that the tensioner pointer is still aligned with the backplate cut-out.

17 If the original belt is being refitted, adjust the tensioner so that the pointer is positioned 4 mm to the left of the cut-out on the backplate **(see illustration)**. Hold the tensioner in the correct position and tighten its retaining bolt to the specified torque. Rotate the crankshaft smoothly through another two complete turns in the normal direction of rotation, to bring the sprocket

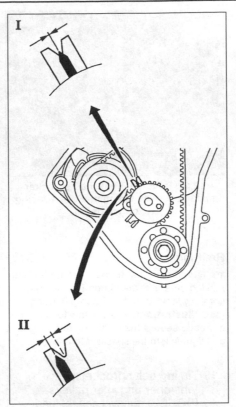

11.17 Timing belt tensioner pointer positions

I Location if a new belt is being fitted
II Location if the original belt is being re-used (pointer should be 4 mm to the left of the backplate cut-out

timing marks back into alignment. Check that the tensioner pointer is still correctly positioned in relation to the backplate cut-out.
18 If the tensioner pointer is not correctly positioned in relation to the backplate, repeat the procedure in paragraph 16 (new belt) or 17 (original belt) (as applicable).
19 Once the tensioner pointer and backplate

remain correctly aligned, refit the timing belt covers and crankshaft pulley as described in Sections 7 and 9. On 1.6 litre models it will be necessary to refit the camshaft sensor to the cylinder head, tighten its retaining bolts to the specified torque, prior to refitting the upper cover.

12 Timing belt tensioner and sprockets (SOHC) - removal and refitting

Camshaft sprocket
Removal
1 Remove the timing belt as described in Section 10.
2 The camshaft must be prevented from turning as the sprocket bolt is unscrewed, and this can be achieved in one of two ways as follows.
a) *Make up a sprocket-holding tool using two lengths of steel strip (one long, the other short), and three nuts and bolts; one nut and bolt forms the pivot of a forked tool, with the remaining two nuts and bolts at the tips of the 'forks' to engage with the sprocket spokes as shown (see illustration).*
b) *Remove the camshaft cover as described in Section 4 and hold the camshaft with an open-ended spanner on the flats provided.*
3 Unscrew the retaining bolt and washer and remove the sprocket from the end of the camshaft.

Refitting
4 Prior to refitting check the oil seal for signs of damage or leakage, if necessary renewing it.
5 Refit the sprocket to the end of the camshaft, aligning its cut-out with the camshaft locating pin, then refit the retaining bolt and washer **(see illustration)**.

12.2 Using a home-made sprocket holding tool to retain the camshaft sprocket whilst the bolt is slackened

12.5 Refit the camshaft sprocket making sure the locating pin (1) engages with the sprocket hole (2)

14A

12.6 Using an open-ended spanner to retain the camshaft whilst the sprocket retaining bolt is tightened to the specified torque

12.11 Refit the crankshaft sprocket making sure its timing marks are facing outwards

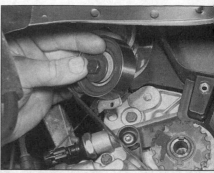

12.14 Slacken and remove the retaining bolt and remove the timing belt tensioner assembly

6 Tighten the sprocket retaining bolt to the specified torque whilst preventing rotation using the method employed on removal **(see illustration)**.
7 Refit the timing belt as described in Section 10 then (where necessary) refit the camshaft cover as described in Section 4.

Crankshaft sprocket

Removal

8 Remove the timing belt (see Section 10).
9 Slide the sprocket off from the end of the crankshaft, noting which way around it is fitted.

Refitting

10 Ensure the Woodruff key is correctly fitted to the crankshaft.
11 Align the sprocket with the crankshaft groove then slide the sprocket into position, making sure its timing mark is facing outwards **(see illustration)**.
12 Refit the timing belt (see Section 10).

Tensioner assembly

Removal

13 Remove the timing belt (see Section 10).
14 Slacken and remove the retaining bolt and remove the tensioner assembly from the oil pump **(see illustration)**.

Refitting

15 Fit the tensioner to the oil pump housing, making sure that the lug on the backplate is correctly located in the oil pump housing hole **(see illustration)**. Ensure the tensioner is correctly seated then refit the retaining bolt and tighten it to the specified torque.

---

13 Timing belt sprockets, tensioner and idler pulleys (DOHC) - removal and refitting

Camshaft sprockets

Note: *New sprocket retaining bolt(s) will be required on refitting.*

Removal

1 Remove the timing belt as described in Section 11.
2 The camshaft must be prevented from turning as the sprocket bolt is unscrewed, and this can be achieved in one of two ways as follows.
a) Make up a sprocket-holding tool using two lengths of steel strip (one long, the other short), and three nuts and bolts; one nut and bolt forms the pivot of a forked tool, with the remaining two nuts and

bolts at the tips of the 'forks' to engage with the sprocket spokes (see illustration 12.2).
b) Remove the camshaft cover as described in Section 5 and hold the camshaft with an open-ended spanner on the flats provided (see illustration).

3 Unscrew the retaining bolt and washer and remove the sprocket from the end of the camshaft. If the sprocket locating pin is a loose fit in the camshaft end, remove it and store it with the sprocket for safe-keeping.
4 If necessary, remove the remaining sprocket using the same method. On 1.6 litre models the inlet and exhaust sprockets are different; the exhaust camshaft sprocket can be easily identified by the lugs which activate the camshaft position sensor. On 1.8 and 2.0 litre models both sprockets are the same.

Refitting

5 Prior to refitting check the oil seal(s) for signs of damage or leakage. If necessary renew them.
6 Ensure the locating pin is in position in the camshaft end.
7 On 1.6 litre models refit the sprocket to the camshaft end, aligning its cut-out with the locating pin, and fit the washer and new retaining bolt **(see illustration)**. If both sprockets have been removed, ensure each

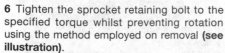

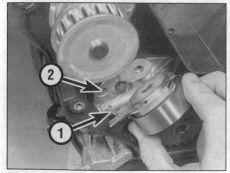

12.15 On refitting ensure the tensioner backplate lug (1) is correctly located in the oil pump housing hole (2)

13.2 Using an open-ended spanner to retain the camshaft whilst the sprocket retaining bolt is slackened

13.7 On 1.6 litre engines ensure the camshaft sprocket cut-out (arrowed) is correctly engaged with the locating pin

...procket is fitted to the correct shaft; the ...xhaust camshaft sprocket can be identified ... the lugs on the sprocket outer face which ...gger the camshaft position sensor.

...On 1.8 and 2.0 litre models both inlet and ...xhaust camshaft sprockets are the same but ...ach one is equipped with two locating pin ...ut-outs. If the sprocket is being fitted to the ...let camshaft, engage the locating pin in the ... cut-out, and if the sprocket is being fitted ... the exhaust camshaft, engage the locating ...in in the EX cut-out **(see illustration)**. Ensure ...e camshaft locating pin is engaged in the ...orrect sprocket cut-out then fit the washer ...nd new retaining bolt.

...On all models, retain the sprocket by the ...ethod used on removal, and tighten the ...ulley retaining bolt to the specified stage 1 ...orque setting then angle-tighten the bolt ...hrough the specified stage 2 angle, using a ...ocket and extension bar, and finally through ...e specified stage 3 angle **(see illustration)**. ...t is recommended that an angle-measuring ...auge is used during the final stages of the ...ightening, to ensure accuracy. If a gauge is ...ot available, use white paint to make ...lignment marks between the bolt head and ...ulley prior to tightening; the marks can then ...e used to check that the bolt has been ...otated through the correct angle.
...0 Refit the timing belt as described in ...Section 11 then (where necessary) refit the ...amshaft cover as described in Section 5.

Crankshaft sprocket - 1.6 litre ...models

Removal

11 Remove the timing belt as described in ...Section 11.
12 Slide the sprocket off from the end of the ...crankshaft, noting which way around it is ...itted.

Refitting

13 Align the sprocket locating key with the ...crankshaft groove then slide the sprocket into ...position, making sure its timing mark is facing ...outwards.
14 Refit the timing belt as described in ...Section 11.

Crankshaft sprocket - 1.8 and 2.0 litre models

Note: *A new crankshaft sprocket retaining bolt will be required on refitting.*

Removal

15 Remove the timing belt as described in Section 11.
16 Slacken the crankshaft sprocket retaining bolt. To prevent crankshaft rotation on manual transmission models, have an assistant select top gear and apply the brakes firmly. On automatic transmission models prevent rotation by removing one of the torque converter retaining bolts and bolting the driveplate to the transmission housing using a metal bar, spacers and suitable bolts.
17 Unscrew the retaining bolt and washer and remove the crankshaft sprocket from the end of the crankshaft.

Refitting

18 Align the sprocket location key with the crankshaft groove and slide the sprocket into position, ensuring its timing mark is facing outwards. Fit the washer and new retaining bolt.
19 Lock the crankshaft by the method used on removal, and tighten the sprocket retaining bolt to the specified stage 1 torque setting then angle-tighten the bolt through the specified stage 2 angle, using a socket and extension bar. It is recommended that an angle-measuring gauge is used during the final stages of the tightening, to ensure accuracy. If a gauge is not available, use white paint to make alignment marks between the bolt head and sprocket prior to tightening; the marks can then be used to check that the bolt has been rotated through the correct angle.
20 Refit the timing belt as described in Section 11.

Tensioner assembly

Removal

21 Remove the timing belt as described in Section 11.
22 Slacken and remove the retaining bolt and remove the tensioner assembly from the engine.

Refitting

23 Fit the tensioner to the engine, making sure that the lug on the backplate is correctly located in the oil pump housing hole. Ensure the tensioner is correctly seated then refit the retaining bolt. Using an Allen key, rotate the tensioner arm clockwise to its stop then securely tighten the retaining bolt.
24 Refit the timing belt as described in Section 11.

Idler pulleys

Removal

25 Remove the timing belt as described in Section 11.
26 Slacken and remove the retaining bolt(s) and remove the idler pulley(s) from the engine. On 1.8 and 2.0 litre models, if necessary, unbolt the pulley mounting bracket and remove it from the cylinder block.

Refitting

27 On 1.8 and 2.0 litre models refit the pulley mounting bracket (where removed) to the cylinder block and tighten its retaining bolts to the specified torque.
28 On all models, refit the idler pulley(s) and tighten the retaining bolt(s) to the specified torque.
29 Refit the timing belt as described in Section 11.

14 Engine right-hand front mounting - removal and refitting

1 Undo the mounting bolts and remove the torque support rod from the right-hand end of the engine unit.
2 Firmly apply the handbrake then jack up the front of the vehicle and support it on axle stands.
3 Support the weight of the engine/transmission using a trolley jack with a block of wood placed on its head.
4 Slacken and remove the nut and washer securing the mounting to the front subframe and the upper nut securing the mounting to its bracket.
5 Raise the engine/transmission unit slightly and manoeuvre the mounting out of position, noting which way up it is fitted. If necessary, undo the bolts securing the mounting bracket to the cylinder block/transmission (as applicable) then manoeuvre the mounting and bracket out of position. **Note:** *Take great care not to place any excess stress on the exhaust system when raising the engine. If necessary, disconnect the front pipe from the manifold.*
6 On reassembly, refit the mounting bracket (where removed) and tighten its bolts to the specified torque.
7 Locate the mounting in the subframe, ensuring it is fitted the correct way up, and lower the engine/transmission back down into

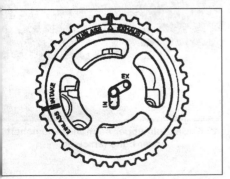

13.8 On 1.8 and 2.0 litre engines ensure the locating pin is engaged in the correct sprocket hole on refitting (see text)

13.9 Using a spanner to prevent camshaft rotation

14A

15.2 Removing the intake duct assembly - 1.8 and 2.0 litre models

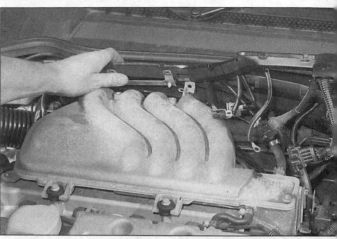

16.2 Free the wiring harness from the rear of the manifold

position. Refit the mounting nuts and tighten them to the specified torque.

8 Lower the vehicle to the ground then refit the torque support rod and tighten its mounting bolts to the specified torque.

15 Air cleaner assembly and intake ducts -
removal and refitting

Removal

1 To remove the air cleaner housing, slacken the retaining clip and disconnect the duct from the outlet then unscrew the retaining nuts and remove the housing from the engine compartment. On single-point injection models, it will be necessary to disconnect the vacuum hose and the hot air intake hose from the housing as it is removed.

2 The various ducts can be disconnected and removed once the retaining clips have been slackened. In some cases it will be necessary to disconnect breather hoses and wiring connectors to allow the duct to be removed; the duct may also be bolted to a support bracket **(see illustration)**.

Refitting

3 Refitting is the reverse of removal, making sure all the ducts are securely reconnected.

16 Inlet manifold upper section (1.6 litre DOHC) -
removal and refitting

1 Remove the oil filler cap then undo the retaining screws and lift off the cover from the top of the engine. Refit the oil filler cap.

2 Slacken and remove the bolts securing the wiring harness plastic tray to the rear of the inlet manifold. Starting at the front and working back, disconnect the wiring connectors from the oxygen sensor, DIS module, purge valve and the various connectors on the left-hand side of the manifold. Undo the nuts securing the earth

leads to the cylinder head and manifold then unclip the plastic tray and position it clear of the manifold **(see illustration)**.

3 Unclip the evaporative emission system purge valve from the left-hand end of the manifold and disconnect the valve hose from the manifold **(see illustration)**.

4 Slacken the union nut and disconnect the braking system vacuum servo hose from the manifold. Also disconnect the breather/vacuum hoses which are situated next to the servo unit union and disconnect the vacuum hose from the fuel pressure regulator **(see illustration)**.

5 Slacken the retaining clip securing the throttle housing connecting hose to the manifold upper section.

6 Slacken and remove the retaining nuts and bolts from the front and rear of the manifold upper section **(see illustration)**. Lift the manifold section out of position, freeing it from the connecting hose, and recover the gasket from the lower section.

7 Refitting is the reverse of removal.

16.3 Unclip the purge valve (arrowed) from the left-hand end of the manifold

16.4 Disconnect the vacuum and breather hose from the manifold

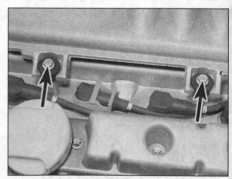

16.6 Manifold upper section-to-camshaft cover bolts (arrowed)

Chapter 14B
Vauxhall/Opel Vectra diesel 1995 to 1998

Contents

Specifications

Timing belt renewal interval . . . . Every 40 000 miles (65 000 km) or 4 years - whichever comes first

Note: *Although the interval for timing belt renewal is increased for later models, it is strongly recommended that this shorter interval is applied to vehicles which are subjected to intensive use, ie, mainly short journeys or a lot of stop-start driving. The actual belt renewal interval is therefore very much up to the individual owner. That being said, it is highly recommended to err on the side of safety, and renew the belt at this earlier interval, bearing in mind the drastic consequences resulting from belt failure.*

Torque wrench settings	Nm	lbf ft
Air conditioning compressor drivebelt centre bolt	45	33
Air conditioning compressor mounting bolt	35	26
Alternator fixings:		
M8 bolts	24	18
M10 bolts	48	35
Camshaft cover bolts	8	6
Camshaft sprocket bolts	10	7
Crankshaft pulley bolts	20	15
Crankshaft sprocket bolt	196	145
Engine/transmission mounting bolts:		
Right-hand mounting:		
Bracket-to-engine bolts	60	44
Mounting-to-bracket/subframe nuts	45	33
Upper bracket nuts	45	33
Left-hand mounting:		
Bracket-to-transmission bolts	60	44
Mounting-to-bracket/subframe nuts	45	33
Rear mounting:		
Bracket-to-transmission bolts	60	44
Mounting-to-bracket bolts	45	33
Mounting-to-subframe bolts	20	15
Injection pump sprocket nut	69	51
Oil pump sprocket nut	44	32
Power steering pump to bracket	25	19
Power steering pump pulley:*		
Stage 1	20	15
Stage 2	Angle-tighten 30°	
Stage 3	Angle-tighten 45°	
Power steering pump tensioner	40	30
Roadwheel bolts	110	81
Timing belt cover bolts	8	6
Timing belt idler pulley bolt	76	56
Timing belt tensioner pulley bolts	19	14

* **Note:** *The manufacturer states that all fasteners secured by the angle-tightening method must be renewed as a matter of course.*

1 Auxiliary drivebelt - removal, refitting and adjustment

1 Remove the air cleaner housing as described in Section 2 then proceed as described under the relevant sub-heading.

Air conditioning compressor drivebelt

2 Slacken the tensioner pulley centre bolt then release the belt tension by rotating the adjuster bolt. Slip the belt off from the pulleys and remove it from the engine.

3 Manoeuvre the belt into position and seat it on the pulleys. Tension the belt, using the adjuster bolt, so that under firm thumb pressure there is about 10 mm of movement at the mid-point on the longest run of the belt.

4 Once the belt is correctly tensioned, tighten the tensioner pulley centre bolt to the specified torque then refit the air cleaner housing.

Power steering pump drivebelt

5 On models with air conditioning, remove the compressor drivebelt (see paragraph 2).

6 Slacken the pump mounting bolts to release the drivebelt tension and slip the belt off from the pulleys.

7 Manoeuvre the belt into position and seat it on the pulleys. Tension the belt by positioning the pump so that under firm thumb pressure there is about 10 mm of movement at the mid-point on the longest run of the belt. Move the pump using an extension bar fitted to the square-section hole in the pump bracket and when its correctly positioned tighten its mounting bolts to the specified torque.

8 Refit the air conditioning compressor drivebelt (where fitted) then refit the air cleaner housing (see Section 2).

Alternator drivebelt

9 Firmly apply the handbrake then jack up the front of the vehicle and support it on axle stands. To improve access, remove the right-hand front roadwheel then undo the fasteners and remove the undercover from beneath the wing.

10 Remove the power steering pump drivebelt as described in this Section.

11 Slacken the alternator mounting bolts to release the drivebelt tension and slip the belt off the pulleys.

12 Manoeuvre the belt into position and seat it on the pulleys. Tension the belt by positioning the alternator so that under firm thumb pressure there is about 10 mm of movement at the mid-point on the longest run of the belt. Move the alternator using an extension bar fitted to the square-section hole in the bracket and when its correctly positioned tighten its mounting bolts to the specified torque.

13 Fit the power steering pump and (where necessary) the air conditioning compressor drivebelt as described in this Section.

14 Refit the undercover and lower the vehicle to the ground and tighten the wheel bolts to the specified torque.

2 Air cleaner assembly and intake ducts - removal and refitting

Removal

1 Slacken the retaining clip and detach the intake duct from the air cleaner housing. If necessary, slacken the other retaining clip then detach the duct from the manifold and remove it from the engine compartment.

2 Undo the nuts securing the air cleaner mountings to the body then free the housing from its air intake and remove the assembly from the engine compartment.

3 The remaining ducts linking the turbocharger, intercooler and inlet manifold can be removed once their retaining clips and (where necessary) bolts have been slackened.

Refitting

9 Refitting is the reverse of removal, ensuring that all intake ducts are properly reconnected and their retaining clips securely tightened.

3 Top dead centre (TDC) for No 1 piston - locating

Note: *If the engine is to be locked in position with No 1 piston at TDC on its compression stroke then a M6 and M8 bolt will be required.*

1 In its travel up and down its cylinder bore, Top Dead Centre (TDC) is the highest point that each piston reaches as the crankshaft rotates. While each piston reaches TDC both at the top of the compression stroke and again at the top of the exhaust stroke, for the purpose of timing the engine, TDC refers to the piston position (usually number 1) at the top of its compression stroke.

2 Number 1 piston (and cylinder) is at the right-hand (timing belt) end of the engine, and its TDC position is located as follows. Note that the crankshaft rotates clockwise when viewed from the right-hand side of the car.

3 Disconnect the battery negative terminal. To improve access to the crankshaft pulley, apply the handbrake, then jack up the front of

3.5 Align the crankshaft pulley notch with the pointer on the base of the oil pump cove[r]

the vehicle and support it on axle stands an[d] remove the right-hand front wheel.

4 Remove the timing belt upper cover a[s] described in Section 6.

5 Using a socket and extension bar on th[e] crankshaft sprocket bolt, rotate the cranksha[ft] until the notch on the crankshaft pulley rim i[s] aligned with the pointer on the base of the oi[l] pump cover **(see illustration)**. Once the mark i[s] correctly aligned, No 1 and 4 pistons are at TDC.

6 To determine which piston is at TDC on it[s] compression stroke, check the position of th[e] timing holes in the camshaft and injection pum[p] sprockets. When No 1 piston is at TDC on it[s] compression stroke, both sprocket holes will b[e] aligned with the threaded holes in the cylinde[r] head/block. If the timing holes are 180° out o[f] alignment then No 4 cylinder is at TDC on it[s] compression stroke; rotate the cranksha[ft] through a further complete turn (360°) to brin[g] No 1 cylinder to TDC on its compression stroke.

7 With No 1 piston at TDC on its compressio[n] stroke, if necessary, the camshaft and fue[l] injection pump sprockets can be locke[d] in position. Secure the camshaft sprocket i[n] position by screwing an M6 bolt through th[e] sprocket hole and into the hole in the cylinde[r] head, then lock the injection pump sprocket i[n] position by screwing an M8 bolt through th[e] arrowed sprocket hole - note that there ar[e] two holes in this sprocket; the correct hole fo[r] timing purposes being indicated by [a] stamped-in arrow mark - into the hole in th[e] cylinder block **(see illustrations)**.

3.7a Lock the camshaft sprocket in position by screwing an M6 bolt (arrowed) into position . . .

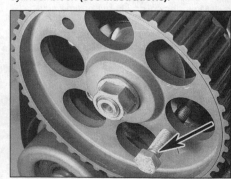

3.7b . . . and lock the injection pump sprocket using an M8 bolt (arrowed) screwed into the block through the sprocket's arrowed hole

4.2 Remove the semi-circular rubber seal from left-hand end of the cylinder head

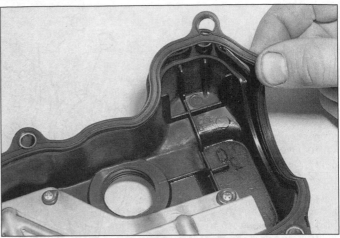

4.4 Ensure the seal is correctly located in the camshaft cover groove

4 Camshaft cover - removal and refitting

Removal

1 Release the retaining clip and disconnect the breather hose from the rear of the camshaft cover.
2 Slacken and remove the camshaft cover retaining bolts, along with their spacers, and lift the camshaft cover and seal away from the cylinder head. Remove the semi-circular rubber seal from the cut-out on the left-hand end of the cylinder head upper surface **(see illustration)**.
3 Examine the cover seal and semi-circular seal for signs of damage or deterioration and renew if necessary.

Refitting

4 Ensure the cover and cylinder head surfaces are clean and dry then fit the seal to the cover groove **(see illustration)**.
5 Apply a smear of sealant to the semi-

circular cut-out on the left-hand end of the cylinder head then fit the seal to the cut-out.
6 Carefully lower the cover into position, ensuring the seal remains correctly seated. Refit the spacers and retaining bolts and tighten them to the specified torque.
7 Reconnect the breather hose to the rear of the cover and secure in position with the retaining clip.

5 Crankshaft pulley - removal and refitting

Removal

1 Apply the handbrake, then jack up the front of the car and support it on axle stands. Remove the right-hand roadwheel.
2 Remove the auxiliary drivebelts as described in Section 1. Prior to removal, mark the direction of rotation on the belts to ensure each belt is refitted the same way around.
3 Slacken and remove the small retaining bolts securing the pulley to the crankshaft sprocket and remove the pulley from the engine. If necessary, prevent crankshaft rotation by holding the sprocket retaining bolt with a suitable socket.

Refitting

4 Refit the pulley to the crankshaft sprocket, aligning the pulley hole with the sprocket locating pin. Refit the pulley retaining bolts, tightening the to the specified torque **(see illustration)**.
5 Refit the auxiliary drivebelt as described in Section 1 using the mark made prior to removal to ensure the belt is fitted the correct way around.
6 Refit the roadwheel then lower the car to the ground and tighten the wheel bolts to the specified torque.

6 Timing belt covers - removal and refitting

Removal

Upper cover

1 Apply the handbrake, then jack up the front of the car and support it on axle stands. Remove the right-hand roadwheel.
2 Remove the air cleaner housing as described in Section 2.
3 Remove the auxiliary drivebelts as described in Section 1. Prior to removal, mark the direction of rotation on each belt to ensure it is refitted the same way around.
4 On models equipped with air conditioning, unbolt the compressor drivebelt tensioner and remove it from the engine.
5 Referring to Section 9, support the engine/transmission unit then undo the retaining nuts and lift off the bracket from the right-hand mounting assembly. Unbolt the mounting bracket and remove it from the side of the cylinder block.
6 Slacken and remove the retaining bolts and remove the timing belt upper cover from the engine, along with its rubber sealing strips. Inspect the sealing strips for signs of damage or deterioration and renew if necessary **(see illustration overleaf)**.

Lower cover

7 Remove the upper cover as described in paragraphs 1 to 6.
8 Remove the crankshaft pulley as described in Section 5.
9 Undo the retaining bolts and remove the lower cover from the engine unit, along with its rubber sealing strips. Inspect the sealing strips for signs of damage or deterioration and renew if necessary.

5.4 Refit the crankshaft pulley, locating it on the sprocket pin (arrowed), and refit the retaining bolts

14B

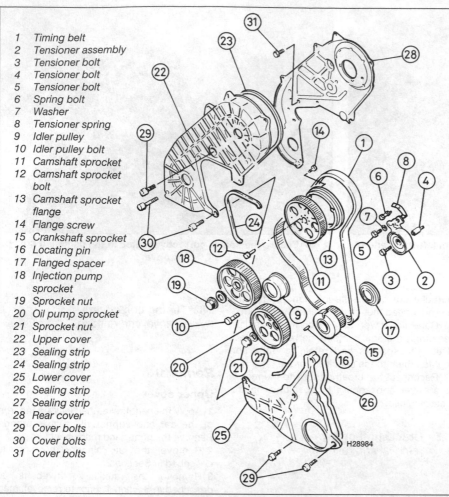

1 Timing belt
2 Tensioner assembly
3 Tensioner bolt
4 Tensioner bolt
5 Tensioner bolt
6 Spring bolt
7 Washer
8 Tensioner spring
9 Idler pulley
10 Idler pulley bolt
11 Camshaft sprocket
12 Camshaft sprocket bolt
13 Camshaft sprocket flange
14 Flange screw
15 Crankshaft sprocket
16 Locating pin
17 Flanged spacer
18 Injection pump sprocket
19 Sprocket nut
20 Oil pump sprocket
21 Sprocket nut
22 Upper cover
23 Sealing strip
24 Sealing strip
25 Lower cover
26 Sealing strip
27 Sealing strip
28 Rear cover
29 Cover bolts
30 Cover bolts
31 Cover bolts

6.6 Timing belt and associated components

Inner cover

10 Remove the timing belt as described in Section 7.

11 Remove the camshaft sprocket, the fuel injection pump sprocket, the timing belt idler pulley and the tensioner assembly as described in Section 8.

12 Unbolt the inner cover from the cylinder head/block and remove it from the engine unit.

Refitting

13 Refitting is the reverse of removal, ensuring the cover sealing strips are correctly fitted and all retaining bolts are tightened to the specified torque **(see illustration)**.

7 Timing belt - removal and refitting

Note: *The timing belt must be removed an refitted with the engine cold.*

Removal

1 Position No 1 cylinder at TDC on it compression stroke as described in Section ? Lock the camshaft and injection pum sprockets in position by screwing the bolt into the threaded holes in the cylinde head/block.

2 Remove the crankshaft pulley as describe in Section 5.

3 Unbolt the timing belt lower cover an remove it along with its rubber sealing strips.

4 Slacken the timing belt tensioner retainin bolts then carefully unhook the tensione spring from its locating pins.

5 Slide the timing belt off from its sprocket and remove it from the engine. If the belt is t be re-used, use white paint or similar to mar the direction of rotation on the belt. **Do no** rotate the crankshaft until the timing belt ha been refitted.

6 If signs of oil contamination are found, trac the source of the oil leak and rectify it, the wash down the engine timing belt area and a related components to remove all traces of oi

Refitting

7 On reassembly, thoroughly clean the timin belt sprockets and ensure the camshaft an injection pump sprockets are locked correctl in position. Temporarily refit the crankshaf pulley to the sprocket and check tha the pulley cut-out is still aligned with the pointer on the oil pump cover; the mark on the crankshaft sprocket should also be aligne with the mark on the oil pump cover **(see illustration)**.

8 Remove the pulley and fit the timing belt over the crankshaft, oil pump, injection pump and camshaft sprockets, ensuring that the belt rear run is taut (ie, all slack is on the

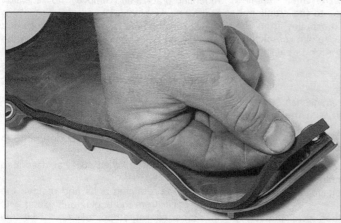

6.13 On refitting ensure the sealing strips are correctly seated in the cover grooves

7.7 Check that the crankshaft sprocket cut-out is aligned with the mark on the oil pump cover (arrowed)

7.11a Rotate the crankshaft 60° backwards to adjust the timing belt tension . . .

7.11b . . . then securely tighten the tensioner pulley bolts

tensioner pulley side of the belt). Do not twist the belt sharply while refitting it. Ensure that the belt teeth are correctly seated centrally in the sprockets, and that the timing marks remain in alignment. If a used belt is being refitted, ensure that the arrow mark made on removal points in the normal direction of rotation, as before.

9 Tension the belt by refitting the tensioner pulley spring, ensuring it is correctly located on its pins.

10 Check that the crankshaft sprocket timing mark is still correctly positioned then unscrew the locking bolts from the injection pump and camshaft sprockets.

11 Slacken the tensioner pulley retaining bolt then rotate the crankshaft pulley approximately 60° **backwards** (anti-clockwise) to automatically adjust the timing belt tension. Hold the crankshaft pulley stationary and securely tighten the tensioner pulley retaining bolt **(see illustrations)**.

12 Rotate the crankshaft smoothly through two complete turns (720°) in the normal direction of rotation to settle the timing belt in position. Realign the crankshaft sprocket timing mark and check that the camshaft and injection pump sprocket locking bolts can be refitted.

13 Slacken the tensioner pulley retaining bolt then rotate the crankshaft pulley approximately 60° **backwards** (anti-clockwise) to automatically adjust the timing belt tension. Hold the crankshaft pulley stationary and tighten the tensioner pulley retaining bolts to the specified torque.

14 Return the crankshaft to TDC and make a final check that the sprocket timing mark/holes are correctly positioned.

15 Refit the timing belt covers then refit the crankshaft pulley as described in Sections 5 and 6.

8 Timing belt tensioner and sprockets - removal and refitting

Camshaft sprocket

Removal

1 Remove the timing belt as described in Section 7.

2 Screw the sprocket locking bolt fully into position then slacken and remove the sprocket retaining bolts, using the locking bolt to prevent rotation.

3 Unscrew the locking bolt and remove the sprocket from the end of the camshaft, noting which way around it is fitted **(see illustration)**. If the sprocket locating pin is a loose fit, remove it from the camshaft end and store it with the sprocket for safe-keeping.

Refitting

4 Ensure the locating pin is in position then refit the sprocket to the camshaft end aligning its locating hole with the pin.

5 Refit the sprocket retaining bolts then align

the timing hole with the cylinder head hole and screw in the lock bolt. Use the locking bolt to retain the sprocket and tighten the sprocket bolts to the specified torque.

6 Refit the timing belt as described in Section 7.

Injection pump sprocket

Note: *The sprocket is a tapered-fit on the injection pump shaft and a suitable puller may be needed to free it from the shaft.*

Removal

7 Remove the timing belt as described in Section 7.

8 In order to prevent sprocket rotation as the retaining nut is slackened, a sprocket holding tool will be required. In the absence of the special Vauxhall tool, a suitable alternative can be made using two lengths of steel strip (one long, the other short), and three nuts and bolts; one nut and bolt forms the pivot of a forked tool, with the remaining two nuts and bolts at the tips of the 'forks' to engage with the sprocket spokes **(see illustration)**.

9 Unscrew the pulley locking bolt and slacken the sprocket retaining nut whilst using the tool to prevent rotation. **Do not** be tempted to use the locking bolt to prevent sprocket rotation.

8.3 Removing the camshaft sprocket (locating pin arrowed)

8.8 Using a sprocket holding tool to prevent rotation as the injection pump sprocket nut is slackened

14B

8.10 Remove the sprocket and recover the Woodruff key from the injection pump shaft

8.17a Unscrew the retaining bolt and washer . . .

8.17b . . . and remove the crankshaft sprocket from the engine

10 Remove the sprocket from the injection pump shaft, noting which way around it is fitted. If the Woodruff key is a loose fit in the pump shaft, remove it and store it with the sprocket for safe-keeping **(see illustration)**.

Refitting

11 Ensure the Woodruff key is correctly fitted to the pump shaft then refit the sprocket, aligning the sprocket groove with the key.
12 Refit the retaining nut and tighten it to the specified torque whilst using the holding tool to prevent rotation.
13 Align the sprocket timing hole with the threaded hole in the cylinder block and screw in the locking bolt.
14 Refit the timing belt as described in Section 7.

Crankshaft sprocket

Removal

15 Remove the timing belt as described in Section 7.
16 Slacken the crankshaft sprocket retaining bolt. To prevent crankshaft rotation, have an assistant select top gear and apply the brakes firmly.
17 Unscrew the retaining bolt and washer and remove the crankshaft sprocket from the end of the crankshaft. If the sprocket is a tight fit, draw it off of the crankshaft using a suitable puller **(see illustrations)**. If the

Woodruff key is a loose fit in the crankshaft, remove it and store it with the sprocket for safe-keeping.
18 Slide the flanged spacer off of the crankshaft, noting which way around it is fitted **(see illustration)**.

Refitting

19 Refit the flanged spacer to the crankshaft with its convex surface facing away from the oil pump housing.
20 Ensure the Woodruff key is correctly fitted then slide on the crankshaft sprocket aligning its groove with the key.
21 Refit the retaining bolt and washer then lock the crankshaft by the method used on removal, and tighten the sprocket retaining bolt to the specified stage torque setting.
22 Refit the timing belt as described in Section 7.

Oil pump sprocket

Removal

23 Remove the timing belt as described in Section 7.
24 Prevent the oil pump sprocket from rotating using a socket and extension bar fitted to one of the oil pump cover bolts then slacken and remove the sprocket retaining nut **(see illustration)**.
25 Remove the sprocket from the oil pump shaft, noting which way around it is fitted.

Refitting

26 Refit the sprocket, aligning it with the fla on the pump shaft, and fit the retaining nu Tighten the sprocket retaining nut to th specified torque, using the socket an extension bar to prevent rotation.
27 Refit the timing belt as described i Section 7.

Tensioner assembly

Removal

28 Remove the timing belt as described i Section 7.
29 Unscrew the retaining bolts and remove the tensioner assembly from the engine **(se illustration)**.

Refitting

30 Fit the tensioner assembly to the engine tightening its retaining bolts by hand only.
31 Refit the timing belt as described i Section 7.

Idler pulley

Removal

32 Remove the timing belt as described i Section 7.
33 Slacken and remove the retaining bolt and

8.18 Slide off the flanged spacer noting which way around it is fitted

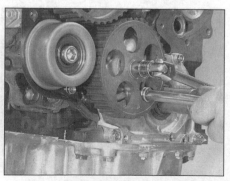

8.24 Lock the oil pump sprocket in position using a socket and extension bar then unscrew the sprocket retaining nut

8.29 Unscrew the retaining bolts and remove the tensioner assembly

8.33 Removing the idler pulley

move the idler pulley from the engine **(see illustration).**

Refitting

4 Refit the idler pulley and tighten the retaining bolt to the specified torque.

5 Refit the timing belt as described in Section 7.

9 Engine right-hand mounting
- removal and refitting

Removal

1 Remove the air cleaner housing and intake duct assembly as described in Section 2.

2 Support the weight of the engine/ transmission using a trolley jack with a block of wood placed on its head.

3 Slacken and remove the nuts securing the mounting bracket to the mounting and engine bracket and lift off the bracket. If necessary, the mounting bracket can then be unbolted from the side of the cylinder block.

4 Raise the engine/transmission unit slightly then unscrew the mounting lower retaining nut and remove the mounting from the body. **Note:** *Take great care not to place any excess stress on the exhaust system when raising the engine. If necessary, disconnect the front pipe from the manifold.*

Refitting

5 Fit the mounting to the vehicle body and tighten its nut to the specified torque.

6 Refit the engine bracket (where removed) to the cylinder block and tighten its bolts to the specified torque. Then refit the mounting bracket to the top of the mounting/ engine bracket and tighten its nuts to the specified torque.

14B

Notes

Whenever servicing, repair or overhaul work carried out on the car or its components, observe the following procedures and instructions. This will assist in carrying out the operation efficiently and to a professional standard of workmanship.

Joint mating faces and gaskets

When separating components at their mating faces, never insert screwdrivers or similar implements into the joint between the faces in order to prise them apart. This can cause severe damage which results in oil leaks, coolant leaks, etc upon reassembly. Separation is usually achieved by tapping along the joint with a soft-faced hammer in order to break the seal. However, note that this method may not be suitable where dowels are used for component location.

Where a gasket is used between the mating faces of two components, a new one must be fitted on reassembly; fit it dry unless otherwise stated in the repair procedure. Make sure that the mating faces are clean and dry, with all traces of old gasket removed. When cleaning a joint face, use a tool which is unlikely to score or damage the face, and remove any burrs or nicks with an oilstone or fine file.

Make sure that tapped holes are cleaned with a pipe cleaner, and keep them free of jointing compound, if this is being used, unless specifically instructed otherwise.

Ensure that all orifices, channels or pipes are clear, and blow through them, preferably using compressed air.

Oil seals

Oil seals can be removed by levering them out with a wide flat-bladed screwdriver or similar implement. Alternatively, a number of self-tapping screws may be screwed into the seal, and these used as a purchase for pliers or some similar device in order to pull the seal free.

Whenever an oil seal is removed from its working location, either individually or as part of an assembly, it should be renewed.

The very fine sealing lip of the seal is easily damaged, and will not seal if the surface it contacts is not completely clean and free from scratches, nicks or grooves. If the original sealing surface of the component cannot be restored, and the manufacturer has not made provision for slight relocation of the seal relative to the sealing surface, the component should be renewed.

Protect the lips of the seal from any surface which may damage them in the course of fitting. Use tape or a conical sleeve where possible. Lubricate the seal lips with oil before fitting and, on dual-lipped seals, fill the space between the lips with grease.

Unless otherwise stated, oil seals must be fitted with their sealing lips toward the lubricant to be sealed.

Use a tubular drift or block of wood of the appropriate size to install the seal and, if the seal housing is shouldered, drive the seal down to the shoulder. If the seal housing is unshouldered, the seal should be fitted with its face flush with the housing top face (unless otherwise instructed).

Screw threads and fastenings

Seized nuts, bolts and screws are quite a common occurrence where corrosion has set in, and the use of penetrating oil or releasing fluid will often overcome this problem if the offending item is soaked for a while before attempting to release it. The use of an impact driver may also provide a means of releasing such stubborn fastening devices, when used in conjunction with the appropriate screwdriver bit or socket. If none of these methods works, it may be necessary to resort to the careful application of heat, or the use of a hacksaw or nut splitter device.

Studs are usually removed by locking two nuts together on the threaded part, and then using a spanner on the lower nut to unscrew the stud. Studs or bolts which have broken off below the surface of the component in which they are mounted can sometimes be removed using a stud extractor. Always ensure that a blind tapped hole is completely free from oil, grease, water or other fluid before installing the bolt or stud. Failure to do this could cause the housing to crack due to the hydraulic action of the bolt or stud as it is screwed in.

When tightening a castellated nut to accept a split pin, tighten the nut to the specified torque, where applicable, and then tighten further to the next split pin hole. Never slacken the nut to align the split pin hole, unless stated in the repair procedure.

When checking or retightening a nut or bolt to a specified torque setting, slacken the nut or bolt by a quarter of a turn, and then retighten to the specified setting. However, this should not be attempted where angular tightening has been used.

For some screw fastenings, notably cylinder head bolts or nuts, torque wrench settings are no longer specified for the latter stages of tightening, "angle-tightening" being called up instead. Typically, a fairly low torque wrench setting will be applied to the bolts/nuts in the correct sequence, followed by one or more stages of tightening through specified angles.

Locknuts, locktabs and washers

Any fastening which will rotate against a component or housing during tightening should always have a washer between it and the relevant component or housing.

Spring or split washers should always be renewed when they are used to lock a critical component such as a big-end bearing retaining bolt or nut. Locktabs which are folded over to retain a nut or bolt should always be renewed.

Self-locking nuts can be re-used in non-critical areas, providing resistance can be felt when the locking portion passes over the bolt or stud thread. However, it should be noted that self-locking stiffnuts tend to lose their effectiveness after long periods of use, and should then be renewed as a matter of course.

Split pins must always be replaced with new ones of the correct size for the hole.

When thread-locking compound is found on the threads of a fastener which is to be re-used, it should be cleaned off with a wire brush and solvent, and fresh compound applied on reassembly.

Special tools

Some repair procedures in this manual entail the use of special tools such as a press, two or three-legged pullers, spring compressors, etc. Wherever possible, suitable readily-available alternatives to the manufacturer's special tools are described, and are shown in use. In some instances, where no alternative is possible, it has been necessary to resort to the use of a manufacturer's tool, and this has been done for reasons of safety as well as the efficient completion of the repair operation. Unless you are highly-skilled and have a thorough understanding of the procedures described, never attempt to bypass the use of any special tool when the procedure described specifies its use. Not only is there a very great risk of personal injury, but expensive damage could be caused to the components involved.

Environmental considerations

When disposing of used engine oil, brake fluid, antifreeze, etc, give due consideration to any detrimental environmental effects. Do not, for instance, pour any of the above liquids down drains into the general sewage system, or onto the ground to soak away. Many local council refuse tips provide a facility for waste oil disposal, as do some garages. If none of these facilities are available, consult your local Environmental Health Department, or the National Rivers Authority, for further advice.

With the universal tightening-up of legislation regarding the emission of environmentally-harmful substances from motor vehicles, most vehicles have tamperproof devices fitted to the main adjustment points of the fuel system. These devices are primarily designed to prevent unqualified persons from adjusting the fuel/air mixture, with the chance of a consequent increase in toxic emissions. If such devices are found during servicing or overhaul, they should, wherever possible, be renewed or refitted in accordance with the manufacturer's requirements or current legislation.

OIL CARE

FOLLOW THE CODE

OIL BANK LINE
0800 66 33 66

Note: It is antisocial and illegal to dump oil down the drain. To find the location of your local oil recycling bank, call this number free.

Introduction

A selection of good tools is a fundamental requirement for anyone contemplating the maintenance and repair of a motor vehicle. For the owner who does not possess any, their purchase will prove a considerable expense, offsetting some of the savings made by doing-it-yourself. However, provided that the tools purchased meet the relevant national safety standards and are of good quality, they will last for many years and prove an extremely worthwhile investment.

To help the average owner to decide which tools are needed to carry out the various tasks detailed in this manual, we have compiled three lists of tools under the following headings: *Maintenance and minor repair, Repair and overhaul*, and *Special*. Newcomers to practical mechanics should start off with the *Maintenance and minor repair* tool kit, and confine themselves to the simpler jobs around the vehicle. Then, as confidence and experience grow, more difficult tasks can be undertaken, with extra tools being purchased as, and when, they are needed. In this way, a *Maintenance and minor repair* tool kit can be built up into a *Repair and overhaul* tool kit over a considerable period of time, without any major cash outlays. The experienced do-it-yourselfer will have a tool kit good enough for most repair and overhaul procedures, and will add tools from the *Special* category when it is felt that the expense is justified by the amount of use to which these tools will be put.

Maintenance and minor repair tool kit

The tools given in this list should be considered as a minimum requirement if routine maintenance, servicing and minor repair operations are to be undertaken. We recommend the purchase of combination spanners (ring one end, open-ended the other); although more expensive than open-ended ones, they do give the advantages of both types of spanner.

☐ *Combination spanners:*
  Metric - 8 to 19 mm inclusive
☐ *Adjustable spanner - 35 mm jaw (approx.)*
☐ *Spark plug spanner (with rubber insert) - petrol models*
☐ *Spark plug gap adjustment tool - petrol models*
☐ *Set of feeler gauges*
☐ *Brake bleed nipple spanner*
☐ *Screwdrivers:*
  Flat blade - 100 mm long x 6 mm dia
  Cross blade - 100 mm long x 6 mm dia
  Torx - various sizes (not all vehicles)
☐ *Combination pliers*
☐ *Hacksaw (junior)*
☐ *Tyre pump*
☐ *Tyre pressure gauge*
☐ *Oil can*
☐ *Oil filter removal tool*
☐ *Fine emery cloth*
☐ *Wire brush (small)*
☐ *Funnel (medium size)*
☐ *Sump drain plug key (not all vehicles)*

Repair and overhaul tool kit

These tools are virtually essential for anyone undertaking any major repairs to a motor vehicle, and are additional to those given in the *Maintenance and minor repair list*. Included in this list is a comprehensive set of sockets. Although these are expensive, they will be found invaluable as they are so versatile - particularly if various drives are included in the set. We recommend the half-inch square-drive type, as this can be used with most proprietary torque wrenches.

The tools in this list will sometimes need to be supplemented by tools from the *Special list*.

☐ *Sockets (or box spanners) to cover range in previous list (including Torx sockets)*
☐ *Reversible ratchet drive (for use with sockets)*
☐ *Extension piece, 250 mm (for use with sockets)*
☐ *Universal joint (for use with sockets)*
☐ *Flexible handle or "breaker bar" (for use with sockets)*
☐ *Torque wrench (for use with sockets)*
☐ *Self-locking grips*
☐ *Ball pein hammer*
☐ *Soft-faced mallet (plastic or rubber)*
☐ *Screwdrivers:*
  Flat blade - long & sturdy, short (chubby), and narrow (electrician's) types
  Cross blade – long & sturdy, and short (chubby) types
☐ *Pliers:*
  Long-nosed
  Side cutters (electrician's)
  Circlip (internal and external)
☐ *Cold chisel - 25 mm*
☐ *Scriber*
☐ *Scraper*
☐ *Centre-punch*
☐ *Pin punch*
☐ *Hacksaw*
☐ *Brake hose clamp*
☐ *Brake/clutch bleeding kit*
☐ *Selection of twist drills*
☐ *Steel rule/straight-edge*
☐ *Allen keys (inc. splined/Torx type)*
☐ *Selection of files*
☐ *Wire brush*
☐ *Axle stands*
☐ *Jack (strong trolley or hydraulic type)*
☐ *Light with extension lead*
☐ *Universal electrical multi-meter*

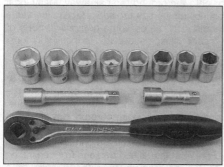

Sockets and reversible ratchet drive

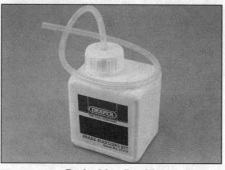

Brake bleeding kit

Torx key, socket and bit

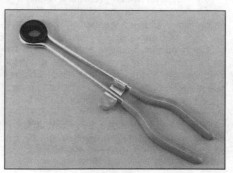

Hose clamp

Angular-tightening gauge

Special tools

The tools in this list are those which are not used regularly, are expensive to buy, or which need to be used in accordance with their manufacturers' instructions. Unless relatively difficult mechanical jobs are undertaken frequently, it will not be economic to buy many of these tools. Where this is the case, you could consider clubbing together with friends (or joining a motorists' club) to make a joint purchase, or borrowing the tools against a deposit from a local garage or tool hire specialist. It is worth noting that many of the larger DIY superstores now carry a large range of special tools for hire at modest rates.

The following list contains only those tools and instruments freely available to the public, and not those special tools produced by the vehicle manufacturer specifically for its dealer network. You will find occasional references to these manufacturers' special tools in the text of this manual. Generally, an alternative method of doing the job without the vehicle manufacturers' special tool is given. However, sometimes there is no alternative to using them. Where this is the case and the relevant tool cannot be bought or borrowed, you will have to entrust the work to a dealer.

- ☐ Angular-tightening gauge
- ☐ Valve spring compressor
- ☐ Valve grinding tool
- ☐ Piston ring compressor
- ☐ Piston ring removal/installation tool
- ☐ Cylinder bore hone
- ☐ Balljoint separator
- ☐ Coil spring compressors (where applicable)
- ☐ Two/three-legged hub and bearing puller
- ☐ Impact screwdriver
- ☐ Micrometer and/or vernier calipers
- ☐ Dial gauge
- ☐ Stroboscopic timing light
- ☐ Dwell angle meter/tachometer
- ☐ Fault code reader
- ☐ Cylinder compression gauge
- ☐ Hand-operated vacuum pump and gauge
- ☐ Clutch plate alignment set
- ☐ Brake shoe steady spring cup removal tool
- ☐ Bush and bearing removal/installation set
- ☐ Stud extractors
- ☐ Tap and die set
- ☐ Lifting tackle
- ☐ Trolley jack

Buying tools

Reputable motor accessory shops and superstores often offer excellent quality tools at discount prices, so it pays to shop around.

Remember, you don't have to buy the most expensive items on the shelf, but it is always advisable to steer clear of the very cheap tools. Beware of 'bargains' offered on market stalls or at car boot sales. There are plenty of good tools around at reasonable prices, but always aim to purchase items which meet the relevant national safety standards. If in doubt, ask the proprietor or manager of the shop for advice before making a purchase.

Care and maintenance of tools

Having purchased a reasonable tool kit, it is necessary to keep the tools in a clean and serviceable condition. After use, always wipe off any dirt, grease and metal particles using a clean, dry cloth, before putting the tools away. Never leave them lying around after they have been used. A simple tool rack on the garage or workshop wall for items such as screwdrivers and pliers is a good idea. Store all normal spanners and sockets in a metal box. Any measuring instruments, gauges, meters, etc, must be carefully stored where they cannot be damaged or become rusty.

Take a little care when tools are used. Hammer heads inevitably become marked, and screwdrivers lose the keen edge on their blades from time to time. A little timely attention with emery cloth or a file will soon restore items like this to a good finish.

Working facilities

Not to be forgotten when discussing tools is the workshop itself. If anything more than routine maintenance is to be carried out, a suitable working area becomes essential.

It is appreciated that many an owner-mechanic is forced by circumstances to remove an engine or similar item without the benefit of a garage or workshop. Having done this, any repairs should always be done under the cover of a roof.

Wherever possible, any dismantling should be done on a clean, flat workbench or table at a suitable working height.

Any workbench needs a vice; one with a jaw opening of 100 mm is suitable for most jobs. As mentioned previously, some clean dry storage space is also required for tools, as well as for any lubricants, cleaning fluids, touch-up paints etc, which become necessary.

Another item which may be required, and which has a much more general usage, is an electric drill with a chuck capacity of at least 8 mm. This, together with a good range of twist drills, is virtually essential for fitting accessories.

Last, but not least, always keep a supply of old newspapers and clean, lint-free rags available, and try to keep any working area as clean as possible.

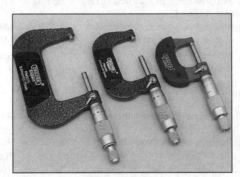

Micrometers

Dial test indicator ("dial gauge")

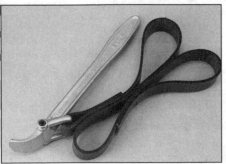

Strap wrench

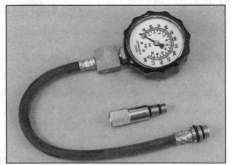

Compression tester

Fault code reader

Conversion Factors

Length (distance)

Inches (in)	x 25.4	= Millimetres (mm)	x 0.0394	= Inches (in)
Feet (ft)	x 0.305	= Metres (m)	x 3.281	= Feet (ft)
Miles	x 1.609	= Kilometres (km)	x 0.621	= Miles

Volume (capacity)

Cubic inches (cu in; in³)	x 16.387	= Cubic centimetres (cc; cm³)	x 0.061	= Cubic inches (cu in; in³)
Imperial pints (Imp pt)	x 0.568	= Litres (l)	x 1.76	= Imperial pints (Imp pt)
Imperial quarts (Imp qt)	x 1.137	= Litres (l)	x 0.88	= Imperial quarts (Imp qt)
Imperial quarts (Imp qt)	x 1.201	= US quarts (US qt)	x 0.833	= Imperial quarts (Imp qt)
US quarts (US qt)	x 0.946	= Litres (l)	x 1.057	= US quarts (US qt)
Imperial gallons (Imp gal)	x 4.546	= Litres (l)	x 0.22	= Imperial gallons (Imp gal)
Imperial gallons (Imp gal)	x 1.201	= US gallons (US gal)	x 0.833	= Imperial gallons (Imp gal)
US gallons (US gal)	x 3.785	= Litres (l)	x 0.264	= US gallons (US gal)

Mass (weight)

Ounces (oz)	x 28.35	= Grams (g)	x 0.035	= Ounces (oz)
Pounds (lb)	x 0.454	= Kilograms (kg)	x 2.205	= Pounds (lb)

Force

Ounces-force (ozf; oz)	x 0.278	= Newtons (N)	x 3.6	= Ounces-force (ozf; oz)
Pounds-force (lbf; lb)	x 4.448	= Newtons (N)	x 0.225	= Pounds-force (lbf; lb)
Newtons (N)	x 0.1	= Kilograms-force (kgf; kg)	x 9.81	= Newtons (N)

Pressure

Pounds-force per square inch (psi; lbf/in²; lb/in²)	x 0.070	= Kilograms-force per square centimetre (kgf/cm²; kg/cm²)	x 14.223	= Pounds-force per square inch (psi; lbf/in²; lb/in²)
Pounds-force per square inch (psi; lbf/in²; lb/in²)	x 0.068	= Atmospheres (atm)	x 14.696	= Pounds-force per square inch (psi; lbf/in²; lb/in²)
Pounds-force per square inch (psi; lbf/in²; lb/in²)	x 0.069	= Bars	x 14.5	= Pounds-force per square inch (psi; lbf/in²; lb/in²)
Pounds-force per square inch (psi; lbf/in²; lb/in²)	x 6.895	= Kilopascals (kPa)	x 0.145	= Pounds-force per square inch (psi; lbf/in²; lb/in²)
Kilopascals (kPa)	x 0.01	= Kilograms-force per square centimetre (kgf/cm²; kg/cm²)	x 98.1	= Kilopascals (kPa)
Millibar (mbar)	x 100	= Pascals (Pa)	x 0.01	= Millibar (mbar)
Millibar (mbar)	x 0.0145	= Pounds-force per square inch (psi; lbf/in²; lb/in²)	x 68.947	= Millibar (mbar)
Millibar (mbar)	x 0.75	= Millimetres of mercury (mmHg)	x 1.333	= Millibar (mbar)
Millibar (mbar)	x 0.401	= Inches of water (inH₂O)	x 2.491	= Millibar (mbar)
Millimetres of mercury (mmHg)	x 0.535	= Inches of water (inH₂O)	x 1.868	= Millimetres of mercury (mmHg)
Inches of water (inH₂O)	x 0.036	= Pounds-force per square inch (psi; lbf/in²; lb/in²)	x 27.68	= Inches of water (inH₂O)

Torque (moment of force)

Pounds-force inches (lbf in; lb in)	x 1.152	= Kilograms-force centimetre (kgf cm; kg cm)	x 0.868	= Pounds-force inches (lbf in; lb in)
Pounds-force inches (lbf in; lb in)	x 0.113	= Newton metres (Nm)	x 8.85	= Pounds-force inches (lbf in; lb in)
Pounds-force inches (lbf in; lb in)	x 0.083	= Pounds-force feet (lbf ft; lb ft)	x 12	= Pounds-force inches (lbf in; lb in)
Pounds-force feet (lbf ft; lb ft)	x 0.138	= Kilograms-force metres (kgf m; kg m)	x 7.233	= Pounds-force feet (lbf ft; lb ft)
Pounds-force feet (lbf ft; lb ft)	x 1.356	= Newton metres (Nm)	x 0.738	= Pounds-force feet (lbf ft; lb ft)
Newton metres (Nm)	x 0.102	= Kilograms-force metres (kgf m; kg m)	x 9.804	= Newton metres (Nm)

Power

Horsepower (hp)	x 745.7	= Watts (W)	x 0.0013	= Horsepower (hp)

Velocity (speed)

Miles per hour (miles/hr; mph)	x 1.609	= Kilometres per hour (km/hr; kph)	x 0.621	= Miles per hour (miles/hr; mph)

Fuel consumption*

Miles per gallon (mpg)	x 0.354	= Kilometres per litre (km/l)	x 2.825	= Miles per gallon (mpg)

Temperature

Degrees Fahrenheit = (°C x 1.8) + 32   Degrees Celsius (Degrees Centigrade; °C) = (°F - 32) x 0.56

It is common practice to convert from miles per gallon (mpg) to litres/100 kilometres (l/100km), where mpg x l/100 km = 282

A

ABS (Anti-lock brake system) A system, usually electronically controlled, that senses incipient wheel lockup during braking and relieves hydraulic pressure at wheels that are about to skid.

Air bag An inflatable bag hidden in the steering wheel (driver's side) or the dash or glovebox (passenger side). In a head-on collision, the bags inflate, preventing the driver and front passenger from being thrown forward into the steering wheel or windscreen.

Air cleaner A metal or plastic housing, containing a filter element, which removes dust and dirt from the air being drawn into the engine.

Air filter element The actual filter in an air cleaner system, usually manufactured from pleated paper and requiring renewal at regular intervals.

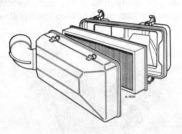

Air filter

Allen key A hexagonal wrench which fits into a recessed hexagonal hole.

Alligator clip A long-nosed spring-loaded metal clip with meshing teeth. Used to make temporary electrical connections.

Alternator A component in the electrical system which converts mechanical energy from a drivebelt into electrical energy to charge the battery and to operate the starting system, ignition system and electrical accessories.

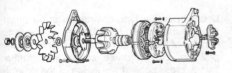

Alternator (exploded view)

Ampere (amp) A unit of measurement for the flow of electric current. One amp is the amount of current produced by one volt acting through a resistance of one ohm.

Anaerobic sealer A substance used to prevent bolts and screws from loosening. Anaerobic means that it does not require oxygen for activation. The Loctite brand is widely used.

Antifreeze A substance (usually ethylene glycol) mixed with water, and added to a vehicle's cooling system, to prevent freezing of the coolant in winter. Antifreeze also contains chemicals to inhibit corrosion and the formation of rust and other deposits that would tend to clog the radiator and coolant passages and reduce cooling efficiency.

Anti-seize compound A coating that reduces the risk of seizing on fasteners that are subjected to high temperatures, such as exhaust manifold bolts and nuts.

Anti-seize compound

Asbestos A natural fibrous mineral with great heat resistance, commonly used in the composition of brake friction materials. Asbestos is a health hazard and the dust created by brake systems should never be inhaled or ingested.

Axle A shaft on which a wheel revolves, or which revolves with a wheel. Also, a solid beam that connects the two wheels at one end of the vehicle. An axle which also transmits power to the wheels is known as a live axle.

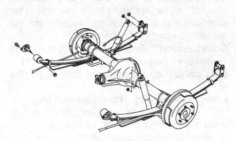

Axle assembly

Axleshaft A single rotating shaft, on either side of the differential, which delivers power from the final drive assembly to the drive wheels. Also called a driveshaft or a halfshaft.

B

Ball bearing An anti-friction bearing consisting of a hardened inner and outer race with hardened steel balls between two races.

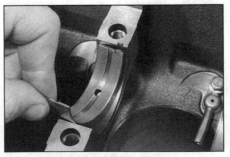

Bearing

Bearing The curved surface on a shaft or in a bore, or the part assembled into either, that permits relative motion between them with minimum wear and friction.

Big-end bearing The bearing in the end of the connecting rod that's attached to the crankshaft.

Bleed nipple A valve on a brake wheel cylinder, caliper or other hydraulic component that is opened to purge the hydraulic system of air. Also called a bleed screw.

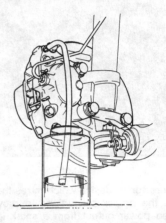

Brake bleeding

Brake bleeding Procedure for removing air from lines of a hydraulic brake system.

Brake disc The component of a disc brake that rotates with the wheels.

Brake drum The component of a drum brake that rotates with the wheels.

Brake linings The friction material which contacts the brake disc or drum to retard the vehicle's speed. The linings are bonded or riveted to the brake pads or shoes.

Brake pads The replaceable friction pads that pinch the brake disc when the brakes are applied. Brake pads consist of a friction material bonded or riveted to a rigid backing plate.

Brake shoe The crescent-shaped carrier to which the brake linings are mounted and which forces the lining against the rotating drum during braking.

Braking systems For more information on braking systems, consult the *Haynes Automotive Brake Manual*.

Breaker bar A long socket wrench handle providing greater leverage.

Bulkhead The insulated partition between the engine and the passenger compartment.

C

Caliper The non-rotating part of a disc-brake assembly that straddles the disc and carries the brake pads. The caliper also contains the hydraulic components that cause the pads to pinch the disc when the brakes are applied. A caliper is also a measuring tool that can be set to measure inside or outside dimensions of an object.

Camshaft A rotating shaft on which a series of cam lobes operate the valve mechanisms. The camshaft may be driven by gears, by sprockets and chain or by sprockets and a belt.

Canister A container in an evaporative emission control system; contains activated charcoal granules to trap vapours from the fuel system.

Canister

Carburettor A device which mixes fuel with air in the proper proportions to provide a desired power output from a spark ignition internal combustion engine.

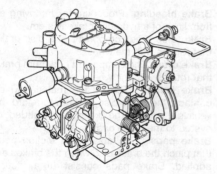

Carburettor

Castellated Resembling the parapets along the top of a castle wall. For example, a castellated balljoint stud nut.

Castellated nut

Castor In wheel alignment, the backward or forward tilt of the steering axis. Castor is positive when the steering axis is inclined rearward at the top.

Catalytic converter A silencer-like device in the exhaust system which converts certain pollutants in the exhaust gases into less harmful substances.

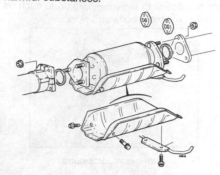

Catalytic converter

Circlip A ring-shaped clip used to prevent endwise movement of cylindrical parts and shafts. An internal circlip is installed in a groove in a housing; an external circlip fits into a groove on the outside of a cylindrical piece such as a shaft.

Clearance The amount of space between two parts. For example, between a piston and a cylinder, between a bearing and a journal, etc.

Coil spring A spiral of elastic steel found in various sizes throughout a vehicle, for example as a springing medium in the suspension and in the valve train.

Compression Reduction in volume, and increase in pressure and temperature, of a gas, caused by squeezing it into a smaller space.

Compression ratio The relationship between cylinder volume when the piston is at top dead centre and cylinder volume when the piston is at bottom dead centre.

Constant velocity (CV) joint A type of universal joint that cancels out vibrations caused by driving power being transmitted through an angle.

Core plug A disc or cup-shaped metal device inserted in a hole in a casting through which core was removed when the casting was formed. Also known as a freeze plug or expansion plug.

Crankcase The lower part of the engine block in which the crankshaft rotates.

Crankshaft The main rotating member, or shaft, running the length of the crankcase, with offset "throws" to which the connecting rods are attached.

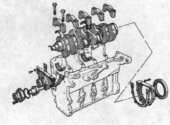

Crankshaft assembly

Crocodile clip See Alligator clip

D

Diagnostic code Code numbers obtained b accessing the diagnostic mode of an engir management computer. This code can b used to determine the area in the syster where a malfunction may be located.

Disc brake A brake design incorporating rotating disc onto which brake pads ar squeezed. The resulting friction converts th energy of a moving vehicle into heat.

Double-overhead cam (DOHC) An engir that uses two overhead camshafts, usuall one for the intake valves and one for th exhaust valves.

Drivebelt(s) The belt(s) used to driv accessories such as the alternator, wate pump, power steering pump, air conditionin compressor, etc. off the crankshaft pulley.

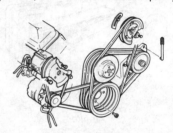

Accessory drivebelts

Driveshaft Any shaft used to transmi motion. Commonly used when referring to th axleshafts on a front wheel drive vehicle.

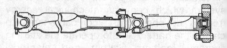

Driveshaft

Drum brake A type of brake using a drum-shaped metal cylinder attached to the inner surface of the wheel. When the brake pedal is pressed, curved brake shoes with friction linings press against the inside of the drum to slow or stop the vehicle.

Drum brake assembly

E

EGR valve A valve used to introduce exhaust gases into the intake air stream.

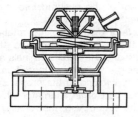

EGR valve

Electronic control unit (ECU) A computer which controls (for instance) ignition and fuel injection systems, or an anti-lock braking system. For more information refer to the *Haynes Automotive Electrical and Electronic Systems Manual.*

Electronic Fuel Injection (EFI) A computer controlled fuel system that distributes fuel through an injector located in each intake port of the engine.

Emergency brake A braking system, independent of the main hydraulic system, that can be used to slow or stop the vehicle if the primary brakes fail, or to hold the vehicle stationary even though the brake pedal isn't depressed. It usually consists of a hand lever that actuates either front or rear brakes mechanically through a series of cables and linkages. Also known as a handbrake or parking brake.

Endfloat The amount of lengthwise movement between two parts. As applied to a crankshaft, the distance that the crankshaft can move forward and back in the cylinder block.

Engine management system (EMS) A computer controlled system which manages the fuel injection and the ignition systems in an integrated fashion.

Exhaust manifold A part with several passages through which exhaust gases leave the engine combustion chambers and enter the exhaust pipe.

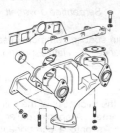

Exhaust manifold

F

Fan clutch A viscous (fluid) drive coupling device which permits variable engine fan speeds in relation to engine speeds.

Feeler blade A thin strip or blade of hardened steel, ground to an exact thickness, used to check or measure clearances between parts.

Feeler blade

Firing order The order in which the engine cylinders fire, or deliver their power strokes, beginning with the number one cylinder.

Flywheel A heavy spinning wheel in which energy is absorbed and stored by means of momentum. On cars, the flywheel is attached to the crankshaft to smooth out firing impulses.

Free play The amount of travel before any action takes place. The "looseness" in a linkage, or an assembly of parts, between the initial application of force and actual movement. For example, the distance the brake pedal moves before the pistons in the master cylinder are actuated.

Fuse An electrical device which protects a circuit against accidental overload. The typical fuse contains a soft piece of metal which is calibrated to melt at a predetermined current flow (expressed as amps) and break the circuit.

Fusible link A circuit protection device consisting of a conductor surrounded by heat-resistant insulation. The conductor is smaller than the wire it protects, so it acts as the weakest link in the circuit. Unlike a blown fuse, a failed fusible link must frequently be cut from the wire for replacement.

G

Gap The distance the spark must travel in jumping from the centre electrode to the side

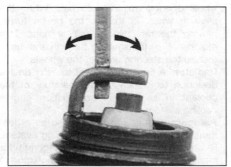

Adjusting spark plug gap

electrode in a spark plug. Also refers to the spacing between the points in a contact breaker assembly in a conventional points-type ignition, or to the distance between the reluctor or rotor and the pickup coil in an electronic ignition.

Gasket Any thin, soft material - usually cork, cardboard, asbestos or soft metal - installed between two metal surfaces to ensure a good seal. For instance, the cylinder head gasket seals the joint between the block and the cylinder head.

Gasket

Gauge An instrument panel display used to monitor engine conditions. A gauge with a movable pointer on a dial or a fixed scale is an analogue gauge. A gauge with a numerical readout is called a digital gauge.

H

Halfshaft A rotating shaft that transmits power from the final drive unit to a drive wheel, usually when referring to a live rear axle.

Harmonic balancer A device designed to reduce torsion or twisting vibration in the crankshaft. May be incorporated in the crankshaft pulley. Also known as a vibration damper.

Hone An abrasive tool for correcting small irregularities or differences in diameter in an engine cylinder, brake cylinder, etc.

Hydraulic tappet A tappet that utilises hydraulic pressure from the engine's lubrication system to maintain zero clearance (constant contact with both camshaft and valve stem). Automatically adjusts to variation in valve stem length. Hydraulic tappets also reduce valve noise.

I

Ignition timing The moment at which the spark plug fires, usually expressed in the number of crankshaft degrees before the piston reaches the top of its stroke.

Inlet manifold A tube or housing with passages through which flows the air-fuel mixture (carburettor vehicles and vehicles with throttle body injection) or air only (port fuel-injected vehicles) to the port openings in the cylinder head.

J

Jump start Starting the engine of a vehicle with a discharged or weak battery by attaching jump leads from the weak battery to a charged or helper battery.

L

Load Sensing Proportioning Valve (LSPV) A brake hydraulic system control valve that works like a proportioning valve, but also takes into consideration the amount of weight carried by the rear axle.

Locknut A nut used to lock an adjustment nut, or other threaded component, in place. For example, a locknut is employed to keep the adjusting nut on the rocker arm in position.

Lockwasher A form of washer designed to prevent an attaching nut from working loose.

M

MacPherson strut A type of front suspension system devised by Earle MacPherson at Ford of England. In its original form, a simple lateral link with the anti-roll bar creates the lower control arm. A long strut - an integral coil spring and shock absorber - is mounted between the body and the steering knuckle. Many modern so-called MacPherson strut systems use a conventional lower A-arm and don't rely on the anti-roll bar for location.

Multimeter An electrical test instrument with the capability to measure voltage, current and resistance.

N

NOx Oxides of Nitrogen. A common toxic pollutant emitted by petrol and diesel engines at higher temperatures.

O

Ohm The unit of electrical resistance. One volt applied to a resistance of one ohm will produce a current of one amp.

Ohmmeter An instrument for measuring electrical resistance.

O-ring A type of sealing ring made of a special rubber-like material; in use, the O-ring is compressed into a groove to provide the sealing action.

O-ring

Overhead cam (ohc) engine An engine with the camshaft(s) located on top of the cylinder head(s).

Overhead valve (ohv) engine An engine with the valves located in the cylinder head, but with the camshaft located in the engine block.

Oxygen sensor A device installed in the engine exhaust manifold, which senses the oxygen content in the exhaust and converts this information into an electric current. Also called a Lambda sensor.

P

Phillips screw A type of screw head having a cross instead of a slot for a corresponding type of screwdriver.

Plastigage A thin strip of plastic thread, available in different sizes, used for measuring clearances. For example, a strip of Plastigage is laid across a bearing journal. The parts are assembled and dismantled; the width of the crushed strip indicates the clearance between journal and bearing.

Plastigage

Propeller shaft The long hollow tube with universal joints at both ends that carries power from the transmission to the differential on front-engined rear wheel drive vehicles.

Proportioning valve A hydraulic control valve which limits the amount of pressure to the rear brakes during panic stops to prevent wheel lock-up.

R

Rack-and-pinion steering A steering system with a pinion gear on the end of the steering shaft that mates with a rack (think of a geared wheel opened up and laid flat). When the steering wheel is turned, the pinion turns, moving the rack to the left or right. This movement is transmitted through the track rods to the steering arms at the wheels.

Radiator A liquid-to-air heat transfer device designed to reduce the temperature of the coolant in an internal combustion engine cooling system.

Refrigerant Any substance used as a heat transfer agent in an air-conditioning system. R-12 has been the principle refrigerant for many years; recently, however, manufacturers have begun using R-134a, a non-CFC substance that is considered less harmful to the ozone in the upper atmosphere.

Rocker arm A lever arm that rocks on a sha or pivots on a stud. In an overhead val engine, the rocker arm converts the upwa movement of the pushrod into a downwa movement to open a valve.

Rotor In a distributor, the rotating devi inside the cap that connects the cent electrode and the outer terminals as it turn distributing the high voltage from the c secondary winding to the proper spark plu Also, that part of an alternator which rotat inside the stator. Also, the rotating assemb of a turbocharger, including the compress wheel, shaft and turbine wheel.

Runout The amount of wobble (in-and-o movement) of a gear or wheel as it's rotate The amount a shaft rotates "out-of-true." Th out-of-round condition of a rotating part.

S

Sealant A liquid or paste used to preve leakage at a joint. Sometimes used conjunction with a gasket.

Sealed beam lamp An older headlight desig which integrates the reflector, lens an filaments into a hermetically-sealed one-pie unit. When a filament burns out or the le cracks, the entire unit is simply replaced.

Serpentine drivebelt A single, long, wic accessory drivebelt that's used on som newer vehicles to drive all the accessorie instead of a series of smaller, shorter belt Serpentine drivebelts are usually tensioned b an automatic tensioner.

Serpentine drivebelt

Shim Thin spacer, commonly used to adjus the clearance or relative positions betwee two parts. For example, shims inserted into under bucket tappets control valv clearances. Clearance is adjusted b changing the thickness of the shim.

Slide hammer A special puller that screw into or hooks onto a component such as shaft or bearing; a heavy sliding handle on th shaft bottoms against the end of the shaft t knock the component free.

Sprocket A tooth or projection on th periphery of a wheel, shaped to engage with chain or drivebelt. Commonly used to refer the sprocket wheel itself.

Starter inhibitor switch On vehicles with a

automatic transmission, a switch that prevents starting if the vehicle is not in Neutral or Park.

Strut See MacPherson strut.

T

Tappet A cylindrical component which transmits motion from the cam to the valve stem, either directly or via a pushrod and rocker arm. Also called a cam follower.

Thermostat A heat-controlled valve that regulates the flow of coolant between the cylinder block and the radiator, so maintaining optimum engine operating temperature. A thermostat is also used in some air cleaners in which the temperature is regulated.

Thrust bearing The bearing in the clutch assembly that is moved in to the release levers by clutch pedal action to disengage the clutch. Also referred to as a release bearing.

Timing belt A toothed belt which drives the camshaft. Serious engine damage may result if it breaks in service.

Timing chain A chain which drives the camshaft.

Toe-in The amount the front wheels are closer together at the front than at the rear. On rear wheel drive vehicles, a slight amount of toe-in is usually specified to keep the front wheels running parallel on the road by offsetting other forces that tend to spread the wheels apart.

Toe-out The amount the front wheels are closer together at the rear than at the front. On front wheel drive vehicles, a slight amount of toe-out is usually specified.

Tools For full information on choosing and using tools, refer to the *Haynes Automotive Tools Manual*.

Tracer A stripe of a second colour applied to a wire insulator to distinguish that wire from another one with the same colour insulator.

Tune-up A process of accurate and careful adjustments and parts replacement to obtain the best possible engine performance.

Turbocharger A centrifugal device, driven by exhaust gases, that pressurises the intake air. Normally used to increase the power output from a given engine displacement, but can also be used primarily to reduce exhaust emissions (as on VW's "Umwelt" Diesel engine).

U

Universal joint or U-joint A double-pivoted connection for transmitting power from a driving to a driven shaft through an angle. A U-joint consists of two Y-shaped yokes and a cross-shaped member called the spider.

V

Valve A device through which the flow of liquid, gas, vacuum, or loose material in bulk may be started, stopped, or regulated by a movable part that opens, shuts, or partially obstructs one or more ports or passageways. A valve is also the movable part of such a device.

Valve clearance The clearance between the valve tip (the end of the valve stem) and the rocker arm or tappet. The valve clearance is measured when the valve is closed.

Vernier caliper A precision measuring instrument that measures inside and outside dimensions. Not quite as accurate as a micrometer, but more convenient.

Viscosity The thickness of a liquid or its resistance to flow.

Volt A unit for expressing electrical "pressure" in a circuit. One volt that will produce a current of one ampere through a resistance of one ohm.

W

Welding Various processes used to join metal items by heating the areas to be joined to a molten state and fusing them together. For more information refer to the *Haynes Automotive Welding Manual*.

Wiring diagram A drawing portraying the components and wires in a vehicle's electrical system, using standardised symbols. For more information refer to the *Haynes Automotive Electrical and Electronic Systems Manual*.

Haynes Manuals – The Complete List

Title	Book No.
ALFA ROMEO	
Alfa Romeo Alfasud/Sprint (74 - 88)	0292
Alfa Romeo Alfetta (73 - 87)	0531
AUDI	
Audi 80 (72 - Feb 79)	0207
Audi 80, 90 (79 - Oct 86) & Coupe (81 - Nov 88)	0605
Audi 80, 90 (Oct 86 - 90) & Coupe (Nov 88 - 90)	1491
Audi 100 (Oct 82 - 90) & 200 (Feb 84 - Oct 89)	0907
Audi 100/A6 (May 91 - May 97)	3504
AUSTIN	
Austin/MG Maestro 1.3 & 1.6 (83 - 95)	0922
Austin/MG Metro (80 - May 90)	0718
Austin Montego 1.3 & 1.6 (84 - 94)	1066
Austin/MG Montego 2.0 (84 - 95)	1067
Mini (59 - 69)	0527
Mini (69 - Oct 96)	0646
Austin/Rover 2.0 litre Diesel Engine (86 - 93)	1857
BEDFORD	
Bedford CF (69 - 87)	0163
Bedford Rascal (86 - 93)	3015
BMW	
BMW 316, 320 & 320i (4-cyl) (75 - Feb 83)	0276
BMW 320, 320i, 323i & 325i (6-cyl) (Oct 77 - Sept 87)	0815
BMW 3-Series (Apr 91 - 96)	3210
BMW 3-Series (sohc) (83 - 91)	1948
BMW 520i & 525e (Oct 81 - June 88)	1560
BMW 525, 528 & 528i (73 - Sept 81)	0632
BMW 5-Series (sohc) (81 - 91)	1948
BMW 1500, 1502, 1600, 1602, 2000 & 2002 (59 - 77)	0240
CITROËN	
Citroën 2CV, Ami & Dyane (67 - 90)	0196
Citroën AX Petrol & Diesel (87 - 94)	3014
Citroën BX (83 - 94)	0908
Citroën C15 Van Petrol & Diesel (89 - 98)	3509
Citroën CX (75 - 88)	0528
Citroën Saxo Petrol & Diesel (96 - 98)	3506
Citroën Visa (79 - 88)	0620
Citroën Xantia Petrol & Diesel (93 - 98)	3082
Citroën XM Petrol & Diesel (89 - 98)	3451
Citroën ZX Diesel (91 - 93)	1922
Citroën ZX Petrol (91 - 94)	1881
Citroën 1.7 & 1.9 litre Diesel Engine (84 - 96)	1379
COLT	
Colt 1200, 1250 & 1400 (79 - May 84)	0600
DAIMLER	
Daimler Sovereign (68 - Oct 86)	0242
Daimler Double Six (72 - 88)	0478
FIAT	
Fiat 126 (73 - 87)	0305
Fiat 127 (71 - 83)	0193
Fiat 500 (57 - 73)	0090
Fiat Cinquecento (June 93 - 98)	3501
Fiat Panda (81 - 95)	0793
Fiat Punto (94 - 96)	3251
Fiat Regata (84 - 88)	1167
Fiat Strada (79 - 88)	0479

Title	Book No.
Fiat Tipo (88 - 91)	1625
Fiat Uno (83 - 95)	0923
Fiat X1/9 (74 - 89)	0273
FORD	
Ford Capri II (& III) 1.6 & 2.0 (74 - 87)	0283
Ford Capri II (& III) 2.8 & 3.0 (74 - 87)	1309
Ford Cortina Mk IV (& V) 1.6 & 2.0 (76 - 83)	0343
Ford Escort (75 - Aug 80)	0280
Ford Escort (Sept 80 - Sept 90)	0686
Ford Escort (Sept 90 - 97)	1737
Ford Escort Mk II Mexico, RS 1600 & RS 2000 (75 - 80)	0735
Ford Fiesta (inc. XR2) (76 - Aug 83)	0334
Ford Fiesta (inc. XR2) (Aug 83 - Feb 89)	1030
Ford Fiesta (Feb 89 - Oct 95)	1595
Ford Fiesta Petrol & Diesel (Oct 95 - 97)	3397
Ford Granada (Sept 77 - Feb 85)	0481
Ford Granada (Mar 85 - 94)	1245
Ford Mondeo (93 - 99)	1923
Ford Mondeo Diesel (93 - 96)	3465
Ford Orion (83 - Sept 90)	1009
Ford Orion (Sept 90 - 93)	1737
Ford Sierra 1.3, 1.6, 1.8 & 2.0 (82 - 93)	0903
Ford Sierra 2.3, 2.8 & 2.9 (82 - 91)	0904
Ford Scorpio (Mar 85 - 94)	1245
Ford Transit Petrol (Mk 2) (78 - Jan 86)	0719
Ford Transit Petrol (Mk 3) (Feb 86 - 89)	1468
Ford Transit Diesel (Feb 86 - 95)	3019
Ford 1.6 & 1.8 litre Diesel Engine (84 - 96)	1172
Ford 2.1, 2.3 & 2.5 litre Diesel Engine (77 - 90)	1606
FREIGHT ROVER	
Freight Rover Sherpa (74 - 87)	0463
HILLMAN	
Hillman Avenger (70 - 82)	0037
HONDA	
Honda Accord (76 - Feb 84)	0351
Honda Accord (Feb 84 - Oct 85)	1177
Honda Civic (Feb 84 - Oct 87)	1226
Honda Civic (Nov 91 - 96)	3199
HYUNDAI	
Hyundai Pony (85 - 94)	3398
JAGUAR	
Jaguar E Type (61 - 72)	0140
Jaguar MkI & II, 240 & 340 (55 - 69)	0098
Jaguar XJ6, XJ & Sovereign (68 - Oct 86)	0242
Jaguar XJ6 & Sovereign (Oct 86 - Sept 94)	3261
Jaguar XJ12, XJS & Sovereign (72 - 88)	0478
JEEP	
Jeep Cherokee Petrol (93 - 96)	1943
LADA	
Lada 1200, 1300, 1500 & 1600 (74 - 91)	0413
Lada Samara (87 - 91)	1610
LAND ROVER	
Land Rover 90, 110 & Defender Diesel (83 - 95)	3017
Land Rover Discovery Diesel (89 - 95)	3016
Land Rover Series IIA & III Diesel (58 - 85)	0529
Land Rover Series II, IIA & III Petrol (58 - 85)	0314

Title	Book No.
MAZDA	
Mazda 323 fwd (Mar 81 - Oct 89)	1608
Mazda 323 (Oct 89 - 98)	3455
Mazda 626 fwd (May 83 - Sept 87)	0929
Mazda B-1600, B-1800 & B-2000 Pick-up (72 - 88)	0267
MERCEDES-BENZ	
Mercedes-Benz 190, 190E & 190D Petrol & Diesel (83 - 93)	3450
Mercedes-Benz 200, 240, 300 Diesel (Oct 76 - 85)	1114
Mercedes-Benz 250 & 280 (68 - 72)	0346
Mercedes-Benz 250 & 280 (123 Series) (Oct 76 - 84)	0677
Mercedes-Benz 124 Series (85 - Aug 93)	3253
MG	
MGB (62 - 80)	0111
MG Maestro 1.3 & 1.6 (83 - 95)	0922
MG Metro (80 - May 90)	0718
MG Midget & AH Sprite (58 - 80)	0265
MG Montego 2.0 (84 - 95)	1067
MITSUBISHI	
Mitsubishi 1200, 1250 & 1400 (79 - May 84)	0600
Mitsubishi Shogun & L200 Pick-Ups (83 - 94)	1944
MORRIS	
Morris Ital 1.3 (80 - 84)	0705
Morris Minor 1000 (56 - 71)	0024
NISSAN	
Nissan Bluebird fwd (May 84 - Mar 86)	1223
Nissan Bluebird (T12 & T72) (Mar 86 - 90)	1473
Nissan Cherry (N12) (Sept 82 - 86)	1031
Nissan Micra (K10) (83 - Jan 93)	0931
Nissan Micra (93 - 96)	3254
Nissan Primera (90 - Oct 96)	1851
Nissan Stanza (82 - 86)	0824
Nissan Sunny (B11) (May 82 - Oct 86)	0895
Nissan Sunny (Oct 86 - Mar 91)	1378
Nissan Sunny (Apr 91 - 95)	3219
OPEL	
Opel Ascona & Manta (B Series) (Sept 75 - 88)	0316
Opel Ascona (81 - 88) (Not available in UK see Vauxhall Cavalier 0812)	3215
Opel Astra (Oct 91 - 96) (Not available in UK see Vauxhall Astra 1832)	3156
Opel Calibra (90 - 98) (See Vauxhall/Opel Calibra Book No. 3502)	
Opel Corsa (83 - Mar 93) (Not available in UK see Vauxhall Nova 0909)	3160
Opel Corsa (Mar 93 - 97) (Not available in UK see Vauxhall Corsa 1985)	3159
Opel Frontera Petrol & Diesel (91 - 98) (See Vauxhall/Opel Frontera Book No. 1985)	
Opel Kadett (Nov 79 - Oct 84)	0634
Opel Kadett (Oct 84 - Oct 91) (Not available in UK see Vauxhall Astra & Belmont 1136)	3196
Opel Omega & Senator (86 - 94) (Not available in UK see Vauxhall Carlton & Senator 1469)	3157
Opel Omega Petrol & Diesel (94 - 98) (See Vauxhall/Opel Omega Book 3510)	

Title	Book No.
Opel Rekord (Feb 78 - Oct 86)	0543
Opel Vectra (88 - Oct 95)	
(Not available in UK see Vauxhall Cavalier 1570)	3158
Opel Vectra Petrol & Diesel (95 - 98)	
(Not available in UK see Vauxhall Vectra 3396)	3523

PEUGEOT

Title	Book No.
Peugeot 106 Petrol & Diesel (91 - June 96)	1882
Peugeot 205 (83 - 95)	0932
Peugeot 305 (78 - 89)	0538
Peugeot 306 Petrol & Diesel (93 - 98)	3073
Peugeot 309 (86 - 93)	1266
Peugeot 405 Petrol (88 - 96)	1559
Peugeot 405 Diesel (88 - 96)	3198
Peugeot 406 Petrol & Diesel (96 - 97)	3394
Peugeot 505 (79 - 89)	0762
Peugeot 1.7/1.8 & 1.9 litre Diesel Engines (82 - 96)	0950
Peugeot 2.0, 2.1, 2.3 & 2.5 litre Diesel Engines (74 - 90)	1607

PORSCHE

Title	Book No.
Porsche 911 (65 - 85)	0264
Porsche 924 & 924 Turbo (76 - 85)	0397

PROTON

Title	Book No.
Proton (89 - 97)	3255

RANGE ROVER

Title	Book No.
Range Rover V8 (70 - Oct 92)	0606

RELIANT

Title	Book No.
Reliant Robin & Kitten (73 - 83)	0436

RENAULT

Title	Book No.
Renault 5 (72 - Feb 85)	0141
Renault 5 (Feb 85 - 96)	1219
Renault 9 & 11 (82 - 89)	0822
Renault 18 (79 - 86)	0598
Renault 19 Petrol (89 - 94)	1646
Renault 19 Diesel (89 - 95)	1946
Renault 21 (86 - 94)	1397
Renault 25 (84 - 92)	1228
Renault Clio Petrol (91 - 93)	1853
Renault Clio Diesel (91 - June 96)	3031
Renault Espace (85 - 96)	3197
Renault Laguna (94 - 96)	3252
Renault Mégane & Scénic Petrol & Diesel (96 - 98)	3395

ROVER

Title	Book No.
Rover 111 & 114 (95 - 96)	1711
Rover 213 & 216 (84 - 89)	1116
Rover 214 & 414 (89 - 96)	1689
Rover 216 & 416 (89 - 96)	1830
Rover 200 Series Petrol & Diesel (95 - 98)	3399
Rover 400 Series Petrol & Diesel (95 - 98)	3453
Rover 618, 620 & 623 (93 - 97)	3257
Rover 820, 825 & 827 (86 - 95)	1380
Rover 3500 (SD1) (76 - 87)	0365
Rover Metro (May 90 - 94)	1711

SAAB

Title	Book No.
Saab 90, 99 & 900 (79 - Oct 93)	0765
Saab 900 (Oct 93 - 98)	3512
Saab 9000 (4-cyl) (85 - 95)	1686

SEAT

Title	Book No.
Seat Ibiza & Malaga (85 - 92)	1609

SKODA

Title	Book No.
Skoda Estelle 105, 120, 130 & 136 (77 - 89)	0604
Skoda Favorit (89 - 92)	1801
Skoda Felicia Petrol & Diesel (95 - 98)	3505

SUBARU

Title	Book No.
Subaru 1600 & 1800 (Nov 79 - 90)	0995

SUZUKI

Title	Book No.
Suzuki SJ Series, Samurai & Vitara (82 - 97)	1942
Suzuki Supercarry (86 - Oct 94)	3015

TALBOT

Title	Book No.
Talbot Alpine, Solara, Minx & Rapier (75 - 86)	0337
Talbot Horizon (78 - 86)	0473
Talbot Samba (82 - 86)	0823

TOYOTA

Title	Book No.
Toyota Carina E (May 92 - 97)	3256
Toyota Corolla (fwd) (Sept 83 - Sept 87)	1024
Toyota Corolla (rwd) (80 - 85)	0683
Toyota Corolla (Sept 87 - 92)	1683
Toyota Corolla (Aug 92 - 97)	3259
Toyota Hi-Ace & Hi-Lux (69 - Oct 83)	0304

TRIUMPH

Title	Book No.
Triumph Acclaim (81 - 84)	0792
Triumph GT6 & Vitesse (62 - 74)	0112
Triumph Spitfire (62 - 81)	0113
Triumph Stag (70 - 78)	0441
Triumph TR7 (75 - 82)	0322

VAUXHALL

Title	Book No.
Vauxhall Astra (80 - Oct 84)	0635
Vauxhall Astra & Belmont (Oct 84 - Oct 91)	1136
Vauxhall Astra (Oct 91 - 96)	1832
Vauxhall/Opel Calibra (90 - 98)	3502
Vauxhall Carlton (Oct 78 - Oct 86)	0480
Vauxhall Carlton (Nov 86 - 94)	1469
Vauxhall Cavalier 1600, 1900 & 2000 (75 - July 81)	0315
Vauxhall Cavalier (81 - Oct 88)	0812
Vauxhall Cavalier (Oct 88 - Oct 95)	1570
Vauxhall Chevette (75 - 84)	0285
Vauxhall Corsa (93 - 97)	1985
Vauxhall/Opel Frontera Petrol & Diesel (91 - 98)	3454
Vauxhall Nova (83 - 93)	0909
Vauxhall/Opel Omega Petrol & Diesel (94 - 98)	3510
Vauxhall Rascal (86 - 93)	3015
Vauxhall Senator (Sept 87 - 94)	1469
Vauxhall Vectra Petrol & Diesel (95 - 98)	3396
Vauxhall/Opel 1.5, 1.6 & 1.7 litre Diesel Engines (82 - 96)	1222

VOLKSWAGEN

Title	Book No.
VW Beetle 1200 (54 - 77)	0036
VW Beetle 1300 & 1500 (65 - 75)	0039
VW Beetle 1302 & 1302S (70 - 72)	0110
VW Beetle 1303, 1303S & GT (72 - 75)	0159
VW Golf Mk 1 1.1 & 1.3 (74 - Feb 84)	0716
VW Golf Mk 1 1.5, 1.6 & 1.8 (74 - 85)	0726
VW Golf Mk 1 Diesel (78 - Feb 84)	0451
VW Golf Mk 2 (Mar 84 - Feb 92)	1081
VW Golf Mk 3 Petrol & Diesel (Feb 92 - 96)	3097
VW Jetta Mk 1 1.1 & 1.3 (80 - June 84)	0716
VW Jetta Mk 1 1.5, 1.6 & 1.8 (80 - June 84)	0726
VW Jetta Mk 1 Diesel (81 - June 84)	0451
VW Jetta Mk 2 (July 84 - 92)	1081
VW LT vans & light trucks (76 - 87)	0637
VW Passat (Sept 81 - May 88)	0814
VW Passat (May 88 - 96)	3498
VW Polo & Derby (76 - Jan 82)	0335
VW Polo (82 - Oct 90)	0813
VW Polo (Nov 90 - Aug 94)	3245
VW Polo Hatchback (95 - 98)	3500
VW Santana (Sept 82 - 85)	0814
VW Scirocco Mk 1 1.5, 1.6 & 1.8 (74 - 82)	0726
VW Scirocco (82 - 90)	1224
VW Transporter 1600 (68 - 79)	0082
VW Transporter 1700, 1800 & 2000 (72 - 79)	0226
VW Transporter with air-cooled engine (79 - 82)	0638
VW Transporter water-cooled (82 - 90)	3452
VW Vento Petrol & Diesel (Feb 92 - 96)	3097

VOLVO

Title	Book No.
Volvo 142, 144 & 145 (66 - 74)	0129
Volvo 240 Series (74 - 93)	0270
Volvo 262, 264 & 260/265 (75 - 85)	0400
Volvo 340, 343, 345 & 360 (76 - 91)	0715
Volvo 440, 460 & 480 (87 - 92)	1691
Volvo 740 & 760 (82 - 91)	1258
Volvo 850 (92 - 96)	3260
Volvo 940 (90 - 96)	3249

YUGO/ZASTAVA

Title	Book No.
Yugo/Zastava (81 - 90)	1453

TECH BOOKS

Title	Book No.
Automotive Brake Manual	3050
Automotive Carburettor Manual	3288
Automotive Diagnostic Fault Codes Manual	3472
Automotive Diesel Engine Service Guide	3286
Automotive Disc Brake Manual	3542
Automotive Electrical and Electronic Systems Manual	3049
Automotive Engine Management and Fuel Injection Systems Manual	3344
Automotive Gearbox Overhaul Manual	3473
Automotive Service Summaries Manual	3475
Automotive Timing Belt Manual - Ford	3474
Automotive Welding Manual	3053
In-Car Entertainment Manual (3rd Edition)	3363

CAR BOOKS

Title	Book No.
Automotive Fuel Injection Systems	9755
Car Bodywork Repair Manual	9864
Caravan Manual (2nd Edition)	9894
Motorcaravan Manual, The	L7322
Small Engine Repair Manual	1755
SU Carburettors	0299
Weber Carburettors (to 79)	0393

CL07.01/99

Preserving Our Motoring Heritage

< *The Model J Duesenberg Derham Tourster. Only eight of these magnificent cars were ever built – this is the only example to be found outside the United States of America*

Almost every car you've ever loved, loathed or desired is gathered under one roof at the Haynes Motor Museum. Over 300 immaculately presented cars and motorbikes represent every aspect of our motoring heritage, from elegant reminders of bygone days, such as the superb Model J Duesenberg to curiosities like the bug-eyed BMW Isetta. There are also many old friends and flames. Perhaps you remember the 1959 Ford Popular that you did your courting in? The magnificent 'Red Collection' is a spectacle of classic sports cars including AC, Alfa Romeo, Austin Healey, Ferrari, Lamborghini, Maserati, MG, Riley, Porsche and Triumph.

A Perfect Day Out

Each and every vehicle at the Haynes Motor Museum has played its part in the history and culture of Motoring. Today, they make a wonderful spectacle and a great day out for all the family. Bring the kids, bring Mum and Dad, but above all bring your camera to capture those golden memories for ever. You will also find an impressive array of motoring memorabilia, a comfortable 70 seat video cinema and one of the most extensive transport book shops in Britain. The Pit Stop Cafe serves everything from a cup of tea to wholesome, home-made meals or, if you prefer, you can enjoy the large picnic area nestled in the beautiful rural surroundings of Somerset.

John Haynes O.B.E., Founder and Chairman of the museum at the wheel of a Haynes Light 12. >

< *Graham Hill's Lola Cosworth Formula 1 car next to a 1934 Riley Sports.*

The Museum is situated on the A359 Yeovil to Frome road at Sparkford, just off the A303 in Somerset. It is about 40 miles south of Bristol, and 25 minutes drive from the M5 intersection at Taunton.

Open 9.30am - 5.30pm (10.00am - 4.00pm Winter) 7 days a week, *except Christmas Day, Boxing Day and New Years Day*

Special rates available for schools, coach parties and outings Charitable Trust No. 292048